WORLD UNMANNED AIRCRAFT

Sunset — or a new dawn?

WORLD
UNMANNED
AIRCRAFT

Kenneth Munson

AMRAeS, ARHistS

JANE'S

First published in the United Kingdom in 1988 by
Jane's Publishing Company Limited
238 City Road, London EC1V 2PU

ISBN 0 7106 0401 7

Distributed in the Philippines and the USA and its
dependencies by
Jane's Publishing Inc
4th Floor
115 5th Avenue
New York, NY 10003

Typeset by Method Limited, Epping, Essex
Printed in the United Kingdom by Biddles Ltd,
Guildford, Surrey

Contents

Preface

The Jane's Pocket Book *Robot Aircraft Today*, published a decade ago, was able to cover all such aircraft then in service or under development with a list of about 120 basic types. To them have been added, in the ensuing ten years, approximately double that number, most of them new designs and many of considerably more advanced concept and capability. They represent a convincing expression of the aerospace industry's continuing faith in the present and future value of this class of aircraft, ranging from the simplest hand-launched 'model aircraft' targets to sophisticated vehicles for real-time surveillance, target acquisition and detection, airborne early warning, electronic warfare and other vital military or naval missions.

Selection of a title for this new volume presented an early problem. 'Pilotless Aircraft' was clearly inappropriate for vehicles controlled by a remote 'pilot' on the ground. The term 'RPV', although the one most widely used, was not ideal, since (a) it can imply equally a ground or underwater vehicle and (b) would be just as inaccurate when applied to UMAs with missions that are entirely pre-programmed. No one much liked the nowadays less descriptive 'drone'; and so, at risk of offending the occasional diehard feminist, 'Unmanned Aircraft' won the day. Adoption of a larger format has allowed each UMA to be presented in a style and depth virtually identical to those in each annual edition of *Jane's All the World's Aircraft*, following the same policy of omitting towed targets, ballistic targets, and such other borderline UMAs as cruise missiles.

It was, however, hard to avoid the thought that the letters 'E & OE' should also have been a part of the title. Unmanned aircraft still receive far less media coverage than their manned brethren, and are in a market area where potential supply far exceeds possible present-day demand. That being so, one hoped for a better response from the manufacturers invited to provide details of their products; but the sad truth is that, of more than 100 companies whose input was requested, approximately half failed even to reply. I can only claim, therefore, to have done the best I could with the material available; if any company or its products are inadequately or inaccurately portrayed, it will not be for want of trying to obtain something better.

That said, my thanks clearly *are* due to those companies that did respond, some of them well beyond the highest expectations, to requests for information and illustrations. To them is due in no small measure any merit that this volume may have. For much other advice, encouragement and assistance I am indebted to (among many others) Reg Austin and Roger Moses, respectively the Chairman and Organising Secretary of the Bristol International RPV Conference; Ron Pretty and Bernard Blake of *Jane's Weapon Systems*; the publisher, for his uncomplaining patience in awaiting completion of the manuscript; and, certainly not least, John W. R. Taylor, with whom I was happily associated in the original *Robot Aircraft Today*, who fully supported this replacement, and who unearthed many elusive last-minute photographs.

Finally, a word of explanation and apology for what may otherwise appear to be my substandard mathematics. Where original dimensions are metric, they were converted to the nearest quarter of an inch and expressed as such in the original manuscript; but midway through production the publisher decided, for typographical reasons, that these vulgar fractions should be 'decimalised'. Thus, while a fully accurate conversion of 3.75 m (for example) would be 12 ft 3.64 in, it will appear as 12 ft 3.75 in. However, the reader should have no problem provided that the *standard* of conversion adopted is borne in mind.

K. M.

Seaford, East Sussex
July 1987

Introduction

The Sperry-Curtiss 'aerial torpedo', built for the US Navy in 1917
(US National Archives)

The ability to steer a flying machine automatically, without the hands-on attention of an onboard human pilot, has been with us ever since Lawrence Sperry first flight tested his gyro stabiliser – the world's first automatic pilot – in a Curtiss biplane in 1913. A mere four years later an improved version became the heart of Sperry's 'aerial torpedo', which made several successful flights for the US Navy from Sperry's Long Island airfield. It would seem incredible to him that, 70 years after those tests, arguments should still be raging over whether or not unmanned aircraft have a serious future.

On the face of it, UMAs have many sound arguments in their favour. They can be developed, produced and operated at a fraction of the cost of manned aircraft in airframes, engines, fuel consumption, pilot training, logistics and maintenance. They can be made smaller, more manoeuvrable, more numerous, more available, and above all more survivable, all without putting a single human operator at risk.

Consider these two quotations:

'This . . . target was . . . flown against the concentrated gunfire of the (British) Home Fleet during an exercise in the Mediterranean. For two hours, every gun in the fleet tried in vain to destroy the lone, slow and fragile target, but it was recovered safely.'

'Thousands of rounds of radar-directed fire from a sophisticated air defense gun, as well as hundreds of rounds of fifty caliber, were expended on an unmanned vehicle flying well within range. The unmanned vehicle flew on without a scratch.'

They are noteworthy not merely as evidence of survivability, but because between the two incidents there is an interval of 47 years. The former achievement, recorded by Richard A. Botzum in his excellent Northrop UMA history *50 Years of Target Drone Aircraft*, was logged in January 1933 by an ancient Fairey Queen biplane; the second was quoted during a US government hearing in 1980. Further irrefutable proof of drone survivability is given in *Lightning Bugs and other Reconnaissance Drones*, William Wagner's superb saga of the Ryan 147 RPVs in Viet-Nam, in which he records that, between 1964 and 1975, a total of 3,435 operational drone sorties was flown by USAF's 100th Strategic Reconnaissance Wing, and from 2,873 of those sorties – nearly 84 per cent – the drone came back. From 1972, as more sophisticated models were introduced, survival rates were well in excess of 90 per cent.

In that same war America lost more than 2,500 manned aircraft, about 5,000 of her airmen were killed, and nearly 90 per cent of *all* US servicemen taken prisoner were pilots and crewmen. Proponents of UMAs were confident that RPVs had proved their case, and were set to become a major new 'force multiplier' in military thinking. Instead, the expected upturn in their fortunes failed to materialise, and five years after Viet-Nam the USA had not one single operational RPV in its inventory. Four years later still, we find the US Navy risking two crewmen, in a 40-million-dollar carrier-based F-14, to obtain non-real-time photographic intelligence of targets in Lebanon – followed by an air strike in which the USN lost two aircraft out of 28, a third damaged, one pilot killed and another taken prisoner. Both missions could have been carried out by suitable UMAs, more cheaply, probably with real-time

Top-scoring Ryan drone was 'Top Cat', a Model 147SC which survived 68 sorties over Viet-Nam, with an average 12 targets per mission, before being lost in 1974

7

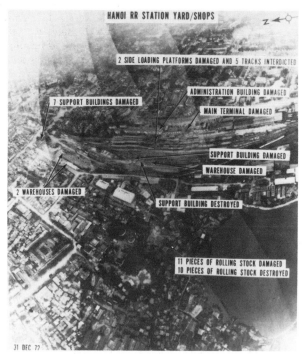

HANOI RR STATION YARD/SHOPS

2 SIDE LOADING PLATFORMS DAMAGED AND 5 TRACKS INTERDICTED

7 SUPPORT BUILDINGS DAMAGED

ADMINISTRATION BUILDING DAMAGED

MAIN TERMINAL DAMAGED

SUPPORT BUILDING DAMAGED

WAREHOUSE DAMAGED

2 WAREHOUSES DAMAGED

SUPPORT BUILDING DESTROYED

11 PIECES OF ROLLING STOCK DAMAGED
10 PIECES OF ROLLING STOCK DESTROYED

31 DEC 72

Typical damage assessment photograph obtained by Ryan 147 reconnaissance drone after the 1972 'Linebacker 2' bombing raids on North Viet-Nam

data, and certainly without human casualties. Small wonder that a few months earlier the Editor of *Armed Forces Journal International*, in his Foreword to *Lightning Bugs*, had written: 'RPVs may have met their enemy. Could it be us?'

Contrast this with Israeli action in Lebanon the same year. Israel first recognised the value of RPVs during the Yom Kippur war of 1973, when it was able to reduce its manned aircraft losses by using inexpensive Chukar decoys to deceive and saturate Egyptian SAM batteries along the Suez Canal. Shortly after that war it charged the IAI and Tadiran companies with developing small, versatile, low-signature RPVs, able to send back real-time intelligence by direct video link, and capable of being operated in the field by ordinary soldiers after only three to six months training. The Scout and Mastiff mini-RPVs came into their own in June 1982 when Israel launched its 'Peace for Galilee' offensive against Syrian forces in Lebanon. While some of the drones, equipped with radar reflectors to simulate full size aircraft, acted as decoys to draw the fire of Syrian gun and missile batteries in the Beka'a Valley, others carrying explosive charges remained undetected by Syrian radars, enabling them to home in on the radars' emissions and destroy them on impact. The air defence batteries, thus 'blinded', were totally vulnerable to attack by manned strike aircraft, which wiped them out completely. In this object lesson in the *combined* use of manned and unmanned aircraft, not one single Israeli pilot was lost, and Syria quickly paid Israel the compliment of acquiring drone systems for its own forces from the USSR.

The conclusion to be drawn from these two scenarios seems obvious enough: that when the need is perceived, and the motivation is strong enough, UMAs will be acquired, will be used, and will be successful at many missions (though not yet all) hitherto performed by manned aircraft. Unfortunately, that perception has all

Most successful operational mini-RPV to date, the Scout formed the basis for Israel's new Pioneer system, now being deployed by the US Navy *(Brian M. Service)*

too often been blunted, both by industry (in overstating its case) and by potential customers (by failing to recognise that UMAs can actually help them to make *better* use of their manned equipment and resources). The day of the RPV as a natural ingredient of military thinking is much nearer than it was a decade ago, but there is still an urgent need for clearer and more widespread understanding, not only of what they can do but also of what they can *not* do better than manned systems – or at least not yet. In short, they need a better image. Given that, and the right user motivation, they also need one other vital ingredient: a fair, and consistent, share of defence spending. Sadly, two of these three ingredients have not always been present in the one major RPV programme that has received more public attention than any other.

Even its staunchest advocates would not deny that Lockheed's Aquila battlefield RPV for the US Army has been an unconscionably long time a-coming. If it does indeed become operational in 1988 as currently predicted (and it was on the Congress 'hit list' again in the autumn of 1987), it will be 14 years, or one year longer than it took four British and French manufacturers to design, develop and put into service the world's first supersonic airliner. Launched in 1974, the initial XMQM-105 demonstration phase was completed successfully in about three years, and the proposed IOC of summer 1984 seemed well within reach when the YMQM-105 FSED phase began on 31 August 1979. But subsequent troubles with the data link and TV payload, and the stop-go failure of several budgets to fund the programme fully, were not helped in mid-1983

After launch and recovery, Aquila can be made ready to fly another three-hour mission after only half an hour's refuelling and refurbishing

when, in a major shifting of the goalposts, the US Army cut its planned purchase from 995 Aquilas to 548, simultaneously expanding the range of required missions to include communications relay, weather reconnaissance and electronic warfare. The effect of this on the timetable was admitted at the end of the following year when, to minimise further delays, the Army terminated development of all but the basic air vehicle, its TV/FLIR/laser designator payloads, the launch/recovery vehicles and the GCS. Even so, by 1985 the FSED period had been stretched from 43 months to 79, overall programme cost was nearing $2,000 million, and procurement plans had been further cut to 376 air vehicles at a unit cost fast rising towards the $1 million mark. When Aquila does enter service, the US Army will be getting fewer than 40 per cent of the air vehicles originally planned, at a cost virtually four times the original estimate. That still compares well with the cost of developing a manned aircraft for the same job, but is not exactly calculated to work wonders for the oft-preached 'quick, cheap and simple' image of mini-RPVs, and must surely have had an adverse knock-on effect upon other UMA programmes already competing for support with more complex and expensive manned systems.

The other side of the coin is that the operational Aquila should be a far more capable and survivable RPV than the little 13·6 kg (30 lb) payload, 54·4 kg (120 lb) gross weight vehicle originally planned back in 1974. Endurance has been doubled to three hours (and could exceed this handsomely if required), payload is almost doubled, and the shape of the 120 kg (265 lb) production Aquila has a much 'stealthier' outline. Moreover, it will be operable worldwide in virtually any climate, unlike some other simpler, fair-weather minis with which it is sometimes unjustly compared.

To its credit, the US Army has sustained its belief in Aquila throughout its protracted development, and it has to be remarked that, around the world, it is armies that have taken the lead in adopting UMA systems. Belgium has its Épervier, four European armies operate the CL-89 surveillance drone, and the British Army is awaiting GEC Avionics' Phoenix battlefield system as eagerly as the US Army looks forward to fielding Aquila. A few navies are at last beginning to look more favourably at UMAs, but navies have their own special operating problems. For example, as the US Navy has discovered during early trials with the Israeli Pioneer, it is one thing to land a UMA on a flat strip of sunlit desert, but quite another to try catching it in a net mounted on the heaving deck of a ship at sea. Moreover, most ships have enough 'top hamper' on deck already, without adding to it such extra clutter as a launching ramp and retrieval system. Some form of rotorcraft or other VTOL air vehicle would seem to offer a better solution to most naval requirements. Air forces, with very few exceptions, apparently still need educating out of the fear that UMAs are going to make all their human pilots redundant overnight.

On the industry/technological side, the most profitable military missions to pursue in the immediate future seem to be those of reconnaissance and data gathering, electronic intelligence, and detecting and attacking hostile radars.

More research and development effort is still needed to improve the effectiveness and reliability of data links, especially over more than local ranges, and to facilitate payload integration. There must also be honesty in the marketplace, to present UMAs as a means of augmenting rather than supplanting existing ways of conducting a mission; and, as in any marketplace, it is necessary to separate the sheep from the goats. As the contents of this book show very clearly, the range of UMAs developed over the past two decades offers vehicles with payloads ranging from 2·5 kg to over 500 kg (5·5 to 1,102 lb), endurances from 15 minutes to 24 hours or more, and virtually every conceivable kind of land, air or shipboard launch and recovery. As a catalogue of industry capability, it may be impressive, but as an example of over-capacity in a market where potential demand is still limited, it is far less reassuring, and only those designs that can prove themselves the most reliable and cost-effective are likely to survive.

From frigates and smaller ships a small RPH like Canadair's Sentinel, with 3-4 hours' endurance, could perform a variety of useful roles (decoy is illustrated here) without the deck clutter of separate launch and recovery systems

Argentina

FÁBRICA MILITAR DE AVIONES (FMA)

Avenida Fuerza Aérea Argentina Km 5½, 5103 Guarnición
Aérea Córdoba

FMA IA 59

Designed to Argentine Air Force requirements by the Instituto
de Investigaciónes Aeronáuticas y Espaciales (Aerospace
Research Institute), the IA 59 target drone was built by the
Grupo Fabricación of the FMA as an experimental aerial
target for anti-aircraft guns and surface-to-air missiles.
Construction of a prototype, designated IA-X-59-1, began in
1975, and this made its first flight in December 1976. A second
prototype flew in July 1977. Series production was not
undertaken.

TYPE: Remotely controlled aerial target.

AIRFRAME: High-wing monoplane, with torpedo-shaped fuselage and twin-fin tail unit. Single-spar duralumin wings of
constant section and chord, fitted with ailerons. Fuselage of
circular cross-section, with steel central section forming fuel
tank; tapered forward and rear sections of duralumin.
All-dural tailplane, with electrically actuated elevator, and
rectangular twin fins (no rudders). Target floats to permit
recovery from water.

POWER PLANT: One 54/67 kW (72/90 hp) McCulloch
O-100-2 flat-four piston engine, driving a two-blade wooden
propeller. Fuel tank in fuselage, capacity 40 litres (8.75 Imp
gallons; 10.6 US gallons).

LAUNCH AND RECOVERY: Zero-length launch, from ground or
ship's deck, using portable launcher and jettisonable booster
rockets. Parachute system for recovery from land or water.

GUIDANCE AND CONTROL: Radio command guidance system,
developed by IIAE, using 30W FM/FM ground transmitter
operating in 138.67MHz bandwidth. Receiver/decoder
separates command signals into two control channels, plus a
third which stops engine and deploys recovery parachute.
Backup system to initiate recovery sequence automatically if
radio control link is broken. IIAE onboard autopilot acts
under command from ground radio controller to govern
pitch and roll. Vertical gyro provides attitude signals which,
when amplified, govern electrical actuators. Aerodynamic
control by ailerons and elevator.

SYSTEM: 24V 15Ah lead-acid battery for general electrical
supply; 18V 0.5Ah nickel-cadmium battery for signal
circuits.

DIMENSIONS:

Wing span	3.60 m (11 ft 9.75 in)
Wing area	2.25 m² (24.2 sq ft)
Length overall	4.06 m (13 ft 3.75 in)
Tailplane span	1 m (3 ft 3.75 in)
Propeller diameter	1.10 m (3 ft 7.25 in)

WEIGHTS:

Max launching weight	170 kg (375 lb)
Max landing weight	150 kg (330 lb)

PERFORMANCE (at max launching weight):

Max level speed at S/L	172 knots (320 km/h; 199 mph)

Prototype of the FMA IA 59

Stalling speed	65 knots (120 km/h; 75 mph)
Max rate of climb at S/L	1,200 m (3,935 ft)/min
Service ceiling	7,000 m (22,950 ft)
Range with max fuel	172 nm (320 km; 199 miles)
Endurance with max fuel	1 h

QUIMAR SA, CONSTRUCCIONES AERONAUTICAS Y ELECTRONICAS

Gorriti, Córdoba 5000

This company produces three drones known as the MQ-1
Chimango, MQ-2 Bigua and MQ-4 Agilucho, all of which are
variants of the Italian Meteor Mirach series. A common
automatic launcher is used for all three vehicles.

QUIMAR MQ-1 CHIMANGO

The Chimango is a licence-built version of the piston-engined
Meteor Mirach-70 (see Italian section). It serves as a training
target for the crews of anti-aircraft artillery and low/medium
altitude surface-to-air missiles, and can be equipped with
smoke or infra-red emitters in underwing pods, or tow banner
targets at the end of a 100 m (330 ft) nylon cable. The airframe
is of glassfibre reinforced polyester resin, and zero-length ramp
launch is by means of an MQ 8785/NNZ solid propellant
rocket booster which gives 18.63 kN (4,189 lb) thrust for 0.7 s
before the 53.7 kW (72 hp) piston engine takes over. The target
is recovered by parachute. Onboard equipment includes a
Rolido y Cabeceo autopilot and a Quimar miss distance
indicator; missions are controlled by a Meteor Alamak ground
station.

The Argentine Navy reportedly ordered 50 Chimangos in
1986, for target use with its 'Meko' class frigates. Chimango is a
falcon-like bird found in central areas of South America.

DIMENSIONS: As for Mirach-70

WEIGHTS:

Mission payload	10 kg (22 lb)
Fuel	34 kg (75 lb)
Launching weight	184 kg (406 lb)

PERFORMANCE:

Max level speed at S/L	194 knots (360 km/h; 224 mph)
Min operating altitude	200 m (656 ft)
Range	65 nm (120 km; 74.5 miles)
Max endurance	1 h

QUIMAR MQ-2 BIGUA

The transonic, turbojet-powered Bigua is a version of the Italian Mirach-100 (which see), intended for both target and RPV applications. Two versions are planned. Version 1 is for use as a recoverable target, or to tow banner targets, for weapons training of gunnery or missile battery crews; to evaluate new weapons systems or special equipment; and as a reconnaissance RPV trainer. Version 2 is intended to undertake operational missions such as battlefield surveillance, intermediate-range reconnaissance, target acquisition, elint, ECM, attack against sea or air targets, defence saturation, infra-red decoy, and close support. Production was about to begin in 1986. Bigua is a bird found on large rivers and seashores in Central and South America.

Basic configuration is that of a sweptback low-wing monoplane with a dorsal air intake, dihedral tailplane and twin ventral fins. Construction, including control surfaces, is almost entirely of light alloy except for the wing leading edges, fins and parachute container, which are of glassfibre reinforced polyester resin. The MQ-2 is normally launched, by RATO booster rockets, from a zero-length ramp, cruising power being provided by a 1.13 kN (253 lb st) turbojet engine. However, provision is also made for air launch from fixed-wing aircraft or helicopters, and a joint Quimar/Meteor programme was inaugurated in 1985 to adapt the Bigua for launch from beneath the fuselage of an IA 58A Pucará close support aircraft.

The Bigua has a two-stage parachute recovery system, and is fitted with impact absorbers to cushion the landing. An inflatable airbag is provided for recovery from water. The drone is equipped with a three-axis autopilot, and can be either remotely piloted (using Meteor's Alamak ground control system) or pre-programmed when fitted with an automatic navigation kit. Real-time sensors, mounted in the nose compartment, can include low light level TV, a panoramic camera, an infra-red linescanner, or a secure elint transceiver.

DIMENSIONS:

Wing span	1.80 m (5 ft 11 in)
Wing area	0.82 m² (8.83 sq ft)
Length overall	3.90 m (12 ft 9.5 in)
Height overall	0.80 m (2 ft 7.5 in)
Body diameter (max)	0.38 m (1 ft 3 in)

Model of Quimar MQ-2 Bigua under fuselage of an IA 58 Pucará (*Brian M. Service*)

WEIGHTS:

Sensors	40-70 kg (88-154 lb)
Max launching weight (excl boosters)	260 kg (573 lb)
Landing weight with 10 litres (2.2 Imp gallons; 2.6 US gallons) fuel remaining	195 kg (430 lb)

PERFORMANCE:

Max level speed	458 knots (850 km/h; 521 mph)
Ceiling	9,000 m (29,525 ft)
Range at 2,000 m (6,560 ft):	
out and back	216 nm (400 km; 248 miles)
one-way mission	485 nm (900 km; 559 miles)
Endurance at max speed at 9,000 m (29,525 ft)	1 h

QUIMAR MQ-4 AGILUCHO

Quimar was reported in 1986 to be developing a reconnaissance/jamming/communications relay version of the Meteor Mirach-20 (see Italian section), powered by an 18.6 kW (25 hp) piston engine. Known as the Agilucho, this is believed to be the previously unidentified RPV bearing the Quimar designation MQ-4. No further details were known at the time of going to press.

Australia

AEROSPACE TECHNOLOGIES OF AUSTRALIA PTY LTD (ATA)

Fishermen's Bend, Private Bag No. 4, Post Office, Port Melbourne, Victoria 3207

ATA (GAF) JINDIVIK

One of the longest-serving target drones in the world, the Jindivik (Aborigine for 'the hunted one') was designed in 1948 at the former Government Aircraft Factories (GAF) and first flew, in piloted form (as the Pika), two years later. Continually improved and updated since that time, it remains a standard weapons target for its principal customers, Australia and the United Kingdom. Total orders for 502 by early 1986 included 249 for the UK, 163 for joint UK/Australian use at the Woomera range and 37 for the Royal Australian Navy; other earlier recipients were the US Navy (42) and Sweden (10). Jindiviks have flown more than 6,600 sorties at the RAE, Llanbedr, North Wales, and in Australia; one particular Mk 3A drone (WRE 418) was destroyed after successfully completing 285 sorties at Woomera.

The following versions have been built:

Mk 103A Jindivik

Mk 2A. Extended span wings and modified intake. First flown 18 September 1958; 3 built.

Mk 2B. Viper ASV.8 engine. First flown 8 October 1959; 76 built.

Mk 3. Viper ASV.11 engine. First flown 12 May 1961; 9 built.

Mk 3A. First flown 10 November 1961; 147 built, including 10 Mk 203A for RAN. One Mk 203A fitted experimentally in 1975–76 with Bell Aerospace air cushion landing system.

Mk 3B. Viper Mk 201 engine. First flown 22 January 1970; 126 built, including 90 Mk 103B and Mk 103BL for UK, 27 Mk 203B for RAN, and 9 Mk 203B for WRE Woomera. Intended for low level trials at speeds of up to 500 knots (925 km/h; 575 mph). GEC Avionics L4 or L5 autopilot; equipment incorporates printed circuit techniques.

Mk 4A. Improved current production version from March 1981; 15 ordered by UK, of which 10 delivered by January 1986. Rationalised electrical power supply system, integrated electronic systems, and increased speed, endurance and manoeuvring capability (up to more than 6*g*).

For low altitude work, the standard span Mk 4A is fitted with Mk 9 wingtip pods each containing two cameras, a microwave reflector and a small amount of fuel. For high altitude work, also with Mk 9 wing pods, constant chord 1.02 m (40 in) wing extension panels can be added outboard of the pods. For extra high altitude flying (with Mk 5 pods only), these panels can be replaced by 2.03 m (80 in) panels, tapered on the leading edge. A ventral fin is fitted for high altitude and maximum turn rate configurations.

Pika. Piloted prototype, to MoS Specification E.7/48. First flown 31 October 1950. Armstrong Siddeley Adder ASA.1 turbojet (4.6 kN; 1,050 lb st). Span 5.79 m (19 ft 0 in), length 7.11 m (23 ft 3 in). First Australian-designed jet aircraft to fly.

Mk 1. First pilotless version, first flown 28 August 1952. Adder engine; 14 built.

Mk 2. Viper ASV.3 engine (8.45 kN; 1,900 lb st). First flown 11 December 1953; 111 built, including 10 for Sweden.

Cutaway drawing of the Jindivik Mk 3B

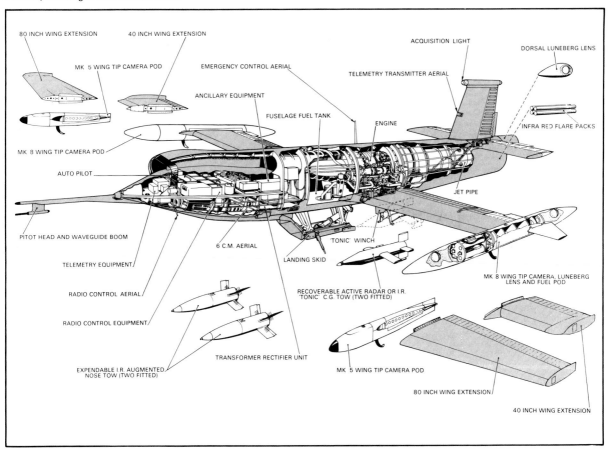

Current production Jindivik 4A with Mk 9 wing pods

The following description applies to the current Mk 4A except where indicated:

TYPE: Recoverable target drone.

AIRFRAME: Low/mid-wing monoplane. Dihedral 2° 30'. Incidence 1°. Bonded multi-spar wing box with integral trailing edge of aluminium alloy. Replaceable foam filled aluminium alloy leading edge. Interspar torsion box forms integral fuel tank. Aluminium alloy monocoque flaps and ailerons. Ailerons fitted with inset geared tab and driven by ATA (GAF) designed twin-motor servo. Flaps operated pneumatically. Aluminium alloy semi-monocoque fuselage. Front portion carries all control equipment, autopilot and telemetry equipment. Pitot head is mounted on nose probe. Moulded glassfibre honeycomb canopy, which lifts off for access to equipment, also forms ram type air intake. Rear end of front fuselage and front end of centre fuselage form bay for all mission equipment. Centre fuselage also houses retractable landing skid. Removable rear fuselage carries engine and jet-pipe. Multi-spar light alloy tailplane. Elevators, with inset geared tabs, driven by ATA (GAF) designed twin-motor servo actuator, operable on one motor. Fin is polyurethane foam filled light alloy skin, bonded to a single spar. No rudder. Ventral fin in max turn rate and high altitude configurations. Pneumatically extended, manually retracted (on ground) central skid. Pneumatic jack acts as shock absorber. Steel auxiliary skids at wingtips. See also paragraph on 'Launch and Recovery'.

POWER PLANT: One Rolls-Royce Viper Mk 201 turbojet engine, rated at 12.36 kN (2,780 lb st). Engine relight capability in the event of flameout. Flexible rubber main fuselage tank, capacity 291 litres (64 Imp gallons; 77 US gallons), and two integral wing tanks, total capacity 173 litres (38 Imp gallons; 45.6 US gallons). Mk 4A has additional 91 litre (20 Imp gallon; 24 US gallon) fuselage tank. Mk 9 pods each hold 86 litres (19 Imp gallons; 22.8 US gallons). Total possible fuel capacity 727 litres (160 Imp gallons; 192 US gallons).

LAUNCH AND RECOVERY: Take-off from aircraft trolley, steered by gyro and servo-controlled nosewheel which responds to signals from ground controller. Aircraft/trolley combination accelerates under normal jet power with flaps retracted and with aircraft set at negative incidence. When unstick speed is reached, aircraft flaps are lowered rapidly. Rotation of aircraft initiates trolley release system and the aircraft climbs away. When Jindivik is in approach run, flaps and skid are selected down for landing. On touchdown, at approx 120 knots (222 km/h; 138 mph), a 'sting' extended below main skid rotates on impact and initiates rapid retraction of flaps. Fuel supply terminated by radio command.

GUIDANCE AND CONTROL: Radio control equipment comprises two UHF receivers and ATA (GAF) auxiliary control unit. GEC Avionics flight control computer, with gyroscope. Telemetry equipment consists of Australian designed transmitter and data unit.

SYSTEMS: Non-regenerative pneumatic system: air stored at 138 bars (2,000 lb/sq in) in power pack which supplies air to flaps and landing skid at reduced pressure of 39.6 bars (575 lb/sq in). Engine driven brushless DC generator, rated at 9 kW at 30V DC. In event of generator failure, a 24V DC battery provides limited power for essential control functions. Automatic orbit and/or destruct systems provided, consistent with range safety requirements.

MISSION EQUIPMENT: Transponders and microwave reflectors for trials of active, semi-active or beam riding missiles. Heat sources, including infra-red flare packs mounted on rear of fuselage, can be fitted to provide low-frequency IR output. Transponders in X, S and C bands can be fitted for target acquisition and to enable Jindivik to be tracked to greater range. Provision for recoverable towed target to be carried under each wing. These tow bodies can carry either active radar, in-flight-commanded IR flares, or forward looking Luneberg lens. They can be towed at 15–150 m (50–500 ft) behind aircraft; recovery by electric winch mounted in centre of fuselage. Other types of special tow may also be carried. Cameras fitted with wide angle lenses are carried in wingtip pods, with all-round viewing capability. Variants are Mk 5 pod with cameras only and Mk 9 with cameras, fuel and provision for fitment of microwave reflectors (Luneberg lenses) in leading edge and/or trailing edge radomes. By fitting rearward-looking prisms to the lower cameras they can record missile performance when Tonic towed targets are used. To simulate different types of aircraft by varying the apparent radar cross-section, Plessey Microwave Ltd has developed a semi-active artificial radar target (SART Mk IV) for operation in a towed configuration with Jindivik as the towing aircraft.

DIMENSIONS:

Wing span:	
short span, low altitude	6.32 m (20 ft 8.99 in)
extended, high altitude	7.92 m (26 ft 6 in)
extended, extra high altitude	9.78 m (32 ft 1.4 in)
Wing area:	
short span	7.06 m² (76 sq ft)
extended span, high altitude	9.48 m² (102 sq ft)
extended span, extra high altitude	10.68 m² (115 sq ft)
Length overall: incl nose probe	8.15 m (26 ft 8.75 in)
excl nose probe	7.11 m (23 ft 3.75 in)
Height overall, skid extended	2.08 m (6 ft 9.85 in)

WEIGHTS (A: Mk 3B, B: Mk 4A):

Weight empty, equipped (min):	
A, B	1,315 kg (2,900 lb)
Max payload:	
A, B (short span versions)	249 kg (550 lb)
A, B (extended span versions)	181 kg (400 lb)
Max T-O weight (short span):	
*A (Mk 5 wing pods)	1,451 kg (3,200 lb)
A (Mk 9 wing pods)	1,655 kg (3,650 lb)
B (Mk 9 wing pods)	1,814 kg (4,000 lb)
Max T-O weight (high altitude):	
*A (Mk 5 wing pods)	1,474 kg (3,250 lb)
A (Mk 9 wing pods)	1,655 kg (3,650 lb)
B (Mk 9 wing pods)	1,814 kg (4,000 lb)

Mk 4A not available in this configuration

Max T-O weight (extra high altitude):
  A and B (Mk 5 wing pods)   1,496 kg (3,300 lb)
PERFORMANCE (A and B as above):
  Max level speed at S/L, all configurations:
    A   530 knots (981 km/h; 610 mph)
    B   540 knots (1,000 km/h; 622 mph)
  Min operating height (short span):
    A (Mk 5 or Mk 9 pods)   15 m (50 ft)
    B (Mk 9 pods)   12 m (40 ft)
  Max operational ceiling (short span):
    A (Mk 5 pods)   17,375 m (57,000 ft)
    A (Mk 9 pods)   16,460 m (54,000 ft)
    B (Mk 9 pods)   15,850 m (52,000 ft)
  Max operational ceiling (high altitude):
    A (Mk 5 pods)   19,200 m (63,000 ft)
    A (Mk 9 pods)   18,595 m (61,000 ft)
    B (Mk 9 pods)   17,985 m (59,000 ft)
  Max operational ceiling (extra high altitude):
    A (Mk 5 pods)   20,420 m (67,000 ft)
    B (Mk 5 pods)   19,810 m (65,000 ft)
  Time to max operational ceiling (A and B):
    short span   26 min
    high altitude   30 min
    extra high altitude   34 min
  Typical max on-station endurance:
    A (short span and high altitude, Mk 5 pods)   1 h 24 min
    A (short span, Mk 9 pods)   1 h 56 min
    B (short span, Mk 9 pods)   1 h 35 min
    A (high altitude, Mk 9 pods)   2 h 17 min
    B (high altitude, Mk 9 pods)   2 h
    A (extra high altitude, Mk 5 pods)   1 h 28 min
    B (extra high altitude, Mk 5 pods)   2 h 5 min
  Max range:
    A (short span, Mk 5 pods)   560 nm (1,038 km; 645 miles)
    A (short span, Mk 9 pods)   800 nm (1,482 km; 921 miles)
    B (short span, Mk 9 pods)   825 nm (1,529 km; 950 miles)
    A (high altitude, Mk 5 pods)
                                740 nm (1,371 km; 852 miles)
    A (high altitude, Mk 9 pods)
                                1,100 nm (2,038 km; 1,266 miles)
    B (high altitude, Mk 9 pods)
                                1,125 nm (2,085 km; 1,295 miles)
    A (extra high altitude, Mk 5 pods)
                                900 nm (1,668 km; 1,036 miles)
    B (extra high altitude, Mk 5 pods)
                                1,160 nm (2,150 km; 1,335 miles)

ATA (GAF) TURANA

First flown on 12 March 1971, Turana was developed by the
Australian Department of Productivity from the Ikara
anti-submarine missile, initially to meet a Royal Australian
Navy staff requirement for a gunnery and guided weapons
target. Construction had to ensure an average life of at least 10
flights per drone, with equipment designed for at least 20
complete missions, including sea-water immersion. Operational
evaluation of 12 drones by the RAN up to 1979 demonstrated
sea-skimming gunnery presentation, from 25 nm (46 km; 29
miles) at 15 m (50 ft), low-altitude flight at 11.25 m (37 ft), and
precision control during gunnery engagements by two ships.
The drone was capable of demand turns of up to 3g,
customer-specified manoeuvres of more than 10g, and demand
heading changes of up to 26°, but the Turana programme was
discontinued in 1980.

Turana on a test flight from the RAN range at Jervis Bay, NSW

TYPE: Recoverable target drone.
AIRFRAME: Mid-wing cropped-delta monoplane, with vertical
  tail fin (all steering by autopilot and full-span symmetrically
  or differentially operated elevons). Detachable wings, with
  metal spars and ribs; remainder of foam-filled glassfibre.
  Aluminium-skinned fin, except for glassfibre tip and trailing
  edge. Aluminium alloy torsion box fuselage, with removable
  glassfibre fairings. No landing gear.
POWER PLANT: One 0.78 kN (176 lb st) Microturbo Couguar
  022 turbojet engine with compressed air starting. Engine
  speed controlled by electronic unit forming part of speed
  demand loop. Stainless steel/airbag fuel tank of 51.8 litres
  (11.4 Imp gallons; 13.7 US gallons) capacity; airbag
  pressurised from engine compressor.
BOOSTER: Single-nozzle PMD41 solid propellant rocket motor
  developed specially for Turana; attached to fuselage by
  swivelling links and two explosive bolts. Nominal burn time
  2 s, nominal thrust 26.7 kN (6,000 lb); jettisoned at end of
  boost phase.
LAUNCH AND RECOVERY: Launched from standard Ikara ship
  launcher, or from lightweight portable launcher, at fixed
  elevation of 22° 30′. Command parachute recovery,
  activated automatically in event of engine, electrical power
  system or command link failure. Parachute housed in
  ejectable nose compartment. Short or long time delays could
  be included in command link failure mode to allow for
  momentary signal fades. Designed for water recovery.
GUIDANCE AND CONTROL: Initial guidance equipment (housed in
  fin) adapted from Ikara system on board RAN ships;
  navigation by Ikara tracking receiver and ship's plotting
  facilities. Control by open loop demands from ground and
  closed loop sensing and autocontrol system in drone.
  Three-axis autopilot; air data unit; provision for radar
  altimeter to permit automatically controlled flight at low
  altitudes.
MISSION EQUIPMENT: All onboard systems powered electrically
  for one hour by rechargeable battery pack in ventral
  compartment. Pyrotechnic charge for ejection of nose
  section. Smoke system for visual augmentation; forward-
  looking passive radar augmentation by 190 mm Luneberg
  lens in nose. Space/weight provisions for active augmentation
  devices, telemetry system, flares, miss distance indicator etc.
DIMENSIONS:
  Wing span   1.53 m (5 ft 0.2 in)
  Wing area   1.23 m² (13.2 sq ft)
  Length overall   3.37 m (11 ft 0.5 in)
  Height: excl booster   1.02 m (3 ft 4 in)
          incl booster   1.19 m (3 ft 10.8 in)

WEIGHTS:

Weight empty	196 kg (432 lb)
Fuel	41 kg (91 lb)
Mission equipment	more than 45 kg (100 lb)
Gross weight (excl booster)	240 kg (529 lb)
Weight at launch	293 kg (646 lb)
Weight at recovery (empty)	187 kg (412 lb)

PERFORMANCE:

Max level speed	500 knots (927 km/h; 576 mph)
Boost acceleration (nominal)	10g
End-of-boost speed	332 knots (534 km/h; 382 mph)
Max rate of climb at S/L	1,219 m (4,000 ft)/min
Service ceiling	20,000 m (65,625 ft)
Range	174 nm (322 km; 200 miles)
Max endurance	34 min

AIRSHIP DEVELOPMENTS AUSTRALIA PTY LTD (ADA)

96 Rankins Road, Kensington, Victoria 3031

Earlier airship designs by Mr Bruce Blake have included a pair of drones, a single- and two-seat non-rigid, a twin-engined, four/six-seat light utility airship (LUA), and a 50-passenger tourist craft. A scaled-down drone version of the LUA is known as the Albatross. First flown in early 1986, the Albatross is intended to prove several innovative features, including a lifting outrigger with a blown flap. The full size LUA, for which preliminary design work has been completed, is known as the **ADA-1200**. The following description relates to the one-third scale prototype:

ADA ALBATROSS

ENVELOPE: The envelope is a two-skin type, the inner (gas cell) being made from metallised laminated nylon film while the outer (load carrying) skin is of stabilised polyester fabric. The inner skin will eventually conform to the shape of the outer skin as it stretches with use. A single spherical ballonet (volume 8 m³; 283 cu ft) is provided, constructed from nylon film. Automatic pressure control is achieved by the use of a pressure switch, an electric centrifugal blower (with a one-way flow valve) and an outflow valve. An overpressure

The Airship Developments Albatross remotely controlled scale prototype *(The Age, Melbourne)*

valve is provided to vent helium, should envelope pressure exceed safe limits. Additionally, a remotely controlled dump valve enables the initiation of a controlled descent if the propulsion system should fail. Albatross has an X-fin tail unit, each fin being fitted with a 'ruddervator' actuated by servos, with electronic mixing, to provide control in pitch and yaw. The fins are constructed from balsa wood and covered with a heat-shrunk polyester film.

POWER PLANT: Two 2.6 kW (3.5 hp) Robin EY15D single-cylinder four-stroke engines, lightened in weight and each fitted with an electric starter/generator. Engines are mounted on stub-wings, each with direct drive to a two-blade wooden propeller. Single fuel tank in spine fairing, max capacity 15 litres (3.3 Imp gallons; 4 US gallons).

GONDOLA, SPINE AND WINGS: The cabin/spine unit is unusually large, in comparison with gondolas fitted to existing non-rigid airships, but is in fact of scale size, and is an innovation of the LUA design. The Albatross is not entirely representative of the full sized ADA-1200, since the CG of the cabin/spine is aft of the appropriate position, and the two-skin envelope precludes a conventional internal suspension system. Instead, cords at the wingtips provide the missing support. Materials used in the cabin/spine are hand layered glass/epoxy/PVC foam sandwich, with aircraft plywood structural reinforcing. The wing, lifting outrigger or lift plane, attached to the rear of the spine, is constructed from light gauge aluminium alloy sheet and provides structural attachment for the engines and main landing gear units. The trailing edge is formed by a 30% chord flap, servo actuated to ±40° deflection. This provides a useful increment of aerodynamic lift control. The tricycle landing gear has gas strut shock absorption and twin wheels, with 5.5 in pneumatic tyres, on each unit.

GUIDANCE AND CONTROL: A standard FM radio control unit is used for line-of-sight operation. Minor modification was made to enable the use of a large external battery for the transmitter, with a similar improvement at the receiver. Control is provided for throttles, 'ruddervators', flaps and dump valve; three channels remain unused. The system provides an electronic discriminator for 'fail-safe' operation in the event of signal interference. Advanced RPV television based guidance is a possibility for future out-of-sight operations.

DIMENSIONS, OVERALL:

Length	12 m (39 ft 4.5 in)
Height	4.40 m (14 ft 5.25 in)
Width	3.60 m (11 ft 9.75 in)

DIMENSIONS, ENVELOPE:

Length	12 m (39 ft 4.5 in)
Max diameter	3.20 m (10 ft 6 in)
Volume	76 m³ (2,684 cu ft)

DIMENSIONS, GONDOLA/WINGS:

Gondola: Length	3.90 m (12 ft 9.5 in)
Height (incl landing gear)	1 m (3 ft 3.25 in)
Wing span	2.10 m (6 ft 10.75 in)
Wheel track	2 m (6 ft 6.75 in)
Wheelbase	2.50 m (8 ft 2.5 in)
Propeller diameter	0.76 m (2 ft 6 in)

WEIGHTS:

Weight empty	64 kg (141 lb)
Max fuel	11 kg (24 lb)
Max payload	11 kg (24 lb)

PERFORMANCE (estimated):
  Max level speed (neutral buoyancy)
                        40 knots (74 km/h; 46 mph)
  Max cruising speed, 75% power
                        38 knots (70 km/h; 44 mph)

HAWKER DE HAVILLAND AUSTRALIA PTY LTD (HDH)

PO Box 30, Milperra Road, Bankstown, NSW 2200

Hawker de Havilland's only known venture into the field of unmanned aircraft is a series of three similar-looking target vehicles produced during the middle and late 1970s.

HDH-10 ENMOTH

HDH developed the Enmoth in 1975 to provide an aiming and scoring system for the Royal Australian Army's Redeye surface-to-air missiles. The complete system comprised the target aircraft, a transport container, and a self-contained ground support package. Twelve production Enmoths were ordered in January 1977. The first of these was flown that April, and deliveries began two months later.

TYPE: Miniature target aircraft.
AIRFRAME: Cropped-delta monoplane, with wings of glassfibre covered foam plastics. Elevon on each trailing edge. Circular-section fuselage, blending into wings at their point of maximum thickness. Cropped-delta fin and rudder. Non-retractable tricycle landing gear, with wide-track main gear and steerable nosewheel.

Hawker de Havilland Enmoth

POWER PLANT: One 1.5 kW (2 hp) K & B 61 piston engine, driving a two-blade propeller. Fuel in four plastic tanks.
LAUNCH AND RECOVERY: Normally by conventional T-O and landing. Parachute recovery optional.
GUIDANCE AND CONTROL: Radio command guidance. Aerodynamic control by elevons (roll and pitch) and rudder.
MISSION EQUIPMENT: Infra-red source, with all-round 'view', on top of fin. Radio control receiver and payload housed in fuselage. Futaba flight controls and actuators.
DIMENSIONS:
  Wing span   1.52 m (5 ft)
  Length overall   1.57 m (5 ft 2 in)
  Height overall   0.56 m (1 ft 10 in)
  Wheel track   0.61 m (2 ft)
  Wheelbase   0.58 m (1 ft 11 in)
WEIGHTS:
  Weight empty   6.8 kg (15 lb)
  Max normal fuel   1.5 kg (3.25 lb)
  *Max normal payload   3 kg (6.75 lb)
  Max normal T-O weight   11.3 kg (25 lb)
  *Payload capability at a min speed of 17 knots (32 km/h; 20 mph) is over 3 kg (6.75 lb) and at a min speed of 29 knots (55 km/h; 34 mph) is over 5 kg (11 lb)
PERFORMANCE (at max T-O weight: A at max power, B at 50% power):
  Max level speed:
    A   70 knots (130 km/h; 81 mph)
    B   57 knots (106 km/h; 66 mph)
  Stalling speed:
    A   20 knots (37 km/h; 23 mph)
    B   30 knots (56 km/h; 35 mph)
  Endurance:
    A   35 min
    B   52 min

HDH-11 BEEMOTH

The Beemoth had a similar planform to Enmoth, double the linear dimensions, greatly increased payload capacity, and a 'pusher' propeller. No other details known.

HDH-12 PROMOTH

The Promoth mini-RPV was designed specifically as a tough, low-cost expendable target for small-arms gunnery practice. Three prototypes were flown, and development was completed, but plans for series production in 1978 did not materialise.

AIRFRAME: Cropped-delta monoplane, with 'flat plate' section wings of glassfibre-covered foam. Elevon on each trailing edge. Rectangular section fuselage. Cropped-delta fin, also of 'flat plate' section. Skid landing gear.
POWER PLANT: One K & B 40 piston engine, driving a pusher propeller; fuel in centre-section.
LAUNCH AND RECOVERY: Catapult launch and net recovery; skid landing on grass also possible. Both methods proved in flight trials.
GUIDANCE AND CONTROL: Standard Futaba radio control link and actuators, providing pitch, roll and throttle control.
DIMENSIONS:
  Wing span   1 m (3 ft 3.25 in)
  Length overall   1.12 m (3 ft 8 in)
  Height overall   0.34 m (1 ft 1.5 in)

HDH-12 Promoth

WEIGHTS:
Weight empty	3.2 kg (7.05 lb)
Max fuel	0.73 kg (1.61 lb)

PERFORMANCE (at average weight of 3.6 kg; 8 lb):
Max level speed	100 knots (185 km/h; 115 mph)
Recommended net recovery speed	
	30–35 knots (56–65 km/h; 34–40 mph)
Max rate of climb at S/L	823 m (2,700 ft)/min
Rate of roll at 100 knots (185 km/h; 115 mph)	
	approx 360°/s

Belgium

MANUFACTURE BELGE DE LAMPES ET DE MATERIEL ELECTRONIQUE SA (MBLE)

80 rue des Deux Gares, B-1070 Brussels

MBLE has contributed to several NATO and national military aircraft programmes such as the F-104G Starfighter, F-16 Fighting Falcon, and refits to Belgian Air Force Mirages. It also developed the all-Belgian Épervier reconnaissance RPV.

MBLE ÉPERVIER (SPARROWHAWK)

Developed and built entirely in Belgium, the Épervier is a complete battlefield reconnaissance system comprising the drone aircraft, their sensors, a short ramp launcher, and a drone control centre (DCC) containing all necessary electronic equipment for guidance and tracking. A mobile unit for photographic processing and interpretation is also part of the system. Initially developed to meet NATO specifications, the Épervier X-1 prototype flew for the first time on 24 April 1965. The programme received Belgian government financial support on 11 July 1969, and after further development to meet Belgian Army requirements an initial production order was placed in 1974. This was for 43 air vehicles and their associated ground equipment, and these were delivered in 1976 to equip two Épervier platoons, one of which is based in West Germany. An identical system (except that it used a programme

MBLE Épervier leaving its mobile launcher

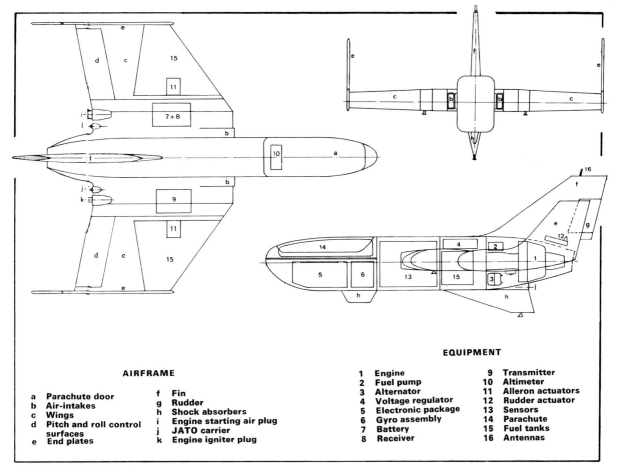

AIRFRAME

a	Parachute door	f	Fin
b	Air-intakes	g	Rudder
c	Wings	h	Shock absorbers
d	Pitch and roll control surfaces	i	Engine starting air plug
e	End plates	j	JATO carrier
		k	Engine igniter plug

EQUIPMENT

1	Engine	9	Transmitter
2	Fuel pump	10	Altimeter
3	Alternator	11	Aileron actuators
4	Voltage regulator	12	Rudder actuator
5	Electronic package	13	Sensors
6	Gyro assembly	14	Parachute
7	Battery	15	Fuel tanks
8	Receiver	16	Antennas

Main features of the MBLE Épervier

encoder/decoder and different radio frequencies) was offered to non-NATO countries under the name **Asmodée**, but did not go into production.

TYPE: Recoverable battlefield reconnaissance drone/RPV.

AIRFRAME: Mid-wing monoplane with single fin and rudder. Very low aspect ratio swept wings, with endplate fin/winglet at each tip and full-span trailing edge elevons. Box-shaped fuselage, with impact absorbing fairings fore and aft on underside. Basic airframe structure, manufactured by Sonaca under subcontract, is of aluminium alloy with a GRP skin.

POWER PLANT: One 0.49 kN (110 lb st) Lucas CT3201 engine; 11.77 kN (2,645 lb st) JATO bottle for launch boost. Fuel tanks in fuselage and each wing.

LAUNCH AND RECOVERY: Launched from short, orientatable truck-mounted launcher with aid of recoverable JATO rocket booster. Parachute recovery, with guaranteed CEP of 150 m (500 ft).

GUIDANCE AND CONTROL: Radio command guidance system. Flight can be pre-programmed, radio guided, or a mixture of the two. Aerodynamic control by elevons and rudder.

MISSION EQUIPMENT: Usual sensors are an Omera 5 in AA3-70 or Oude-Delft 70 mm TA8 daytime camera, or an Omera 70 mm AA6-62 night camera with Alkan 505 16-round flare launcher. Also suitable for carriage of SAT Cyclope infra-red linescan or Teledyne Brown LLLTV, both with real-time transmission. Aircraft is capable of photographing either pinpoint targets or large areas of terrain during guided and/or programmed flights up to more than 50 nm (93 km; 57 miles) from launch site.

DIMENSIONS:

Wing span	1.72 m (5 ft 7.75 in)
Length overall	2.38 m (7 ft 9.75 in)
Height overall	0.92 m (3 ft 0.25 in)
Payload compartment volume	0.024 m³ (0.85 cu ft)

WEIGHTS:

Payload (max)	20 kg (45 lb)
Fuel	26 kg (57.3 lb)
Max launching weight	147 kg (324 lb)

PERFORMANCE:

Cruising speed	270 knots (500 km/h; 310 mph)
Max rate of climb at S/L	720 m (2,362 ft)/min
Max mission radius	more than 50 nm (93 km; 57 miles)
Endurance	more than 25 min

Brazil

AERONAVES E MOTORES SA (AEROMOT)

Aeroporto Internacional, Salgado Filho (PO Box 8031),
90201 Porto Alegre, RS

AEROMOT K1 AM

The K1 AM is an Aeromot design, based on the airframe of imported Northrop KD2R-5 target drones but using a Brazilian engine and equipment. Design began in December 1984, and construction of a prototype started in April 1985; this was due to make its first flight in early 1987. Ten K1 AMs have been ordered, including six pre-production examples, for the Brazilian Navy's Grupo de Alvos da Esquadra (Fleet Target Group).

TYPE: Recoverable target drone.

AIRFRAME: Tapered high-wing monoplane, of duralumin construction, with oval section monocoque fuselage and conventional tail surfaces. Fuel tank, in forward fuselage, is made of stainless steel. Wingtip radar reflector pods are of epoxy resin, reinforced with glassfibre. No landing gear.

POWER PLANT: One 65.6 kW (88 hp) Aeromot AM 11003 flat-four two-stroke engine, driving a two-blade fixed-pitch wooden propeller.

LAUNCH AND RECOVERY: Platform-launched, using a 12.75 kN (2,866 lb st) solid propellant booster rocket motor. Recovery is made by 11.58 m (38 ft) diameter parachute stowed in fuselage immediately aft of wings; deployment is initiated normally by ground control operator, or automatically in the event of communications or engine failure. Recovery can be made on land or from water.

GUIDANCE AND CONTROL: Radio command guidance system, transmitting to digital autopilot via onboard receiver/decoder to eliminate interference from other frequencies. Vertical gyro, distribution box, receiver computer, battery box and dual servos, and their connecting cables, are all sealed against sea water infiltration. Conventional aerodynamic control surfaces. In the event of communications failure, autopilot is programmed to continue flight until link is restored, or to deploy parachute if this is not achieved within a specified time.

DIMENSIONS:
Wing span:	
without reflector pods	3.502 m (11 ft 5.875 in)
with reflector pods	4.02 m (13 ft 2.25 in)
Wing area	1.73 m² (18.62 sq ft)
Length overall	3.84 m (12 ft 7.25 in)
Fuselage (oval section):	
Max depth	0.346 m (1 ft 1.5 in)
Max width	0.243 m (9.5 in)
Propeller diameter	1.12 m (3 ft 8 in)

WEIGHTS:
Basic operating weight empty	130 kg (287 lb)
Fuel	33 kg (73 lb)
Max launching weight	163 kg (360 lb)

PERFORMANCE (estimated at max launching weight):
Never-exceed speed	240 knots (444 km/h; 276 mph)
Max level speed at S/L	194 knots (360 km/h; 224 mph)
Stalling speed	68 knots (125 km/h; 78 mph)
Max rate of climb at S/L	1,000 m (3,280 ft)/min
Max operating height	4,000 m (13,125 ft)
Max range at S/L	150 nm (278 km; 173 miles)
Endurance at S/L	50 min

CENTRO TÉCNICO AEROESPACIAL (CTA)

PO Box 6001, 12200 São José dos Campos, SP

CTA ACAUÃ (HAWK)

Development was continuing in 1987 of this small propeller-driven RPV, which flew for the first time in March 1986. A number of minor accidents were incurred during the first year or so of flight testing, involving several prototypes. One with a GRP/epoxy airframe was due to fly in 1987.

As the illustration shows, the Acauã is a shoulder-wing aircraft, having a box-section fuselage, twin tailbooms supporting a twin tail unit, and non-retractable tricycle landing gear. Payload is a nose mounted TV camera.

POWER PLANT: One 14.9 kW (20 hp) two-cylinder two-stroke engine, driving a two-blade pusher propeller.

DIMENSIONS:
Wing span	5.00 m (16 ft 4.75 in)
Length overall	4.72 m (15 ft 5.75 in)
Propeller diameter	0.80 m (2 ft 7.5 in)

Aeromot K1 AM Brazilian Navy target

CTA Acauã experimental mini-RPV (*Francisco V. S. Ferro*)

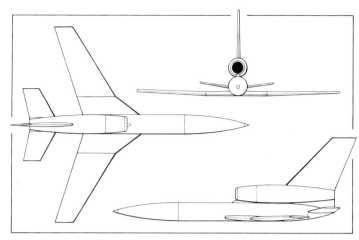

Three-view drawing of the CBT BQM-1BR
(Michael A. Badrocke)

WEIGHT:
    Max T-O weight   100 kg (220.5 lb)
PERFORMANCE:
    Max level speed   65 knots (120 km/h; 74 mph)
    Stalling speed   less than 33 knots (60 km/h; 37 mph)
    T-O run   less than 150 m (492 ft)

COMPANHIA BRASILEIRA DE TRATORES (CBT)

Caixa Postal 376, 13560 São Carlos, SP

CBT BQM-1BR

Claimed to be Brazil's first remotely piloted vehicle, the BQM-1 BR was designed by the Aeronautical Division of CBT, a long established tractor manufacturer; the power plant was developed by the PMO-Divisão de Mecânica (Mechanics Division) of the CTA (Aerospace Technical Centre) and manufactured by CBT.

General appearance of the BQM-1 BR is shown in the accompanying drawing. Missions envisaged included aerial target, tactical reconnaissance (with TV camera), and attack; a version for civil applications, including crop-dusting, was also projected. The BQM-1 BR was intended to make its first flight in 1983, but no confirmation of this, or any other news of the RPV, has been seen.

TYPE: Multi-purpose mini-RPV.
AIRFRAME: All-metal (light alloy) low-wing monoplane. Wings have 3° dihedral, 4° incidence, and are sweptback 33° over most of span, increasing to 55° at root. Conventional semi-monocoque fuselage, of circular cross-section. Fixed incidence tailplane, with 5° dihedral and 30° leading edge sweep. Fin sweptback 45°.
POWER PLANT: One 0.30 kN (67.5 lb st) PMO/CBT Tietê turbojet engine, mounted in nacelle on top of rear fuselage at base of fin.
LAUNCH AND RECOVERY: Takes off on tricycle type landing gear which is jettisoned after take-off.
GUIDANCE AND CONTROL: Radio command guidance system, using a six-channel VHF-FM radio with a range of 11 nm (20 km; 12.5 miles).

DIMENSIONS:
    Wing span   3.18 m (10 ft 5.25 in)
    Length overall   3.89 m (12 ft 9.25 in)
    Fuselage: Length   3.50 m (11 ft 5.75 in)
        Max diameter   0.28 m (11 in)
    Height overall   1.28 m (4 ft 2.5 in)
    Tailplane span   1.10 m (3 ft 7.25 in)
WEIGHT:
    Max T-O weight   93 kg (205 lb)
PERFORMANCE (estimated):
    Max level speed at 6,100 m (20,000 ft)   Mach 0.7
    Max endurance   45 min

INDUSTRIA GAÚCHA DE AERONAVES ESPECIAIS LTDA (IGAE)

Rua Padre Henrique Koelher 87, 90000 Porto Alegre, RS

IGAE LAH/EB

The designation of this delta-winged mini-RPV is derived from the names of its joint designers (1st Lt Luis Arcari and engineer Airton Hoch) and the fact that it was developed for the Brazilian Army (Exército Brasileiro). It is powered by a Japanese 2.6 kW (3.5 hp) OS Max 1.08 model aircraft engine, installed in the nose and driving a two-blade fixed-pitch wooden propeller, with a 1 litre (0.22 Imp gallon; 0.26 US

IGAE's LAH/EB mini-delta target for the Brazilian Army
(Antonio F. Rosa Dini)

gallon) fuel tank. The LAH/EB has a tricycle landing gear, no horizontal tail surfaces, and is operated under line-of-sight radio control. Deliveries were due to begin in late 1986.

DIMENSIONS:
Wing span	1.50 m (4 ft 11 in)
Length overall	1.20 m (3 ft 11.25 in)

WEIGHTS:
Not known
PERFORMANCE:
Endurance	35 min

Canada

BOEING OF CANADA LTD (Winnipeg Division)

99 Murray Park Road, Winnipeg, Manitoba R3J 3M6

Boeing of Canada's Winnipeg Division has for many years produced a wide variety of aerial targets including the Milkcan towed target, passive radar-augmented projectile (PRAP), and Robot-5, and Robot-9 rocket-boosted ballistic targets. These are outside the scope of this volume. Manoeuvring aircraft-type vehicles have included the DRES Robot-X, Targetair TATS 102 (which see), Dragon Fly, and Continental scale simulations of the MiG-27 'Flogger-D' (see US section). A scale representation of the 'Hind-D' helicopter is under development.

BOEING 'HIND-D' TARGET

Eight prototypes have been ordered of this one-fifth scale representation of the Mil Mi-24 'Hind-D' attack helicopter, the first one being flown in mid-1985. It was developed to simulate both attack and evasive manoeuvres by the Mi-24, but modular front and rear fuselage sections can be replaced with others to represent any modern single main rotor helicopter.

The target was originally developed, and the first prototype manufactured, by Gorham Model Products of Calabasas, California. Gorham is now teamed with Boeing Canada (which holds a world product mandate for the target) to carry out advanced development of the system.

TYPE: Recoverable miniature helicopter target.
AIRFRAME: Glassfibre fuselage shell with replaceable front and rear sections. Two-blade main and tail rotors, with simple but reliable drive train. Non-retractable tricycle landing gear.

Boeing Canada's one-fifth scale 'Hind-D' target

POWER PLANT: One 18.6 kW (25 hp) 342 cc Normalair-Garrett WAEL 342 two-cylinder piston engine. Fuel for 30 min operation initially.
GUIDANCE AND CONTROL: PCM radio control system. Remote flight operations include jinking, hovering, and 'S' turns in slow forward flight. Rate gyro to assist yaw control. Control system may be developed to permit fully automatic flight.
DIMENSIONS:
Main rotor diameter	3.35 m (11 ft)
Tail rotor diameter	0.66 m (2 ft 2 in)
Wing span	1.37 m (4 ft 6 in)
Fuselage: Max width	0.36 m (1 ft 2 in)
Height overall	0.99 m (3 ft 3 in)
Wheel track	0.55 m (1 ft 9.5 in)

WEIGHTS:
Max payload	27.2 kg (60 lb)
Normal T-O weight (incl 7.7 kg; 17 lb ballast)	47.5 kg (105 lb)
Max permissible T-O weight	56.7 kg (125 lb)

PERFORMANCE (required by specification):
Max level speed at 5–25 m (15–80 ft) above S/L	60 knots (111 km/h; 69 mph)
Min ascent/descent velocity at 5–25 m (15–80 ft) above S/L	55 m (180 ft)/min
Ceiling	3,050 m (10,000 ft)
Endurance	1 h

BOEING DRAGON FLY

The Dragon Fly was designed in 1980 by Boeing Commercial Airplane Company in Seattle, originally as a maritime RPV to provide expendable sea-launched surveillance in various tactical situations. It can be stored complete with its launcher within a 5.33 × 1.12 × 0.86 m (17 ft 6 in × 3 ft 8 in × 2 ft 10 in) container. Payloads are mounted in port and starboard pods beneath the forward fuselage.

The programme was later transferred to Boeing Canada, which in 1986 had suspended marketing pending completion of further development and updating of the system. The following description applies to the original version:

TYPE: Expendable surveillance mini-RPV.
AIRFRAME: High-wing monoplane with V tail surfaces and non-retractable tricycle landing gear.
POWER PLANT: One 13.4 kW (18 hp) Herbrandson Dyad 220 two-stroke engine, driving a two-blade propeller.

LAUNCH AND RECOVERY: Rail-launched by semi-automatic electro-pneumatic device using compressed air at 86 bars (1,250 lb/sq in) to accelerate the RPV along the launch tube. After launch the Dragon Fly climbs to cruise altitude, manoeuvres as programmed, and flies to designated target co-ordinates.

GUIDANCE AND CONTROL: Normally pre-programmed, but autopilot can respond to command changes (i.e. to alter loiter pattern), and can control and dispense onboard stores.

MISSION EQUIPMENT: Payload pod each side beneath forward fuselage. Port pod houses ESM equipment which can scan a frequency band and provide a directional heading for targets radiating in that band. Starboard (TV) pod provides capability to identify and visually monitor the horizon; it incorporates a zoom lens and an automatic iris control.

DIMENSIONS AND WEIGHTS:
Not known

PERFORMANCE (A: non-loiter mode, B: loiter mode at 610 m; 2,000 ft):
Cruising speed:

A	51 knots (95 km/h; 59 mph)
B	32 knots (60 km/h; 37 mph)
Operating altitude (A and B):	
min	30 m (100 ft)
max	3,660 m (12,000 ft)
Range:	
A	238 nm (441 km; 274 miles)
B	360 nm (667 km; 414 miles)
Endurance:	
A	2 h 30 min
B	6 h

BOEING (CONTINENTAL) MiG-27 'FLOGGER-D' TARGET

Boeing of Canada is marketing outside the USA the C125M and other scale versions of the MiG-27 'Flogger-D' target designed by Continental RPVs of Barstow, California. Details of these can be found under the Continental heading in the US section. The Boeing versions are updated with electronic control and stability systems, have increased flight duration, and are marketed as a low-cost target aircraft recognition training system (TARTS).

Robot-X rocket powered target, built for DRE Suffield by Boeing of Canada *(Brian M. Service)*

BOEING (DRES) ROBOT-X

Newest and most sophisticated addition to the Robot family, the Robot-X was designed by Defence Research Establishment Suffield (which see). It is intended primarily to simulate a low-altitude anti-ship missile or invader aircraft, able to exercise point defence missile systems such as Sea Sparrow. It can also be used as a lookdown/shootdown target for aircraft, or as a low level air defence target for ground forces.

Ten Robot-Xs have been ordered. First flight took place on 4 November 1986.

TYPE: Recoverable rocket-powered target drone.

AIRFRAME: Bullet-shaped body with sweptback rear-mounted wings, with endplate fins, and sweptback, all-moving nose-mounted foreplanes; modular construction, entirely of composite materials. Wings have a shockless symmetrical section, 37° sweepback at quarter chord, and no anhedral or dihedral. Foreplanes and ailerons actuated by Simmonds Precision electric servo. No landing gear.

POWER PLANT: Nineteen 2.75 in CRV-7 rocket motors fired sequentially to achieve over-the-radar-horizon ranges.

LAUNCH AND RECOVERY: Rocket launch (see preceding paragraph); normally surface-launched, but air or sea-borne launch optional. Parachute recovery system.

GUIDANCE AND CONTROL: Pre-programmed manoeuvres using microprocessor-based onboard three-axis digital autopilot.

MISSION EQUIPMENT: Payload capability for miss distance scoring system, chaff dispenser, infra-red flares or radar or visual augmentation devices. 28V battery supply for DC power.

DIMENSIONS:

Wing span	2.40 m (7 ft 10.5 in)
Wing area	1.25 m² (13.45 sq ft)
Foreplane span	1.10 m (3 ft 7.25 in)
Foreplane area	0.35 m² (3.77 sq ft)
Length overall	3.40 m (11 ft 2 in)
Length of fuselage	2.80 m (9 ft 2.25 in)
Body diameter (max)	0.415 m (1 ft 4.25 in)

WEIGHTS:

Max payload	22.7 kg (50 lb)
Max launching weight	250 kg (550 lb)

PERFORMANCE (surface launch):

Never-exceed speed	Mach 0.95
Max level speed at S/L	Mach 0.85
Operating altitude (surface launch):	
min	30 m (100 ft)
max	4,575 m (15,000 ft)
Max range at S/L	21 nm (40 km; 25 miles)
Endurance at S/L	6 min
Max endurance	30 min

BRITISH COLUMBIA RESEARCH COUNCIL (Division of Environment and Health)
3650 Wesbrook Mall, Vancouver, British Columbia
V6S 2L2

In 1982 BC Research began investigating the feasibility, advantages and limitations of using inexpensive RPA (remotely piloted aircraft) systems to acquire small format aerial photography in environmental applications. The Council's first such research RPAs were the Aerie and Condor. Research work on RPAs is reported to have ended, but is believed to have benefited the commercial types produced by Control Technologies Inc (which see).

BC RESEARCH AERIE

This Phase 1 RPA was assembled from a commercially available hobbyist model aircraft and modified to carry a 35 mm camera with autowinder which was operated from the ground by radio control. It was also equipped with removable twin floats, permitting operation from lakes, rivers and coastal waters. The Aerie was used primarily to obtain operating experience, and to demonstrate the value of low-altitude aerial photography, but its usefulness was limited by the low payload capability.

DIMENSIONS:
Wing span	2.70 m (8 ft 10.25 in)
Wing area	1.51 m² (16.25 sq ft)
Length overall	2.24 m (7 ft 4.25 in)

WEIGHTS:
Weight empty	11.4 kg (25 lb)
Max payload	4.5 kg (10 lb)

PERFORMANCE (1.5 kW; 2 hp engine):
Speed range	21–43 knots (40–80 km/h; 25–50 mph)
Rate of climb at S/L (without payload)	300 m (984 ft)/min

BC RESEARCH CONDOR

Condor was a custom designed system, developed to demonstrate RPA technology to interested government agencies and private companies. The prototype was completed in spring 1983, and three were flying by the spring of 1984. These were of conventional tractor monoplane configuration. Of modular design, the Condor could be operated from either land or water. Its specification limited its deployment to study areas of less than 5 km² (1.9 sq miles) and operating altitudes not exceeding 1,000 m (3,280 ft). However, in many applications it provided timely and inexpensive aerial photographs suitable for localised and detailed environmental mapping and monitoring programmes. Normal or infra-red photography could be undertaken.

The description which follows applies to a modified version proposed for 1984 production. So far as is known, however, this was not built.

AIRFRAME: High-wing monoplane, with central fuselage nacelle and twin-boom tail unit. Detachable wings of Clark Y aerofoil section, made of epoxied glassfibre with a foam core, with crushable wingtips and aluminium tube spars. Wooden frame fuselage pod with aluminium skin; nosecone of epoxied glassfibre. Tail unit, of similar construction to wings, carried on twin tailbooms of PVC coated aluminium tube. Four-wheel landing gear (compression springs on front pair, spring steel legs on steerable rear wheels), but prototype operated successfully with removable twin-float gear.

POWER PLANT: One 4.8 kW (6.5 hp) Ekco DP-210 Fire Twin flat-twin two-stroke engine, driving a two-blade pusher propeller.

LAUNCH AND RECOVERY: Conventional take-off and landing.

GUIDANCE AND CONTROL: Digitally encoded radio command (Skyleader PCM control system); automatic flight controllers.

MISSION EQUIPMENT: Two gimbal-mounted 35 mm cameras (panchromatic and/or infra-red) in payload bay; video surveillance camera.

DIMENSIONS:
Wing span	3.65 m (11 ft 11.75 in)
Wing area	2.23 m² (24 sq ft)
Length overall	2.31 m (7 ft 7 in)
Length of fuselage nacelle	1.04 m (3 ft 5 in)
Height overall	1.07 m (3 ft 6 in)
Propeller diameter	0.61 m (2 ft)

WEIGHTS:
Weight empty	18.2 kg (40 lb)
Max payload	9.2 kg (20.3 lb)

PERFORMANCE (estimated, at max T-O weight except where indicated):
Max level speed at S/L	54 knots (100 km/h; 62 mph)
Stalling speed	17 knots (30 km/h; 19 mph)
Max rate of climb at S/L (without payload)	350 m (1,148 ft)/min
T-O run with 7.7 kg (17 lb) payload	35 m (115 ft)

CANADAIR LTD

PO Box 6087, Montreal, Quebec H3C 3G9

Originating as the aircraft division of Canadian Vickers in the 1920s, Canadair assumed its own identity in 1944. It was acquired in 1947 by the Electric Boat Co of the USA, forming the basis for what became General Dynamics Corporation in 1952, but reverted to Canadian government ownership in 1976. Canadair has been active in the area of unmanned airborne surveillance systems since 1961.

CANADAIR CL-89

NATO designation: AN/USD-501
British Army name: Midge

The Canadair CL-89 airborne surveillance drone system evolved from a need of the western Allied armed forces for an intelligence gathering device for battlefield commanders.

With a very high probability of survival against all known air defence systems, it can acquire timely and accurate battlefield intelligence using its photographic and infra-red linescanning equipment. The system, consisting of the air vehicles plus the related ground support and operational maintenance

Truck launch of a Canadair CL-89

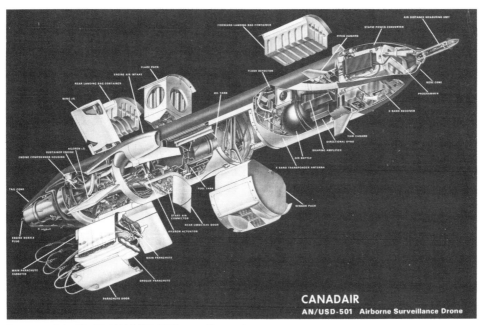

Cutaway of the CL-89 (AN/USD-501) surveillance drone

equipment, is totally integrated, mobile, and independent of such external services as electrical power supplies.

Development began in 1961 as a joint Canadair/Canadian government venture. First flight was made in 1964, and production began in 1967. More than 500 CL-89s have been delivered to the armed forces of the UK, Federal Germany, France and Italy.

TYPE: Recoverable airborne surveillance drone system.

AIRFRAME: Cylindrical metal body, with curved nosecone and tapering tailcone. Three detachable dorsal packs for forward and rear landing bags and flare container; two detachable ventral packs for sensor equipment and parachute recovery system. Four rectangular stub wings at rear of body, in 'X' configuration at 45° to horizontal and vertical centrelines. Upper pair fold out of way when landing airbags are inflated. Ailerons on port upper and starboard lower stub wings. Two pairs of foreplanes aft of nosecone on horizontal and vertical centrelines, for pitch and yaw trim respectively.

POWER PLANT: One 0.56 kN (125 lb st) Williams International WR2-6 turbojet, with variable exhaust nozzle, installed in tailcone aft of wings. Air intake duct on each side of fuselage, forward of wings. Fuel and oil tanks in central body compartment, forward of air intakes. One 22.24 kN (5,000 lb) average thrust PERME Wagtail booster rocket motor, attached to body of drone by three V-shaped thrust arms and cable.

LAUNCH AND RECOVERY: Launched from truck-mounted zero-length ramp; booster separates automatically after 2.5 s of flight. Irvin GB recovery system, for release within speed bracket of 310–440 knots (575–815 km/h; 357–506 mph), comprises a 0.91 m (3 ft) diameter flat ribbon drogue parachute and 5.99 m (19 ft 8 in) diameter main parachute. After final positioning by ground homing beacon, drone is slowed by drogue parachute to approx 61 m (200 ft)/s, when main parachute deploys. Drone is then inverted, and forward and rear airbags are inflated and deployed automatically to absorb landing impact.

GUIDANCE AND CONTROL: Flight path, altitude and sensor on/off commands are controlled by preset programmer which receives information from onboard air distance measuring unit and combines this with preset programme to control flight path. Ground homing beacon positions drone in final stages of flight to ensure accuracy of landing.

MISSION EQUIPMENT: Engine-driven alternator for electrical power during flight. Two main sensor systems currently in use: Carl Zeiss KRb8/24C camera system and British Aerospace Type 201 infra-red linescan system. Aft of sensor pack is compartment for fuel and oil tanks. Compartment aft of tanks has ventral forward-hinged door providing access to engine start air connector, and dorsal pack containing 12 photoflares just forward of rear landing bag container. Final cylindrical compartment houses rear landing bag container and parachute recovery pack, between dorsal and ventral pairs of wings respectively. Other onboard equipment includes forward and rear landing airbags; air distance measuring unit (ADMU); programmer; static power converter; homing receiver; amplifier; flash detector; directional and vertical gyros; transponder antenna; and air bottle to inflate airbags.

DIMENSIONS:

Span: wings	0.94 m (3 ft 1 in)
foreplanes	0.48 m (1 ft 7 in)
Length overall, excl nose probe:	
with booster	3.73 m (12 ft 3 in)
without booster	2.60 m (8 ft 6.5 in)
Body diameter	0.33 m (1 ft 1 in)

WEIGHTS:

Weight dry (excl fuel, oil and mission equipment)	78.2 kg (172.4 lb)
Mission equipment	17–20 kg (37.5–44 lb)
Max launching weight: with booster	156 kg (343 lb)
without booster	108 kg (238 lb)

PERFORMANCE:

Max speed	400 knots (741 km/h; 460 mph)

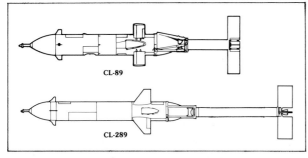

Comparative sizes and configurations of the CL-89 and CL-289

Max operating altitude	3,050 m (10,000 ft)
Max range: standard	65 nm (120 km; 74 miles)
with extended range fuel tank	75 nm (140 km; 87 miles)

CANADAIR/DORNIER CL-289

NATO designation: AN/USD-502

The CL-289 was designed to meet the needs of army corps commanders for timely and accurate battlefield intelligence. It is a development of the CL-89 (which see); however, since the latter was designed for intelligence gathering at division level, it does not have the range and target coverage capability needed at corps level. The requirement for increased range led to a larger air vehicle, able to incorporate a more complex navigation system (to achieve the necessary navigation accuracy at greater range); two kinds of sensor (photographic and infra-red linescan), to permit both day and night intelligence gathering; and a real-time data link to provide virtually instant IRLS imagery.

Development began in July 1976 as a joint programme between the governments of West Germany and Canada. Canadair is prime contractor and system manager, sharing the work equally with Dornier as principal subcontractor. France joined the programme in March 1977, nominating Société Anonyme de Télécommunications to develop an IRLS sensor with real-time data transmission for ground recording. Canadian Marconi and Lear Siegler supply major elements of the navigation system, and Klöckner-Humboldt-Deutz the sustainer engine.

Launch of a CL-289 from a MAN German Army vehicle

CL-289 data receiving ground station

Operation is similar to that of the CL-89. The drone is launched from a mobile zero-length launcher by a jettisonable rocket booster, sustained flight being maintained by a ground-started turbojet engine controlled by the onboard computer. The navigation system uses an advanced heading reference unit, together with a Doppler system and a precise airspeed transducer, all supplying data to the airborne computer, to provide accurate navigation. The Doppler system provides a quasi-terrain-following height control mode, which enables the drone to be flown at low altitude with a consequent reduction in vulnerability. The flight mission programme is stored in the launcher computer and fed into the drone's computer just before launch.

Towards the end of the flight, the drone's terminal guidance unit is switched on by the onboard computer, and the drone homes on to a ground beacon. At the appropriate point on the homing leg the drone intercepts a radio fan marker beam which initiates the recovery sequence. The drone then makes a heading correction (to arrive upwind of the landing site), and a drogue parachute is deployed to slow it down to a safe speed for main parachute deployment. Emergence of the main parachute initiates inflation of the airbags, which cushion the landing impact. Any exposed films are removed for processing and interpretation, the landed drone being transported to the maintenance area for preparation for its next flight.

The first launch of a CL-289 was made on 3 March 1980. Contractors' flight trials at the US Army Proving Grounds at Yuma, Arizona, were completed in March 1981; customer evaluation and troop trials, to ensure that the system met its military technical objectives and was acceptable for service use, took place between December 1981 and May 1983.

Pre-production was approved in January 1986; full scale production was due to begin in mid-1987 and reach peak rate in late 1988. Both the French and West German armies have announced their intention to procure the system. Other NATO member nations have expressed interest.

TYPE: Recoverable airborne surveillance drone system.

AIRFRAME: Cylindrical metal body, with ogival nosecone and tailcone of plastics. Four stub wings, with sweptback leading edges, near rear of body in 'X' configuration at 45° to vertical and horizontal centrelines; upper pair ejected when landing airbags are inflated. Ailerons on port upper and starboard lower stub wings. Two pairs of small foreplanes aft of nosecone, on vertical and horizontal centrelines, to control pitch and yaw; dorsal foreplane is ejected when airbags are inflated. Detachable dorsal packs for forward and rear airbags; detachable ventral packs for camera and linescan installations (forward), and for ribbon type parachute recovery system (aft of stub wings).

POWER PLANT: One 1.07 kN (240 lb st) KHD T117 turbojet engine, installed in tailcone, with an air intake duct on each side of body aft of stub wings. Fuel and oil tanks in central body compartment, forward of wings. One 32.0 kN (7,200 lb) max thrust Bristol Aerospace solid propellant booster rocket motor, attached to rear of drone body. Booster is jettisoned a few seconds after launch; turbojet is controlled by onboard computer to allow a near-constant airspeed, and to alter thrust as necessary during programmed turns, climbs and descents.

LAUNCH AND RECOVERY: Launched from mobile (truck-mounted) zero-length launcher; booster separates automatically shortly after launch. For recovery, drone is slowed down by the drogue parachute until main parachute deploys. Drone is then inverted; forward and rear airbags are inflated and deployed automatically to absorb landing impact. Parachute and airbag system (latter of Kevlar fabric) by Irvin GB Ltd.

GUIDANCE AND CONTROL: Pre-programmed operation. Navigation and control system comprises a Lear Siegler tuned rotor heading reference, a Canadian Marconi Doppler sensor, and a Dornier System airborne digital computer. Mission programme is stored in computer, which generates the command signals required for navigation, attitude control and sensor activation. Ground homing beacon positions drone in final stages of flight to ensure accuracy of landing.

MISSION EQUIPMENT: 28V DC regulator for electrical power during flight. Two main sensor systems comprise Carl Zeiss KRb8/24D three-lens reconnaissance camera and SAT Corsaire infra-red linescan, with SAT real-time video data link transmitter. Other onboard equipment includes air distance measuring unit (ADMU); heading reference unit; power supply unit; barometric altitude reference unit; radar transponder; fuel expulsion unit; non-tactical telemetry for mission equipment; terminal guidance unit; command receiver/decoder; vertical gyro; air reservoir and air pressure regulator for airbag inflation.

DIMENSIONS:

Wing span	1.32 m (4 ft 4 in)
Length overall, excl ADMU nose probe:	
with booster	4.98 m (16 ft 4 in)
without booster	3.52 m (11 ft 6.5 in)
Body diameter (max)	0.38 m (1 ft 3 in)

WEIGHTS AND PERFORMANCE:
Not released, but performance 'considerably higher' than that of CL-89.

CL-227 Sentinel in a typical maritime environment

CANADAIR CL-227 SENTINEL

The CL-227 was designed as a highly survivable real-time surveillance and target acquisition RPV for use at medium range. It has VTOL capability, and can translate to horizontal flight or hover. It is launched either from the ground or from a mobile platform. The CL-227 can be landed free, or winched down to a simple landing device to provide an automatic landing capability. It can also fly tethered or untethered from small surface craft. With a CL-227 on a 200 m (655 ft) tether, the craft's horizon would be extended to 26 nm (48 km; 30 miles). With a 500 m (1,640 ft) tether, the range of view would be 43 nm (80 km; 50 miles).

Phase 1 of the system development programme utilised a prototype powered by a Wankel rotary combustion engine. This made its first flight, tethered, on 25 August 1978.

The Phase 2 vehicle was slightly larger, carried a bigger load of mission equipment, and was powered by a 24 kW (32 shp) Williams International WR34-15-2 turboshaft engine. Flight demonstrations of the Phase 2 configuration took place in Montreal in October and December 1981, the first completely untethered flight being made on 14 December. Further flight trials in a quasi-tactical environment were conducted at Suffield Canadian Forces Base, Alberta, during January/February 1982, culminating in a series of demonstration flights for NATO observers in March 1982. In May 1983 the Sentinel was demonstrated to representatives of the US Army and NATO.

The full scale development Phase 3 started in 1984 and is due for completion in early 1988. Ten air vehicles, of near production standard, plus two ground control stations and six mission payloads, are being produced for customer evaluation beginning with a joint US/Canadian demonstration starting in October 1987. The air vehicles are each powered by a Williams International 37.3 kW (50 shp) WTS-34 turboshaft engine and have a more sophisticated navigation and control system (Bendix Avelex/Incosym INS) than the Phase 2 version. Much attention has been paid in the Phase 3 design to increased reliability and survivability.

The Canadian government agreed on 7 May 1985 to share initial funding of the final development phase.

The CL-227 has a peanut-shaped body made of composite materials, housing the power plant in the upper segment, with the sensors and autopilot in the lower segment. A non-retractable skid landing gear is fitted. Two Kevlar three-blade contra-rotating rigid rotors/propellers, mounted amidships, provide the lift and attitude control, the main gearbox having a single input from the engine and twin outputs to the rotors. The Phase 3 vehicles are equipped with a daylight TV camera with zoom lens. Sensors can include low light level TV, a laser designator, thermal imager, radiation detector or decoy equipment; a starter/alternator provides 1 kW of electrical power for all onboard equipment.

DIMENSIONS:
Rotor diameter (each)	2.80 m (9 ft 2.25 in)
Rotor disc area (each)	6.16 m² (66.3 sq ft)
Height overall	1.64 m (5 ft 4.5 in)
Body diameter (max)	0.64 m (2 ft 1 in)

WEIGHTS:
*Mission payload (max)	45 kg (99.2 lb)
*Fuel (max)	54 kg (119 lb)
Max T-O weight	190 kg (419 lb)

*Combined total of 88 kg (194 lb) permits various trade-offs between fuel and payload

PERFORMANCE:
Max level speed	70 knots (130 km/h; 81 mph)
Max forward and vertical rate of climb at 1,500 m (4,920 ft)	180 m (591 ft)/min
Max operating altitude	3,000 m (9,850 ft)
Typical operating radius	27 nm (50 km; 31 miles)
Typical mission endurance at 500 m (1,640 ft)	3–4 h

CONTROL TECHNOLOGIES INC (Subsidiary of CTI Technologies Corporation)

12151 Horseshoe Way, Richmond, British Columbia V7A 4V4

Control Technologies Inc was formed in 1984 to specialise in development and production of robotic air, land and sea vehicles. In 1986 the company had a workforce of approximately 40 people. Its family of small unmanned aircraft addressed a wide range of needs, all of them having a variety of capabilities at the lower end of the aircraft performance spectrum. All three of the models listed were then in production, initially for the civil market, and built to withstand considerable rough treatment while being simple and inexpensive to repair in the field. Information received shortly before closing for press suggested that, despite its apparently healthy order book, the company may have gone out of business.

CONTROL TECHNOLOGIES ISIS

The Isis can be tailored for a wide range of civil applications, including law enforcement, agriculture, forestry, wildlife surveys, land management, urban planning, rural development, search and rescue, and marine studies. Ten complete Isis systems were ordered in the autumn of 1986 by the Coeur d'Alene Leasing Co Inc of Idaho, USA, for delivery by the end of that year. These were for use in forest aerial survey and on other forestry management work, and the contract included options for larger orders in 1987 and 1988. Isis was produced in two sizes, **Isis I** and **Isis II**; a larger Isis III was projected.

Possible military uses include electro-optical, ESM, infra-red and acoustic reconnaissance; ECM (deception and jamming); and attack against threat emitters, C³I facilities and other point or area targets. Isis I was demonstrated to the US Army in 1986 as a candidate for that service's BOSS (battalion operated surveillance system) requirement, being sponsored in that demonstration by the Advanced Systems Development Division of Gould Inc, USA, whose Electronics Warfare Group provided the payload. By carrying threat emitter simulators, the Isis can also be used to evaluate the effectiveness of countermeasures.

The following description applies to both Isis production models, except where a specific version is indicated:

TYPE: Multi-purpose mini-RPV.
AIRFRAME: Of modular construction, using composites materials. Rectangular section fuselage, with low-mounted main wings at rear and a high-mounted foreplane with elevators. Twin fins and rudders mounted on main wings. Non-retractable tricycle landing gear standard; float gear optional.
POWER PLANT: One 4.1 kW (5.5 hp) piston engine, driving a two-blade pusher propeller.
LAUNCH AND RECOVERY: Conventional take-off and landing standard. Zero-length catapult launch/skid recovery, and parachute recovery, under development.
GUIDANCE AND CONTROL: Degree of sophistication of flight control system depends upon customer requirements; aircraft and payload can be tailored as required. Capability can range from remote piloting via onboard video sensor to incorporation of Tracor Omega-based waypoint navigation system to support semi-autonomous operation. Ailerons, elevators and rudders for aerodynamic control.
MISSION EQUIPMENT: Can include lightweight TV and/or 35 mm still camera, with E-Systems digital image analysis equipment, in nose bay. Other payloads can include digital or infra-red cameras, SLAR, magnetometers and sampling equipment.

DIMENSIONS:
Wing span: Isis I	2.54 m (8 ft 4 in)
Isis II	3.35 m (11 ft)
Length overall: Isis I	2.13 m (7 ft)
Isis II	2.79 m (9 ft 2 in)

WEIGHTS:
Max payload (incl fuel): Isis I	15.9 kg (35 lb)
Isis II	20.4 kg (45 lb)
Max T-O weight: Isis I	45.4 kg (100 lb)
Isis II	61.2 kg (135 lb)

PERFORMANCE:
Max level speed: Isis I	65 knots (121 km/h; 75 mph)
Isis II	61 knots (112 km/h; 70 mph)
Cruising speed: Isis I and II	43 knots (80 km/h; 50 mph)
Stalling speed: Isis I	31 knots (57 km/h; 35 mph)
Isis II	28 knots (52 km/h; 32 mph)
Service ceiling: Isis I	2,440 m (8,000 ft)
Isis II	3,050 m (10,000 ft)
Remote control radius: Isis I and II	22 nm (40 km; 25 miles)
Endurance (Isis I and II):	
with 25% payload	6 h
with max payload	3 h

CONTROL TECHNOLOGIES SWALLOW

Swallow is a much smaller air vehicle than Isis, produced in one size only. It, too, is of canard configuration, and was also demonstrated in the 1986 US Army BOSS competition.

The general description of Isis applies also to the Swallow, except in the following details:

DIMENSIONS:
Wing span	1.42 m (4 ft 8 in)
Length overall	1.36 m (4 ft 5.5 in)

WEIGHTS:
Max payload (incl fuel)	5.4 kg (12 lb)
Max T-O weight	15.9 kg (35 lb)

PERFORMANCE:
Max level speed	56 knots (105 km/h; 65 mph)
Cruising speed	35 knots (64 km/h; 40 mph)
Stalling speed	18 knots (33 km/h; 20 mph)
Service ceiling	1,525 m (5,000 ft)
Endurance:	
with 25% payload	3 h
with max payload	1 h

DEFENCE RESEARCH ESTABLISHMENT SUFFIELD (DRES)
Ralston, Alberta T0J 2N0

One of the Defence Research Laboratories of the Canadian Department of National Defence, DRES has been responsible for the Robot series of aerial targets, including the Robot-5 and Robot-9 rocket-boosted ballistic tagets. Its latest design is the Robot-X, built for DRES by Boeing of Canada Ltd and described under that company's entry.

MAGNUS AEROSPACE CORPORATION
PO Box 599, Station B, Ottawa, Ontario K1P 5P7

MAGNUS LTA

Magnus Aerospace, then known as Van Dusen, started a programme in 1978 for a literally revolutionary airship utilising a principle known as the Magnus effect (a force which will raise the flight path of a spinning ball). The ball in this case is the airship envelope, a pressurised helium filled sphere made of high strength Kevlar. Through the centre of the sphere is a horizontal axle, at each end of which the engines are mounted; a gondola of unique shape is suspended from this axle. Internal gas pressure enables the envelope to maintain constant volume and shape over a wide range of pressures, temperatures and wind conditons. The engines can rotate independently through 90° to vector thrust from vertical take-off mode to a horizontal cruising position. Additional lift is thus generated by the vertical thrust of the engines during take-off and by the large Magnus force created by the sphere's rotation in forward flight.

Flight testing of a one-tenth scale radio controlled **LTA 20-1** began in October 1981, and was successful enough to lead to construction of three more scaled drone vehicles in 1984. These have been used as additional testbeds for configuration changes, flight dynamics testing and in-flight structural testing. Magnus' plans are then to utilise the concept for much larger heavy-lift manned airships with payloads of up to 55 tonnes.

The following data apply to the original one-tenth scale prototype:

DIMENSIONS:
Envelope diameter	5.79 m (19 ft)
Envelope volume	101.94 m³ (3,600 cu ft)
Gondola length	5.44 m (17 ft 10 in)

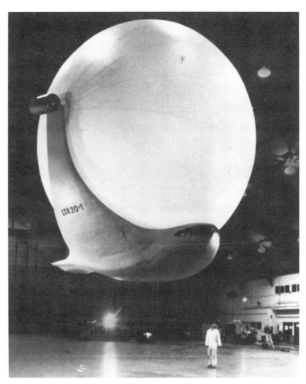

Magnus LTA

Width overall	6.86 m (22 ft 6 in)
Height overall	6.25 m (20 ft 6 in)

WEIGHTS:
Envelope	12.7 kg (28 lb)
Gondola	48.5 kg (107 lb)
Complete vehicle	95.5 kg (211 lb)

PERFORMANCE:
Max level speed	13 knots (24 km/h; 15 mph)
Range at max speed	0.9 nm (1.6 km; 1 mile)

TARGETAIR LTD
RR4, Moncton, New Brunswick E1C 8J8

TARGETAIR TATS 102

Developed to meet a Canadian Forces' need for a low-cost, recoverable aerial target for low-level air defence weapons

Targetair TATS 102 and line of sight operator

training, the TATS 102 is designed for use against man-portable weapons such as Blowpipe and in anti-aircraft gunnery training.

TYPE: Recoverable miniature aerial target.

AIRFRAME: Low-wing monoplane of typical 'model aeroplane' appearance, built of glassfibre, wood and foam plastics.

POWER PLANT: One 13.8 kW (18.5 hp) 100 cc modified Yamaha piston engine, driving a two-blade propeller. Fuel capacity 8.2 litres (1.8 Imp gallons; 2.2 US gallons).

LAUNCH AND RECOVERY: Catapult-launched from mechanical deadweight launcher. Recovery by parachute or wheel/skid landing.

GUIDANCE AND CONTROL: Radio command and control within visual range, using a binocular-based ground control system. Initially this restricted max operational range to less than 1.6 nm (3 km; 1.9 miles), but later utilised Canadian Forces' CHAIR (control handling aid for increased range) system, allowing visual control at ranges of up to 3.2 nm (6 km; 3.7 miles).

MISSION EQUIPMENT: Smoke and light augmentation systems for visual tracking. Can also be equipped with infra-red target source, 9A electrical power source, or DSQ-40, DSQ-41 or similar miss distance scoring system.

DIMENSIONS:
Wing span	3.35 m (11 ft)
Length overall	3.05 m (10 ft)
Height overall	0.29 m (11.25 in)

WEIGHTS:
Basic weight empty	29.5 kg (65 lb)
Max T-O/launching weight	35.5 kg (78 lb)

PERFORMANCE:
Max speed in dive	239 knots (444 km/h; 276 mph)
Max level speed	130 knots (241 km/h; 150 mph)
Stalling speed	31 knots (57 km/h; 35 mph)
Max rate of climb at S/L	305 m (1,000 ft)/min
T-O distance: on wheels	152 m (500 ft)
on launcher	12 m (38 ft)
Landing distance:	
on wheels	152–305 m (500–1,000 ft)
on skids	152 m (500 ft)
Radio range:	
whip antenna	1.6 nm (2.9 km; 1.8 miles)
linear amp and dipole antenna	
	7.8 nm (14.5 km; 9 miles)
Endurance of drone: at full throttle	1 h 15 min
at econ power setting	1 h 45 min
Max battery life after full charge	2 h

ZENAIR LTD

King Road, Nobleton, Ontario LoG 1No

ZENAIR CRICKET

Two Zenair Crickets (Canadian version of the French Colomban Cricri homebuilt aircraft) were tested as pilotless pipeline patrol aircraft. The first was fitted with an automatic pilot in 1983 and flight tested in Texas with a safety pilot on board. The pilot's seat was later removed (see accompanying photograph), and two TV cameras and a still camera were installed. Both aircraft later entered service with a state agency in Qatar. Each aircraft has a range of 863 nm (1,600 km; 994

Fuselage of the pilotless conversion of the Zenair Cricket

miles) at 87 knots (161 km/h; 100 mph), and can patrol oil pipelines at a fraction of the cost of conventional aircraft.

Further details of this programme are classified.

ZENAIR RPV-007

Combining simple and proven construction methods with a well-known small power plant, Zenair designed the RPV-007 pod and boom mini-RPV primarily for such civilian surveillance missions as fishery, coastguard and ice patrol, search and rescue, forest firewatch and pipeline patrol. It has sufficient inbuilt flexibility to perform many other civilian and military reconnaissance or associated missions. Features include simplicity of assembly and operation, low acquisition and operating costs, and an exceptionally good all-round 'view' for the nose-mounted sensors. Prototype construction had not begun in spring 1987.

TYPE: Recoverable surveillance mini-RPV.

AIRFRAME: Low-wing monoplane, with dihedral on outer panels; latter can be folded upwards to facilitate storage. Pod type fuselage nacelle, accommodating mission payload at front and engine at rear. Twin tailbooms, each with sweptback fin. Two-axis aerodynamic control (ailerons and one-piece elevator); no rudders. Standard landing gear has 10-in diameter mainwheels and small tailskid. Ski or float

General arrangement of the Zenair RPV-007
(Michael A. Badrocke)

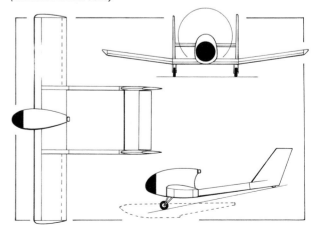

gear available optionally. Entire airframe is bolted together from simple components, none of which is more than 1.83 m (6 ft) long.

POWER PLANT: One 20 kW (27 hp) Rotax 277 single-cylinder two-stroke engine, with hand starting; reduction drive to a two-blade fixed-pitch pusher propeller. Two fuel tanks, combined capacity 45.5 litres (10 Imp gallons; 12 US gallons).

LAUNCH AND RECOVERY: Conventional T-O and landing. Net recovery optional.

EQUIPMENT: According to mission. Payload in vibration damped nose compartment which offers a sensor field of 'view' of 300° in horizontal plane and 270° in vertical plane.

DIMENSIONS:
Wing span	5.49 m (18 ft)
Wing area	5.02 m² (54 sq ft)
Width, wings folded	2.13 m (7 ft)
Length overall	3.66 m (12 ft)
Fuselage: Max width	0.61 m (2 ft)
Height over tail fins	1.70 m (5 ft 7 in)
Height overall (wings folded)	2.10 m (6 ft 10.75 in)
Tailplane span (incl fins)	1.83 m (6 ft)
Propeller diameter	1.52 m (5 ft)

WEIGHTS:
Weight empty	90.7 kg (200 lb)
Max T-O weight	181.4 kg (400 lb)

PERFORMANCE (estimated at max T-O weight):
Max level speed	104 knots (193 km/h; 120 mph)
Cruising speed: 75% power	95 knots (177 km/h; 110 mph)
60% power	87 knots (161 km/h; 100 mph)
Stalling speed	35 knots (65 km/h; 40 mph)
Max rate of climb at S/L	396 m (1,300 ft)/min
Ceiling	4,270 m (14,000 ft)
T-O and landing run (wheel gear, hard surface)	85 m (280 ft)
g limits	± 6 vertical
	± 10 horizontal (net retrieval)

China (People's Republic)

CHANGCHENG SCIENTIFIC INSTRUMENTATION FACTORY (CSIF)
PO Box 2351, Beijing

CSIF B-2

Displayed at the Guangzhou Fair in April 1982, the B-2 radio-controlled target drone has a compact, rigid airframe constructed of lightweight GRP/honeycomb sandwich, is fitted with conventional three-axis control surfaces, and can be launched from various kinds of surface using a zero-length launcher and rocket-assisted take-off. Onboard avionics include the 3W radio command guidance system, an autopilot, heading/azimuth/altitude/distance telemetry, and a number of safety devices. Frequencies used are 49.525MHz (remote control) and 129MHz (telemetry).

Designed for weapon system training and gunnery practice, the B-2 is a variant of the BJ7104 manufactured by the Yuhe Machine Factory in Nanjing (which see), differing chiefly in the power plant fitted. Now in series production, the B-2 is said to be simple to operate, requiring a minimum of crew training. In this configuration operational equipment comprises two towed targets, plus four other devices which give a realistic representation of descending paratroops. The B-2 can also be modified to extend the range of applications, according to individual user requirements.

POWER PLANT: One 12 kW (16 hp) Huosai-16 flat-four two-stroke engine, with pull cord starting, driving a two-blade fixed-pitch wooden propeller. Fuel is a mixture of automobile gasoline and lubrication oil; tank capacity 8 litres (1.8 Imp gallons; 2.1 US gallons).

DIMENSIONS:
Wing span	2.70 m (8 ft 10.25 in)
Length overall	2.55 m (8 ft 4.5 in)
Height overall	0.60 m (1 ft 11.5 in)

WEIGHTS:
Weight empty	53 kg (116.8 lb)
Effective payload	3 kg (6.6 lb)
Fuel	6 kg (13.2 lb)
Max launching weight	62 kg (136.6 lb)

PERFORMANCE:
Max level speed at 1,000 m (3,280 ft)	119–129 knots (220–240 km/h; 137–149 mph)
Max rate of climb at S/L	480–600 m (1,575–1,968 ft)/min
Max controllable range	10.75 nm (20 km; 12.5 miles)
Endurance	1 h

CSIF (Changcheng) B-2 glassfibre target drone on its zero-length launcher

NANJING AERONAUTICAL INSTITUTE (NAI)

Department of RPV Research, 29 Yudaojei Street, Nanjing, Jiangsu Province

NAI CHANG KONG 1C (WIDE BLUE SKY)

The Nanjing Aeronautical Institute began its research work for this series of unmanned aircraft at the end of the 1960s, and finalised the design of a CK1 prototype in late 1976. In the following year it developed a version with underwing equipment pods, known as the CK1A, and in 1982 replaced these pods with non-jettisonable auxiliary fuel tanks, the designation then becoming CK1B.

The definitive version, tested successfully in the autumn of 1984, is the Chang Kong 1C or CK1C. This is described as the first high-manoeuvrability pilotless aircraft researched and developed by the People's Republic of China, and subsequent test flights have demonstrated its suitability for use as an aerial target for various types of missile, including a capability for high-manoeuvre flights at bank angles of up to 70–77°. About 50 had been built by spring 1987, at which time a new version was under study. An alternative Chinese designation is **D-5**.

The following description applies to the CK1C. Its overall configuration, which outwardly resembles that of the Lavochkin La-17 (see USSR section), is shown in the accompanying illustrations.

TYPE: Subsonic jet-powered recoverable target drone.

Nanjing Aeronautical Institute Chang Kong 1C jet powered target drone

Cutaway drawing of the NAI CK1C

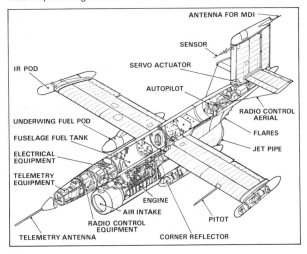

AIRFRAME: Mid-wing monoplane. Constant chord wings, with 2° anhedral. Fuselage built in three sections, those at front (housing radio control, telemetry and electrical equipment) and rear (autopilot and flares) being of aluminium alloy. Central portion, made from steel sheet, forms integral fuel tank. Rectangular conventional tail surfaces, with tailplane mounted near base of fin. No landing gear.

POWER PLANT: One 25.5 kN (5,732 lb st) turbojet (Shenyang Wopen-6 from retired J-6 fighter, minus afterburner section), mounted in nacelle underslung beneath centre of fuselage. Main fuel in steel integral tank forming central portion of fuselage; auxiliary fuel in underwing pods. (See under 'Weights' for capacities.)

LAUNCH AND RECOVERY: Launched from re-usable trolley, upon which drone is mounted on three short guiderails and attached by a single connecting pin at base of engine nacelle. Complete ensemble accelerates along runway under engine power, connecting pin being withdrawn automatically by pneumatic release system when speed reaches 151–154 knots (280–285 km/h; 174–177 mph). Drone then lifts off trolley and enters climbout phase, trolley decelerating and being brought to halt under radio command by brake chute and wheel brakes. Drone can enter firing area two or three times during mission. If not shot down, it can be directed to a preselected landing site, where engine is shut down at a predetermined speed and altitude and drone completes an unpowered landing. Engine nacelle is reinforced to absorb landing impact, resulting in only minor damage which can be repaired easily before re-use.

GUIDANCE AND CONTROL: Four-channel autopilot (pitch, roll, yaw and altitude) in rear of fuselage stabilises aircraft and controls its flight in response to radio commands from ground station; it incorporates gyroscope, directional gyro, three-axis rate gyro, programmer, electrical actuator, amplifier and converter. After drone's separation from trolley, first 85 s of flight are programme-controlled; mission then comes under pre-planned radio command from ground controller. Aerodynamic control by ailerons, elevators and rudder.

AVIONICS AND EQUIPMENT: Onboard radar transponder for identification and tracking from ground. Airborne radio equipment comprises receiver/decoder which enables up to 24 command signals to be conveyed to autopilot and other components and equipment. A 52-channel telemetry system provides ground controller with continuous indication of altitude, speed, angle of bank, engine rpm and temperature, and other functions. Mission equipment includes miss distance indicator (antenna at rear of fin tip); infra-red augmentation pod at each wingtip; five corner reflectors for radar signature augmentation; and three flares or smoke canisters (on undersurface of each wing and on rear edge of engine nacelle fairing) to provide visual augmentation to aid tracking by ground based optical aids. Main electrical power for avionics and equipment provided by engine-driven generator, with alternator for AC power; emergency battery supplies DC power for continued safe flight in the event of main system or engine failure.

DIMENSIONS:

Wing span	7.50 m (24 ft 7.25 in)
Wing area	8.55 m² (92.03 sq ft)
Length overall	8.439 m (27 ft 8.25 in)
Body diameter (max)	0.55 m (1 ft 9.75 in)
Height overall	2.955 m (9 ft 8.33 in)

WEIGHTS:

Weight empty	1,537 kg (3,388 lb)
Fuel: fuselage tank	600 kg (1,323 lb)
underwing tanks (total)	280 kg (617 lb)
Max launching weight	2,450 kg (5,401 lb)

PERFORMANCE:

Operating speed range	
	458–491 knots (850–910 km/h; 528–565 mph)
Operating height range	
	500–16,500 m (1,640–54,135 ft)
Range	324–485 nm (600–900 km; 373–559 miles)
Endurance at low and medium altitude	45–60 min

NANJING RESEARCH INSTITUTE FOR SIMULATION TECHNIQUE (NRIST)
PO Box 1607, Nanjing, Jiangsu Province

The Z-2 remotely piloted helicopter was developed by the NRIST as an RPH feasibility study. It was preceded by a small Z-1 model built primarily to train the ground control operator of the Z-2.

NRIST Z-1

The Z-1 was designed in January 1983 and made its first flight in the following May. Its purpose was to train those responsible for ground control of the Z-2 in remote control operating techniques.

TYPE: Miniature remotely piloted helicopter.

AIRFRAME: Fuselage of aluminium tube and sheet, with non-stressed plastics outer shell. Hiller type two-blade main rotor; wooden main and tail rotor blades.

POWER PLANT: One 10 cc single-cylinder two-stroke glow-plug engine.

GUIDANCE AND CONTROL: FM digital proportional radio control system and heading stabiliser.

DIMENSIONS:

Main rotor diameter	1.60 m (5 ft 3 in)
Fuselage length	1.44 m (4 ft 8.75 in)

WEIGHTS:

Basic weight empty	4.4 kg (9.7 lb)
Fuel	0.6 kg (1.3 lb)
Max T-O weight	5 kg (11 lb)

NRIST Z-1 (left) and Z-2 experimental RPHs: note airbags fitted to landing skids

PERFORMANCE:

Max level speed	58 knots (108 km/h; 67 mph)
Endurance	25 min

NRIST Z-2

From 1976 onward, three Chinese organisations developed RPHs with take-off weights of more than 20 kg (44 lb). Two were single main/single tail rotor types, with 3.7 kW (5 hp) and 11.2 kW (15 hp) engines respectively, and the third, also with a 5 hp engine, had a coaxial rotor configuration. None, however, proved capable of stable flight, and their further development was terminated.

The Z-2 research RPH programme began in January 1982, and two prototypes were built, the first of these being flown in June 1983. Preliminary ground and flight tests took place during the remainder of 1983, more than 70 flights being completed by the end of that year. A number of modifications were made in 1984, in which year over 20 more flights were made. The results confirmed that the Z-2 had achieved its primary design goals of stability and controllability, without exhibiting unacceptable levels of vibration or dynamic structural stress. The Z-2 was thus the first successful RPH in the 20–30 kg (44–66 lb) class to be developed entirely by the Chinese aviation industry, and the experience gained will be used in the development of more advanced RPHs.

For test flying, the Z-2 was generally flown for 10–15 min at a time, usually at a height of 10–15 m (33–50 ft). Maximum flying height on test was 120 m (394 ft).

TYPE: Experimental remotely piloted helicopter.

AIRFRAME: Single two-blade teetering main rotor and two-blade tail rotor. Main rotor is of modified Hiller type, with auxiliary flaps carried on stabilising bar mounted above and at right angles to main blades. Blades are attached to hub by two bolts and a metal bracket. Each blade has a 'C' shape glassfibre spar forming the leading edge, the rear portion consisting of glassfibre/epoxy cloth (layers reducing gradually from root to tip) wrapping a core of polystyrene foam plastics. Outer leading edge of each blade has a nose balance weight of lead. Tail rotor (mounted originally on starboard side of tail pylon, later reversed and transferred to port side) is of similar construction. Fuselage has a central load-bearing frame of welded steel alloy tube and a forward section of riveted aluminium, covered with a non-stressed shell of laminated glassfibre; tailboom is a composites monocoque. Sweptback fins above and below end of tailboom; horizontal stabiliser mid-mounted on tailboom forward of fins. Non-retractable aluminium tube landing skids, with legs of steel alloy tubing; optional flotation bags for impact absorption. Tailskid attached to underfin, to protect tail rotor.

POWER PLANT AND TRANSMISSION: One 3.7 kW (5 hp) 85 cc single-cylinder two-stroke modified chain-saw engine, driving main rotor via a centrifugal friction clutch and Maximizer belt to main gearbox, and tail rotor via two bevel gears and a driveshaft. Fuel tank in centre fuselage.

LAUNCH AND RECOVERY: Conventional helicopter take-off and landing.

GUIDANCE AND CONTROL: Digital proportional control by FM radio and heading stabiliser. Signals are transmitted to onboard receiver, which decodes them and commands onboard actuators (three for collective pitch, longitudinal and lateral manoeuvres, two others for engine throttle and tail rotor pitch) to produce required control movement. Separate main rotor controls for cyclic and collective pitch; tail rotor has collective pitch function only.

EQUIPMENT: Battery pack, radio receiver and control actuators.

DIMENSIONS:

Main rotor diameter	3.25 m (10 ft 8 in)
Main rotor disc area	8.30 m² (89.3 sq ft)
Tail rotor diameter	0.65 m (2 ft 1.5 in)
Tail rotor disc area	0.33 m² (3.6 sq ft)
Distance between rotor centres	2.105 m (6 ft 11 in)
Length overall, rotors turning	4.105 m (13 ft 5.5 in)
Fuselage: Length	2.74 m (9 ft)
Max width	0.385 m (1 ft 3.25 in)
Height to top of rotor head	1.10 m (3 ft 7.25 in)
Skid track	1.18 m (3 ft 10.5 in)

WEIGHTS:

Basic weight empty	23.5 kg (51.8 lb)
Fuel	1.5 kg (3.3 lb)
Max T-O weight	25 kg (55.1 lb)

PERFORMANCE (calculated):

Max level speed	60 knots (111 km/h; 69 mph)
Max rate of climb at S/L	262 m (860 ft)/min
Service ceiling	4,785 m (15,700 ft)
Hovering ceiling: IGE	2,195 m (7,200 ft)
OGE	1,278 m (4,195 ft)
Endurance	40 min

NRIST YK-7

Details of this new fixed-wing target are given in the Addenda.

NORTHWESTERN POLYTECHNICAL UNIVERSITY (NPU)

Xian, Shaanxi 710036

The NPU was formed in 1957 by amalgamating the aeronautics departments of several Chinese universities. Today it is one of China's major aerospace and avionics institutions, with about 6,000 students on campus and a teaching staff of more than 1,300. It has departments for aircraft, aero-engine and astronautical engineering, automatic control systems, avionics, marine equipment engineering, computer and other sciences, and several wind tunnels, including transonic and supersonic.

NPU D-4 RD

Developed by the NPU, the D-4 RD bears some outward resemblance to early piston-engined Beech and Northrop target drones, but is in production as a reconnaissance RPV for the Chinese armed forces. The NPU is believed to have built four prototypes of the D-4, which is of honeycomb and GRP construction and is powered by a nose-mounted 22.4 kW (30 hp) Huosai-510 piston engine driving a two-blade propeller. First flight is believed to have taken place on 5 October 1983. Production began in late 1985 at an initial rate of 15 a year, which may have been increased subsequently.

As shown in the accompanying photograph, the D-4 RD is launched from a mobile zero-length launcher by an underfuselage rocket booster. Recovery is by parachute stowed in a dorsal compartment near the tail. It can be operated under remote control (with telemetry tracking) or automatically by

Prototype of the NPU D-4 RD reconnaissance RPV *(Hangkong Zhishi)*

pre-programming the onboard analog autopilot. Payloads can include a still camera, or a video camera with a real-time data link.

DIMENSIONS:

Wing span	4.30 m (14 ft 1.25 in)
Length overall	3.30 m (10 ft 10 in)

WEIGHTS:

Payload	25 kg (55.1 lb)
Max launching weight	140 kg (308.6 lb)

PERFORMANCE:

Max level speed at S/L	92 knots (170 km/h; 105 mph)
Operating height range	100–3,000 m (330–9,850 ft)
Range	140 nm (260 km; 161 miles)
Endurance	2 h

YUHE MACHINE FACTORY (YMF)

2 Jie Fang Road, Nanjing, Jiangsu Province

This state-owned factory manufactures the BJ7104, a target drone designed and developed by the Nanjing Research Institute for Simulation Technique (which see).

YMF BJ7104

Design, prototype construction and first flight of the BJ7104 took place in 1971, and series production began two years later. A total of 2,400 had been built by the Yuhe Machine Factory by February 1986, with production continuing, primarily for use as a training target for small and medium-sized anti-aircraft artillery weapons.

Suitably re-equipped, the BJ7104 is said to have a number of civil applications including geological prospecting/surveying/mapping, weather monitoring, artificial rainmaking, powerline inspection and crop-spraying. By adding a microcomputer to the system, the BJ7104 can fly pre-programmed missions, including formation flights by several drones under simultaneous control.

TYPE: Recoverable target drone.

AIRFRAME: Mid-wing monoplane with circular section fuselage and conventional tail surfaces. Wings have 6° dihedral from roots. Skid under tailcone and each wingtip to minimise damage on landing. Constructional details probably similar to those of Changcheng B-2, except for greater use of metal instead of composites.

Yuhe Machine Factory BJ7104 target/RPV

POWER PLANT: One 11.2 kW (15 hp) Yuhe Machine Factory YH280 (280 cc) four-cylinder two-stroke engine, driving a two-blade wooden propeller.

LAUNCH AND RECOVERY: Rocket-assisted take-off from zero-length launcher. Skid landing.

GUIDANCE AND CONTROL: 22-channel radio control system. Provision for pre-programmed flights under microcomputer ground control. Aerodynamic control by ailerons, elevators and rudder.

EQUIPMENT: Onboard autopilot, radio receiver and telemetry.

DIMENSIONS:

Wing span	2.70 m (8 ft 10.25 in)
Wing area	1.14 m² (12.27 sq ft)
Length overall	2.55 m (8 ft 4.5 in)
Fuselage: Max diameter	0.28 m (11 in)
Height overall, incl landing skid	0.74 m (2 ft 5 in)

WEIGHTS:

Weight empty	34 kg (75 lb)
Fuel	8 kg (17.6 lb)
Payload	10 kg (22 lb)
Max launching weight	52 kg (114.6 lb)

PERFORMANCE:

Max level speed	135 knots (250 km/h; 155 mph)
Max rate of climb at S/L	600 m (1,968 ft)/min
Operating height range	100–2,000 m (330–6,560 ft)
Service ceiling	6,000 m (19,685 ft)
Control range	8.1 nm (15 km; 9.3 miles)
Endurance	1 h

France

AÉRAZUR EFA (Division Équipements Aéronautiques)

58 Boulevard Galliéni, 92130 Issy-les-Moulineaux

AÉRAZUR DINOSAURE

Designed in 1975, the Dinosaure is an unusual twin-hulled 'catamaran' airship, the hulls each having internal ballonets, a gondola and separate tail surfaces, and being joined together in 'Siamese twin' fashion by a rigid central structure. A single engine, mounted at the rear between the hulls, drives a pusher propeller.

Intended originally for meteorological work, the Dinosaure was evaluated during the first half of the 1980s for remotely piloted surveillance and other potential military missions. The outcome of these trials was not known at the time of going to press.

DIMENSIONS (envelope):

Length overall	9.80 m (32 ft 2 in)
Width overall	7.90 m (25 ft 11 in)
Height overall	3.57 m (11 ft 8.5 in)
Volume, gross	95 m³ (3,355 cu ft)

WEIGHTS AND PERFORMANCE:
Not known

Aérazur Dinosaure twin-hull airship

AÉROSPATIALE SNI (Division Engins Tactiques)

2 rue Béranger, BP 84, 92322 Châtillon Cédex

AÉROSPATIALE CT.20

The CT.20 was produced from 1958 to 1982 as a medium performance target aircraft, capable also of use as a tug for a towed target. About 1,500 were built, including more than 300 for export to NATO and non-NATO countries. In French service, it has been standard equipment for training military units in the use of air-to-air and surface-to-air missiles, and variants included the **CT.20 TBA** (très bas altitude) for very low level use. The **R.20** (which see) was a reconnaissance version for the French Army. The Swedish Navy's RB08 anti-ship missile, licence built by Saab-Scania, was developed from the CT.20.

TYPE: Turbojet-powered recoverable target.

AIRFRAME: Body in three main sections. Forward section, of aluminium alloy, contains command guidance, autopilot, batteries, and principal recovery parachute. Central section consists of structural steel tank divided into two parts, one for fuel and one containing chemicals for tracking smoke. Rear fuselage, of aluminium alloy, contains engine and supports aluminium alloy V tail. Braking parachute in cone above jet nozzle. Mid-mounted swept wings, of aluminium alloy, have wingtip spoilers for lateral control; elevators controlled simultaneously by single jack. Ventral fin under tailcone.

POWER PLANT: One 3.92 kN (882 lb st) Turbomeca Marboré II turbojet engine in Version IV; 4.7 kN (1,058 lb st) Marboré VI in Version VII.

LAUNCH AND RECOVERY: Launched by two 35.3 kN (7,936 lb thrust) solid propellant booster rockets from nearly-zero-length vehicle-mounted ramp. Recovery by parachute and impact absorbing airbag, deployed after engine is shut down by transmission of landing signal. Can be recovered from land or water.

GUIDANCE AND CONTROL: Thomson-CSF radio command guidance system, operated by controller on ground or in airborne director aircraft. Nine basic signals can be transmitted: turn right, turn left, nose up, nose down, increase power, decrease power, trace smoke, operate cameras, and land.

MISSION EQUIPMENT: Can be used to tow Dornier target which is pylon-mounted under starboard wing at launch; or can be used with trailed target system developed for the Centre

Aérospatiale CT.20 with Dornier tow target underwing

d'Essais des Landes, primarily for training in use of air-to-air missiles with electromagnetic (BEY) or infra-red (EMIR) homing systems. TBA version has TRT AVH-6 radio altimeter for very low altitude capability (about 30 m; 100 ft), and an improved remote guidance system.

DIMENSIONS (A: standard version; B: extended version with trailed target):

Wing span	3.16 m (10 ft 4.5 in)
Wing area	3.20 m² (33.34 sq ft)
Length overall: A	5.45 m (17 ft 10.5 in)
B	5.60 m (18 ft 4.5 in)
Body diameter (max)	0.66 m (2 ft 2 in)

WEIGHTS:

Weight empty: A	490 kg (1,080 lb)
B	610 kg (1,344 lb)
Fuel: A	164 kg (361 lb)
B	192 kg (423 lb)
Max launching weight: A	660 kg (1,455 lb)
B	800 kg (1,763 lb)

PERFORMANCE (A and B as above):

Max level speed at 10,000 m (32,800 ft):	
Marboré II	485 knots (900 km/h; 560 mph)
Marboré VI	512 knots (950 km/h; 590 mph)
Max Mach number (A, B)	0.85
Service ceiling:	
Marboré II	12,000 m (39,375 ft)
Marboré VI	15,000 m (49,200 ft)
Max operating altitude: A	14,000 m (45,925 ft)
B	13,000 m (42,650 ft)
Time to 10,000 m (32,800 ft)	6 min
Time to max operating altitude:	
A, B	15 min
Min operating height: A, B	30 m (100 ft)
Practical range of command guidance and tracking system:	
A, B	135 nm (250 km; 155 miles)
Endurance at max operating altitude:	
A	50 min
B	1 h 10 min
Endurance at min operating height:	
A	15 min
B	21 min
Average endurance at 10,000 m (32,800 ft):	
A, B	45 min

AÉROSPATIALE R.20

The R.20 battlefield reconnaissance drone was developed from the CT.20 target, to which it is externally similar. Powered by a Marboré IID turbojet, it is launched by two solid propellant booster rockets from a short ramp on a standard Berliet GB-C8-KT Army lorry; two other standard vehicles carry the support equipment, including the radio control gear and antenna system. When close to its launch post, the R.20 is controlled directly from the ground. Over longer distances, it is controlled automatically by a gyroscopic platform and an electronic programmer, enabling it to follow a prearranged flight plan.

Standard NATO cameras or other surveillance equipment, including an SAT Cyclope infra-red linescanning device, are carried in the R.20's modified nose and in interchangeable wingtip pods. The drone can photograph more than 200 km² (77 sq miles) of territory during a single low-altitude sortie, using three synchronised Omera 114 × 114 mm cameras. Data can be sent back during flight by radio link, and flares can be

Aérospatiale R.20 battlefield observation/target identification RPV

carried for night photography. It has been claimed that the R.20 offers an over-the-target accuracy of within 300 m (985 ft) at a distance of 54 nm (100 km; 62 miles) from its launch site. Average operating height is 1,000 m (3,280 ft), but it can be set to fly higher or lower as required.

A total of 62 R.20s was built for the French Army, production ending in 1976.

DIMENSIONS:
Wing span over pods	3.72 m (12 ft 2.5 in)
Wingtip pods: Length	1.90 m (6 ft 3 in)
Diameter	0.40 m (1 ft 3.75 in)
Length overall	5.71 m (18 ft 9 in)
Body diameter (max)	0.66 m (2 ft 2 in)
Height overall	1.35 m (4 ft 5.25 in)

WEIGHTS:
Payload	150 kg (330 lb)
Fuel	185 kg (408 lb)
Max launching weight:	
incl boosters	1,100 kg (2,425 lb)
excl boosters	850 kg (1,875 lb)

PERFORMANCE:
Operating speed range	311–427 knots (576–792 km/h; 358–492 mph)
Operating height range	200–10,000 m (660–32,800 ft)
Operating radius at low altitude	86 nm (160 km; 100 miles)

AÉROSPATIALE D.15

Aérospatiale develped the D.15 as a small, experimental inexpensive radio-controlled target for anti-aircraft artillery training; it flew for the first time on 10 April 1975.

Of high-wing configuration, with a conventional tail unit, the D.15 was built mostly of plastics materials and could be assembled in 5 minutes. Landing gear was of the reverse tricycle type, the 'tail' wheel actually being located under the centre of the fuselage. Power plant comprised two 1.3 kW (1.7 hp) piston engines, with small two-blade propellers, mounted on outriggers on the fuselage sides. Fuel capacity was 2 litres (0.44 Imp gallons; 0.53 US gallons).

Although demonstrated successfuly, no production was undertaken.

DIMENSIONS:
Wing span	2.40 m (7 ft 10.5 in)
Wing area	1.00 m² (10.76 sq ft)
Length overall	2.20 m (7 ft 2.5 in)

WEIGHTS:
Payload	6 kg (13.2 lb)
T-O weight	18 kg (39.7 lb)

PERFORMANCE:
Max speed:	
simulated low-level strike	108 knots (200 km/h; 124 mph)
simulated diving attack	162 knots (300 km/h; 186 mph)
Endurance at full power	1 h

Aérospatiale D.15 experimental mini-RPV

AÉROSPATIALE C.22

The C.22, which first flew on 6 June 1980, was designed in 1977 as a successor to the CT.20 for use as a variable speed target for anti-aircraft weapons and, especially, for training fighter pilots and anti-aircraft system crews. Its dimensions, radar signature and high performance enable it to simulate combat aircraft flying at any altitude, and also sea skimming missiles.

Ten prototypes and 24 pre-production C.22s were built for the French Ministry of Defence, and the drone is currently in use on French firing ranges. Series production was to begin in 1987. There are two versions: the **C.22T** with remote control only, for use on French ranges, and the **C.22L** with added telemetry and tracking system.

TYPE: Recoverable variable speed subsonic target.

AIRFRAME: Moulded sweptback plastics wings, with light alloy main spar, glassfibre skin and foam core, symmetrical profile and no control surfaces. Fuselage of wound glassfibre on a central metal frame, impregnated with epoxy resin, reinforced by metal inserts at attachment points. Nosecone and tailcone of moulded plastics. 'X' configuration aluminium alloy tail fins, with four electrically actuated control surfaces.

POWER PLANT: One 3.73 kN (838 lb st) Microturbo TRI 60-2 turbojet, mounted in pod on top of fuselage; and two jettisonable solid propellant booster rockets (each 28.3 kN; 6,360 lb st for 1.25 s) attached beneath wings on sides of fuselage. Fuel tanks for TRI 60 in centre of fuselage, capacity 240 litres (52.8 Imp gallons; 63.4 US gallons).

LAUNCH AND RECOVERY: Launched by jettisonable rockets from ground or ship base. Parachute system for recovery from land or sea. Inflatable airbags beneath fuselage to absorb landing impact.

GUIDANCE AND CONTROL: Radio command digital guidance system. Flight control, based upon a minicomputer, permits complex manoeuvres at up to 6.5g. Aerodynamic control by four movable surfaces inset in tail fins indexed at 45° from vertical axis.

MISSION EQUIPMENT: Operational equipment depends upon weapon systems to be fired at target. Nose compartment available for equipment, including tow winch. Tail compartment includes 25 kg (55 lb) smoke generator tank and recovery parachutes. Nosecone houses up to 60 kg (132 lb) of mission equipment; active or passive countermeasures; recording equipment for assessing the effectiveness of weapon systems during training; two 30 kg (66 lb) underfuselage pods; or equipment for towing successively two 30 kg (66 lb) secondary targets at speeds of more than 485 knots (900 km/h; 559 mph), with 800 m (2,625 ft) cable

Aérospatiale C.22 variable speed subsonic target

for each target. Onboard 28V battery (engine driven generator to come later) for electrical power. LCT TTL (Télémesure, Télécommande et Localisation) system for remote control, telemetry and tracking.

DIMENSIONS:
Wing span	2.50 m (8 ft 2.5 in)
Wing area	1.6 m² (17.22 sq ft)
Span over tail fins	1.40 m (4 ft 7.25 in)
Fin area (total)	0.6 m² (6.46 sq ft)
Length overall	5.25 m (17 ft 2.75 in)
Height overall	1.15 m (3 ft 9.25 in)
Body diameter	0.40 m (1 ft 3.75 in)

WEIGHTS:
Weight empty	300 kg (661 lb)
Max fuel	192 kg (423 lb)
Total internal/external payload, incl towed targets	130 kg (286 lb)
Max launching weight (excl boosters)	650 kg (1,433 lb)

PERFORMANCE:
Max speed (all altitudes)	Mach 0.9
Max level speed at S/L	600 knots (1,112 km/h; 691 mph)
Max rate of climb at S/L	4,200 m (13,780 ft)/min
Time to 12,000 m (39,375 ft)	less than 6 min
Service ceiling	14,000 m (45,930 ft)
Min operating height	10 m (33 ft)
Range with max payload	593 nm (1,100 km; 683 miles)
Max endurance at 12,000 m (39,375 ft)	2 h
g limit	+6.5

ÉCOLE NATIONALE SUPÉRIEURE DE L'AÉRONAUTIQUE ET DE L'ESPACE (ENSAE)

10 avenue E. Belin (BP 4032), 31400 Toulouse Cédex

ENSAE EIDER

First details were released at the 1985 Paris Air Show of this small RPV designed by ENSAE students. Built as an aerodynamic and systems testbed, it is of 'canard' configuration, powered by a rear-mounted 2.5 or 4.5 kW (3.3

ENSAE Eider experimental mini-RPV *(Jane's/Mike Keep)*

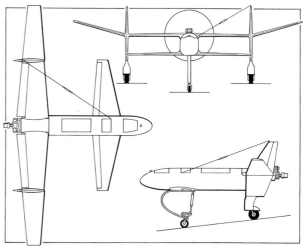

or 6 hp) single-cylinder engine driving a two-blade fixed-pitch wooden pusher propeller. General appearance is shown in the accompanying drawing.

Construction is of glassfibre and foam plastics, with control surfaces on the foreplane (elevators), main wing (ailerons) and vertical fin (rudder), and the Eider has a sprung tricycle landing gear for conventional T-O and landing. It is operated under radio command via a three-axis autopilot, and equipped with a radio altimeter and rate gyro for control at very low altitude (3 m; 10 ft), and a digital microprocessor for data recording.

Two Eider prototypes have been built, the first flight taking place in November 1985.

DIMENSIONS:
Wing span	2.70 m (8 ft 10.25 in)
Wing area	0.71 m² (7.64 sq ft)
Foreplane span	1.50 m (4 ft 11 in)
Foreplane area	0.36 m² (3.88 sq ft)
Length overall	1.70 m (5 ft 7 in)
Body diameter (max)	0.25 m (9.75 in)

WEIGHT:
Weight empty, equipped	17.5 kg (38.6 lb)
Max T-O weight	27 kg (59.5 lb)

PERFORMANCE:
Max level speed	68 knots (126 km/h; 78 mph)
Stalling speed	32 knots (58 km/h; 36 mph)
g limit	+4

ÉTABLISSEMENT D'ÉTUDES ET DE RECHERCHES MÉTÉOROLOGIQUES (EERM)
Direction de la Météorologie Nationale, 77 rue de Sèvres, 92106 Boulogne-Billancourt Cédex

Several types of SAM (Sonde Aérologique Motorisée) have been used in considerable numbers by the EERM since 1976 as pilotless atmospheric sounding vehicles.

EERM SAM-B

SAM-B is an extremely simple vehicle, of disc-shaped planform with the trailing edges hinged to act as control surfaces. It is powered by a 1.2 kW (1.6 hp) Webra 61 10 cc two-stroke piston engine, driving a two-blade glassfibre propeller, and is used under line-of-sight radio control for low altitude sounding flights up to 500 m (1,640 ft).

EERM SAM-C MP atmospheric sounding vehicle

EERM SAM-C

SAM-C is an atmospheric sounding vehicle for work at higher altitudes than SAM-B, up to cloud level. Design began in January 1977, and the first of two prototypes made its initial flight on 5 May that year. This version, with the engine pod-mounted on a pylon above the centre fuselage, is designated **SAM-C MP** (moteur en pylône). A later version, which began flight testing in July 1978, is known as the **SAM-C MAR** (moteur arrière) and has the engine mounted at the rear, driving a pusher propeller.

First high altitude (3,200–4,000 m; 10,500–13,125 ft) tests with a SAM-C MP were made in May 1978 at Deux-Alpes, and in the following month one was flown over the 3,300 m (10,825 ft) Mount Etna in Sicily, to measure thermal conditions in the vicinity of the volcano and to take gas samples to determine their chemical composition.

The following description applies to the SAM-C MAR:

TYPE: Pilotless atmospheric sounding vehicle.

AIRFRAME: Shoulder-wing monoplane, with inverted-V tail surfaces. Wings have 10° dihedral and 3° incidence, and are of glassfibre/polystyrene foam construction without spars or ribs. Schempp-Hirth metal airbrakes, or electrically actuated plastics trailing edge flaps, with upward travel only. Glassfibre frameless monocoque fuselage, in four sections: nose, front, centre and tail. Tail surfaces of similar construction to wings; elevators actuated electrically. No landing gear.

POWER PLANT: One 1.2 kW (1.6 hp) Webra 61 10 cc two-stroke piston engine, mounted in rear fuselage and driving a two-blade glassfibre pusher propeller. Fuel tank in centre fuselage section, capacity 0.5 to 2.0 litres (0.9 to 3.5 Imp pints; 1.1 to 4.2 US pints). NACA-type flush air intake in top of rear fuselage.

LAUNCH AND RECOVERY: Launched by catapult from 3.10 m (10 ft 2 in) ramp.

GUIDANCE AND CONTROL: Line-of-sight radio control. Aerodynamic control by airbrakes/flaps and elevators.

SYSTEM: 12V 0.5Ah nickel-cadmium battery for sounding systems; 4.8V 1.2Ah nickel-cadmium battery for radio controls.

MISSION EQUIPMENT: Temperature, humidity and atmospheric pressure sensors.

DIMENSIONS:
Wing span	3.15 m (10 ft 4 in)
Wing area	1.10 m² (11.85 sq ft)
Length overall	2.10 m (6 ft 10.75 in)
Body diameter	0.16 m (6.3 in)
Height overall (on ground)	0.20 m (7.9 in)
Propeller diameter	0.30 m (11.8 in)

WEIGHTS:
Weight empty:	
MP with minimum 0.5 kg (1.1 lb) ballast in forward fuselage	6.5 kg (14.3 lb)
MAR with 2 kg (4.5 lb) ballast	8 kg (17.6 lb)
Max payload	2.5 kg (5.5 lb)
Max fuel	1.3 kg (2.9 lb)
Max launching and landing weight	9.5 kg (20.9 lb)

PERFORMANCE (at max launching weight except where indicated):
Max level speed at S/L	50 knots (92 km/h; 57 mph)
Max cruising speed	30 knots (55 km/h; 34 mph)
Econ cruising speed at S/L	25 knots (46 km/h; 29 mph)
Stalling speed, power off	15 knots (28 km/h; 17.5 mph)

The canard configuration EERM SAM-D

Max rate of climb at S/L at 8.5 kg (19 lb) normal operating
 weight   210 m (690 ft)/min
Service ceiling   5,000 m (16,400 ft)

EERM SAM-D

Design of SAM-D began at the same time as that of SAM-C,
and the first of two prototypes made its initial flight in March
1978. To be used to obtain aerological measurements under
difficult conditions (wind speeds of up to 29 knots; 54 km/h;
33 mph), it has a wide speed range and entered production in
1979.

TYPE: Pilotless atmospheric sounding vehicle.
AIRFRAME: Cropped-delta mid-mounted main wings at rear
 and shoulder-mounted foreplanes with elevons. Main wings
 have 4° dihedral, 2° incidence and 20° sweepback at
 quarter-chord; they are of glassfibre/polystyrene foam
 construction, without spars or ribs, and have no movable
 control surfaces. Foreplanes are of similar construction, the
 elevons being actuated by electrical servos. Single sweptback
 fin; no rudder. Glassfibre frameless monocoque fuselage, of
 rectangular cross-section. No landing gear.
POWER PLANT: As for SAM-C. Single plastics fuel tank, capacity
 0.5 to 1.0 litre (0.9 to 1.75 Imp pints; 1.1 to 2.1 US pints), in
 fuselage centre section beneath wing roots.
LAUNCH AND RECOVERY: As for SAM-C.
GUIDANCE AND CONTROL: As for SAM-C.
SYSTEM: Electrical power sources as for SAM-C.
EQUIPMENT: Not known.

DIMENSIONS:
 Wing span   1.40 m (4 ft 7.25 in)
 Wing area   0.63 m² (6.78 sq ft)
 Length overall   1.55 m (5 ft 1 in)
 Fuselage: Max width   0.14 m (5.5 in)
 Height overall   0.47 m (1 ft 6.5 in)
 Propeller diameter   0.30 m (11.75 in)
WEIGHTS:
 Weight empty   4.4 kg (9.7 lb)
 Max payload   1 kg (2.2 lb)
 Max fuel load   0.6 kg (1.3 lb)
 Max launching weight   6 kg (13.2 lb)
PERFORMANCE (at max launching weight):
 Max level speed   60 knots (111 km/h; 69 mph)
 Max cruising speed   50 knots (92 km/h; 57 mph)
 Stalling speed, power off   15 knots (28 km/h; 17.5 mph)
 Max rate of climb at S/L   360 m (1,180 ft)/min
 Service ceiling   4,000 m (13,125 ft)

ÉTABLISSEMENT TECHNIQUE CENTRAL DE L'ARMEMENT (ETCA)

16 bis avenue Prieur de la Côte d'Or, 94114 Arcueil Cédex

ETCA MA2

This small experimental observation RPV was first flown in the
spring of 1983 and displayed at the Paris Air Show later that
year. It is a high-wing monoplane with constant chord wings, a
pod and boom fuselage, cruciform tail surfaces, twin
mainwheels and a tail bumper. The airframe was built by CEA
(Commissariat à l'Energie Atomique), the remote piloting
telemetry by Sintra-Alcatel, and the colour TV camera by
Sofretec. In addition to the TV camera, the payload included a
TV transmitter and three-axis autopilot.

DIMENSIONS:
 Not known
WEIGHT:
 Payload   4 kg (8.8 lb)
PERFORMANCE:
 Operating altitude   1,000 m (3,280 ft)
 Range   5.4 nm (10 km; 6.2 miles)
 Endurance   more than 1 h

SOCIÉTÉ ANONYME FRANCE-ENGINS

Chemin du Pont de Rupé, BP 2089, 31019 Toulouse Cédex

French engine manufacturer Microturbo SA joined forces with
Société Soulé in early 1975 to form France-Engins for the
specific purpose of developing a jointly designed UMA known
as the Mitsoubac.

FRANCE-ENGINS MITSOUBAC

The Mitsoubac was designed initially as a low-cost modular
drone/RPV envisaged for use in several versions, including
those of expendable or recoverable target, decoy, reconnaissance drone, and harassment/defence saturation RPV. It was of
modular concept, and capable of air or catapult launch.
 Flight testing began as a private venture in 1975 with a Bell
47 helicopter as the launch aircraft, and continued later at

France-Engins Mitsoubac mounted for air launch from an
Alouette III

Cazaux using an Alouette III. Attention then was focused on possible naval use as a high-*g* manoeuvring target for medium altitudes and for very low level flight over water. In this capacity it was intended to provide a target for ships' armament without the need for land-based support, and most of its equipment was installed in watertight containers to minimise the amount of refurbishing necessary before re-use.

The Mitsoubac appeared to be a versatile and promising programme, and development of a longer-range version was said to have begun in 1980, but the project foundered shortly afterwards from lack of support.

TYPE: Recoverable or expendable target or RPV.
AIRFRAME: Tapered cylindrical body, with low-mounted clipped-delta wings and sweptback fins, moulded from laminated polyester. Modular construction to facilitate changes of equipment and role. No rudder or horizontal tail surfaces: moving surfaces comprised elevon on each wing, actuated electrically using a lightplane autopilot with vertical reference gyro.
POWER PLANT: One 0.98 kN (220 lb st) Microturbo TRS 18-056 turbojet engine with dorsal intake. Fuel capacity 31 litres (6.8 Imp gallons; 8.2 US gallons).
LAUNCH AND RECOVERY: Normally launched from helicopter or fixed-wing aircraft, in latter case being mounted inverted on aircraft's external pylons. Alternative capability for catapult launch. Recoverable by parachute descent and helicopter pickup.
GUIDANCE AND CONTROL: Radio control via five-channel VHF or UHF link to onboard autopilot system comprising roll/pitch gyro, stabilised in roll axis, which provided electrical output via analog computer and synchro system to position elevons for required manoeuvre. Provision to close control loop for pre-programmed missions. Onboard receiver/decoder provided functions for straight flight, left and right turns, climb, descent, maintain height, emit smoke, switch on test installation, hold signal, and recovery.

DIMENSIONS:
Wing span	1.35 m (4 ft 5.25 in)
Length overall	2.86 m (9 ft 4.5 in)
Height overall	0.72 m (2 ft 4.3 in)
Payload volume	0.02 m³ (0.7 cu ft)

WEIGHTS:
Weight empty	83 kg (183 lb)
Payload	20 kg (44 lb)
Max launching weight	150 kg (330 lb)

PERFORMANCE:
Max level speed at 100 m (330 ft)	
	437 knots (810 km/h; 503 mph)
Max cruising speed at 1,500 m (4,920 ft)	
	324 knots (600 km/h; 373 mph)
Range, no reserves:	
at max level speed	71 nm (131 km; 81 miles)
at max cruising speed	93 nm (173 km; 107 miles)
Endurance at 450 knots (834 km/h; 518 mph)	15 min

GIRAVIONS DORAND INDUSTRIES
5 rue Jean Macé, 92151 Surèsnes

GIRAVIONS DORAND DS.7

Developed under contract from the Direction des Recherches et Moyens d'Essais of the French Ministry of Defence, the DS.7 was a small experimental gyro-glider intended for use under pre-programmed control to recover loads dropped from aircraft, including recovery at very low altitudes (down to 15 m; 50 ft) or in high wind conditions. The idea was to provide the load with a means of autorotative descent to a soft landing, and theoretically was capable of adaptation to payloads of up to 15,000 kg (33,070 lb).

The DS.7 'airframe' incorporated a two-blade telescopic rotor, control and suspension systems, a load container fitted with a fantail stabiliser (to keep the load pointed into wind) and an approach height detector. After release, the rotor was started automatically by the airflow, the blades being extended by centrifugal force; glideslope was determined by swashplate setting and the collective pitch angle of the blades. The programmer generated the control movement necessary for changing cyclic and collective pitch angles, following flare-out at a predetermined altitude. Actuated by the height detector, it tilted the rotor backward to reduce forward speed for landing, a second movement returning the rotor to a horizontal plane at the instant of touchdown, which was accomplished at a vertical descent rate of less than 2 m (6 ft)/s.

Initial flight testing was followed in 1974 by a series of tests with half-scale working models, with a view to simplifying the rotor head and control system before considering series production, but the latter did not materialise. Among potential applications listed at the time were the steering of a dropped load towards a predetermined point under remote control; automatic recovery of a helicopter following an engine failure; ejection seat recovery; and use as a man-carrying gyro-glider.

DIMENSIONS:
Rotor diameter (max)	4.00 m (13 ft 1.5 in)
Load container	0.35 × 0.35 × 1.00 m
	(1 ft 1.75 in × 1 ft 1.75 in × 3 ft 3.25 in)

WEIGHTS:
Payload	220 kg (485 lb)
Gross weight, incl load	250 kg (551 lb)

SA CHARLES MARCHETTI
80 avenue de la Grande Armée, 75017 Paris

Under contract to the Direction des Recherches et Moyens d'Essais, Marchetti carried out design and development studies in the mid-1970s for a variety of rotating-wing pilotless aircraft.

MARCHETTI ROTORMOBILE

Developed in the early 1970s, the Rotormobile was a jet-driven, remotely controlled rotor without an airframe, the only non-rotating parts being the avionics platform and the cargo sling. Basis of the system was a rotor consisting of three hollow 'motor blades', with a small turbojet engine mounted at the blade roots. Engine exhaust gases passed through the blades, expanding in nozzles at the tips to provide the reaction that drove the rotor. By reversing blade-tip thrust, the rotor could be stopped in a few seconds. Flaps were fitted to the blades for command and control of the vehicle, which was fitted with an air cushion landing gear.

Tests confirmed the efficiency of the system, and Marchetti used the data to project two larger vehicles of 28 and 50 tonnes gross weight, with respective useful loads of 20 and 35 tonnes.

Marchetti Heliscope tethered flying platform

MARCHETTI HELISCOPE

The Heliscope electrically powered flying platform consisted basically of two three-blade fixed-pitch light alloy rotors of coaxial, contra-rotating design, attached respectively to the rotor and stator of an electric motor located between their hubs. Power supply for the motor was provided by a generator mounted on the vehicle which served as the mobile ground station, and was fed through a cable running to the centre of the base of the Heliscope.

Test results were used to project a platform using three Heliscopes, each with a 1.60 m (5 ft 3 in) diameter four-blade rotor. It was calculated that such a platform could support a useful load of 100 kg (220 lb) with a simplified load stabilisation system at an altitude of 230 m (755 ft) above ground.

SA MATRA

BP No. 1, 78146 Vélizy-Villacoublay Cédex

MATRA SCORPION

The Scorpion experimental battlefield surveillance mini-RPV was being developed by Matra and Thomson-CSF under French government contract. Primary sensor is a Thomson-CSF TV camera, for real-time video data transmission, mounted on a gyro stabilised platform. Principal roles envisaged for the Scorpion were reconnaissance and daytime target designation, with a laser designator as optional equipment.

The accompanying drawing shows the Scorpion to be a pod and boom high-wing monoplane with twin fins and rudders, and is the only known illustration. Despite numerous requests, Matra has declined to confirm whether the Scorpion made its first flight in April 1984, or to provide any other details of the RPV or its development programme.

General appearance of the Matra Scorpion mini-RPV
(Jane's/Mike Keep)

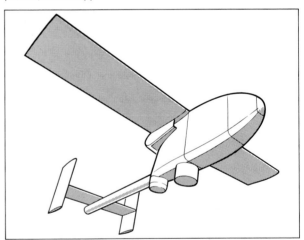

Germany (Federal Republic)

DORNIER GmbH

Postfach 1420, 7990 Friedrichshafen 1

Dornier is active in the fields of tactical RPVs, stand-off missiles, mini-RPVs, helicopter drones, and the DATS series of towed targets. Under sub-contract to LMSC (see US section), it is supplying the net recovery system for the Aquila mini-RPV for the US Army.

Jointly with Canadair and SAT, Dornier is developing the AN/USD-502 (Canadair CL-289), details of which can be found under the Canadair heading.

DORNIER AERODYNE E 1

Development of the Aerodyne wingless high-speed VTOL aircraft was begun by the late Dr A. M. Lippisch in the USA. It was resumed in 1967 by Dornier under an experimental programme for the Federal Ministry of Defence.

Dornier Aerodyne E 1

The Aerodyne principle is marked by the combination of the means of lift and propulsion in a single unit, namely a shrouded propeller, the slipstream from which is deflected downward by cascade-type vanes for vertical take-off and landing. Control is by deflection of the turboshaft exhaust, which emerges at the end of the tailboom, and vanes in the propeller slipstream.

A radio-controlled prototype vehicle, known as the Aerodyne E 1, was built in 1971 and made its first flight, tethered, on 18 September 1972. Hovering tests were concluded successfully on 30 November 1972, after 74 flights totalling almost 1 ½ hours in the air. The last of these was, unintentionally, a free flight, from which the E 1 was successfully brought down from the hover to a normal landing.

In 1974, studies confirmed that the Aerodyne, due to its unique launch and recovery characteristics, could be a suitable V/STOL RPV for a variety of naval applications, and proposals for such applications were submitted to NATO.

Work on the Aerodyne, under Federal Defence Ministry contract, continued in 1975–76 and involved detailed investigation of a ship-based application of an operational vehicle for over-the-horizon fire control missions. Test flights from a moving platform were carried out in the autumn of 1976. For

Proposed Dornier/HSD maritime Aerodyne

these tests a tail unit, reinforced landing gear and a more powerful engine (a Lycoming LTS 101-650C) were installed. Further development was halted in 1977.

TYPE: VTOL experimental RPV.

AIRFRAME: Annular fan shroud and deflection chamber, with bullet-shaped pod attached centrally in mouth of fan duct. Pod houses electronics system and control unit. Power plant mounted on top of fan shroud, with a hollow tailboom to the rear. Non-retractable vertical landing gear, comprising two main legs and a shorter leg under tailboom. Shock absorption by interchangeable aluminium honeycomb damper in each leg. Vertical tail surfaces added for later testing.

POWER PLANT: One 276 kW (370 shp) MTU 6022A-3 turboshaft engine originally, driving a five-blade variable-pitch Hoffmann fan via a Zahnradfabrik/Dornier Z-type reduction gear. (Replaced in 1976 by a 441.5 kW; 592 shp Avco Lycoming LTS 101-650C turboshaft.) Fuel in two tanks located between inner and outer walls of deflection chamber.

FLIGHT CONTROLS: Fan shroud and deflection chamber form an inner flow channel, at end of which airflow is deflected by cascade-type vanes. In prototype, this deflection amounted to approx 60° during hovering flight. Cascades not moved during hovering. Engine exhaust directed aft through tailboom to provide pitch and yaw control during hovering. For this purpose jet could be deflected up and down as well as sideways by hydraulically operated cascades. Roll control effected during both hovering and forward flight by a vertical keel flap, immediately aft of main cascade flaps, supplying a roll moment when deflected. Keel flap and fan pitch control mechanism operated hydraulically.

GUIDANCE AND CONTROL: Radio command, developed by Dornier. During hovering flight, remote control pilot commanded flight vehicle's attitude via a small control stick. Bodenseewerk onboard attitude control system, to keep attitude command within very small limits, incorporating a vertical gyro, three rate gyros and three accelerometers. Telemetry system, with more than 50 channels, for transmitting data to ground station. Battery for emergency power in event of generator failure.

DIMENSIONS (approx):

Max diameter	1.90 m (6 ft 2.75 in)
Fan diameter	1.10 m (3 ft 7.25 in)
Length overall	5.50 m (18 ft 0.5 in)
Height overall	2.60 m (8 ft 6.5 in)

WEIGHT:

Max T-O weight	430 kg (948 lb)

DORNIER MARITIME AERODYNE

Applications of the Aerodyne principle to operational RPV systems were studied under a 1971 agreement between Dornier and Hawker Siddeley Dynamics and included a naval RPV proposal. The Maritime Aerodyne was proposed for a number of naval applications, including reconnaissance, weapon control and delivery, ASW, ECM and in-flight missile guidance. It featured a single engine driving twin ducted fans and could have carried two homing torpedoes in the ASW role.

DIMENSIONS:

Width overall	3 m (9 ft 10 in)
Length overall	4.90 m (16 ft 9.25 in)
Height overall	2.60 m (8 ft 6.25 in)

WEIGHT:
Max T-O weight	1,360 kg (3,000 lb)

PERFORMANCE (estimated):
Max level speed	329 knots (610 km/h; 379 mph)
Service ceiling	6,700 m (22,000 ft)
Hovering ceiling	1,200 m (3,940 ft)
Range at max level speed with 100 kg (220.5 lb) payload	809 nm (1,500 km; 932 miles)
Endurance:	
with 100 kg (220.5 lb) payload	3 h 20 min
with 400 kg (882 lb) payload	1 h 20 min

DORNIER LA-RPV

First proposed in 1977, when it was known as the UKF (Unbemanntes Kampfflugzeug; unmanned combat aircraft), the LA-RPV (Luft Angriffs: air attack) was a Dornier entry in a Federal Defence Ministry programme to study the basic problems of target acquisition, armament and flight guidance for ground support RPVs. The principal tasks envisaged were air strike (especially battlefield interdiction) against highly defended ground targets, tactical reconnaissance, and electronic warfare (including air defence suppression). The configuration favoured was that of a re-usable, ground-launched high-wing monoplane with a dorsally-mounted turbojet engine, V tail surfaces and retractable landing gear. Missions were to be undertaken at high speed and low altitudes, pre-programmed out and back, with provision for overriding by the ground controller. Target attack was to be by means of scatter weapons (Streuwaffen), ejected from an onboard munitions container.

Dornier was assisted in the programme by VFW, and in 1978–79 a manually piloted Fiat G91R was modified as a testbed to carry an AEG-Telefunken TV camera, an Eltro FLIR sensor, a two-axis stabilisation system and a TV transmitter, all housed in an underwing pod.

Dornier UKF (LA-RPV) model at the 1977 Paris Air Show (*Kenneth Munson*)

An LA-RPV flight test article had not been built when the development programme was suspended in 1981; the only known details are as follows:

DIMENSIONS:
Wing span	3.80 m (12 ft 5.5 in)
Length overall	6.50 m (21 ft 4 in)
Height overall	1.90 m (6 ft 2.75 in)

DORNIER Do 32 K EXPERIMENTAL KIEBITZ (PEEWIT)

The Experimental Kiebitz was developed to evaluate the feasibility of an automatically stabilised tethered rotor platform, capable of utilising sensors for reconnaissance, communications and ECM purposes at an altitude which considerably increases their effectiveness. The system consisted of the Do 32 K tethered rotating-wing platform (first demonstrated in flight in late 1970) and a mobile ground vehicle which served as transporter, take-off and landing ramp, and power supply station. The drone was powered by a KHD T212 turbocompressor, supplying compressed air to drive a two-blade 'cold-jet' rotor, and was equipped with a three-axis autostabiliser working through the cyclic pitch and compressor exhaust centre systems. It could be reeled in and out by a winch mounted on the ground vehicle.

Five Do 32 Ks were built, and these completed approx 100 hours of successful test flying. The basic flight programme was followed by tests to evaluate the vehicle's infra-red radiation and radar profile, the distances at which the rotor platform was discernible acoustically and optically, and applications sensors. These included an RDF system, developed by Dornier, and a Grundig television camera with oscillation-damping suspension

Do 32K Experimental Kiebitz tethered rotor platform

and Dynalens lens-stabilisation. The experimental programme provided data for the proposed Do 34 operational version.

DIMENSIONS:
Rotor diameter	7.50 m (24 ft 7.25 in)
Height overall	1.60 m (5 ft 3 in)
Body diameter at bottom edge	0.75 m (2 ft 5.5 in)

WEIGHTS:
Weight without tether or payload	200 kg (440 lb)
Max payload to 200 m (660 ft), ISA	50 kg (110 lb)

PERFORMANCE:
Reel-in/reel-out speed	1.5 m (4.9 ft)/s
Operating altitude	200 m (660 ft)

DORNIER Do 34 KIEBITZ (PEEWIT) and ARGUS I

Based on experience with the experimental Do 32 K, Dornier designed the Do 34 in 1972 as an operational reconnaissance, fire control, communications and traffic monitoring system. A Federal Defence Ministry contract for the first development phase was awarded in August 1972, leading to the completion of two prototype flight vehicles and two ground stations. First flight was made on 1 February 1978, and maximum flight altitude of 300 m (985 ft) was attained just over a month later. Under a Franco-German agreement of March 1974, both flight vehicles were then fitted with an advanced version of the French LCT Orphée II radar to define, integrate and test a new battlefield reconnaissance system known as **Argus** (Autonomes Radar Gefechtsfeld Überwachungs System). Dornier had the main contract for co-ordinating, integrating and testing the system, and continued with Argus for a time as a German national programme following the withdrawal of

Dornier Do 34, the proposed operational version of Kiebitz

French interest in September 1981, but eventually this too was cancelled, and the proposed shipborne Seekiebitz did not materialise.

The first Argus made its initial flight on 14 May 1979 and the second at the end of 1979. The first part of the troop demonstration was also completed in that year. The second part, using an improved Orphée II airborne radar and ground control station, was completed at the end of 1980. The Argus system successfully demonstrated reconnaissance of individual targets and convoys over various distances, and reconnaissance of several vehicle convoys in an assumed tactical situation. By March 1981, the two Argus vehicles had accumulated 150 h flying time and made a total of 306 flights, of which 47 were at the design operating height.

The following details apply to the basic Do 34 flight vehicle:

TYPE: Tethered rotating-wing platform.

AIRFRAME: Roughly cone-shaped body, to reduce radar signature. Approximately cylindrical payload compartment located beneath this, enabling sensors to be changed quickly and allowing space for large-volume radome. Two-blade rotor, with blades attached by straps and driven by cold air expelled through blade-tip nozzles. Air to nozzles supplied by MTU radial compressor driven by engine.

POWER PLANT: One 313 kW (420 shp) Allison 250-C20B turboshaft engine, installed at an angle to optimise air intake position.

LAUNCH AND RECOVERY: Not applicable (cable-tethered, housed in ground vehicle which incorporated landing platform, winch, control post, fuel tank and auxiliary equipment).

GUIDANCE AND CONTROL: After arrival on site, could be in position at operational height of 300 m (985 ft) in 8 min; limiting factors included wind speed of 14 m (46 ft)/s, added gusts of 8 m (26 ft)/s, available thrust reserves, and sensor requirements. Control system aligned drone according to airframe attitude and position in relation to ground. Electromagnetic sensor measured any drift from desired position.

EQUIPMENT: Bodenseewerk autopilot and Lear Siegler 3 kW starter/generator. Appropriate payload packages for reconnaissance, target acquisiton, fire control, communications relay or traffic monitoring.

DIMENSIONS:
Rotor diameter	8 m (26 ft 3 in)
Height overall	2.70 m (8 ft 10.25 in)
Body diameter (max) at bottom	2 m (6 ft 6.75 in)

WEIGHTS:
Weight without cable or mission load	350 kg (772 lb)
300 m (985 ft) cable	85 kg (187 lb)
Max mission load to 300 m (985 ft), ISA	140 kg (309 lb)
Max T-O weight	550 kg (1,212 lb)

PERFORMANCE:
Reel-in/reel-out speed	3 m (9.8 ft)/s
Operating altitude	300 m (985 ft)
Mission endurance	more than 24 h

DORNIER SPÄHPLATTFORM

The Spähplattform (spotting platform) was a tethered camera-carrying device for battlefield surveillance. To improve mobility, the experimental system was installed, under government contract, in a Unimog 1.4 ton truck with a two-wheeled trailer. Development has been completed.

Dornier Spähplattform

TYPE: Tethered observation platform.
AIRFRAME: Small, domed mission load compartment, mounted on top of an upper gyroscopic ring encircling a four-blade rotor, and a lower stationary ring, in which four control vanes are mounted.
POWER SOURCE: 25 kW (33.5 hp) available for initial rotor spin-up; 90 N required to maintain the hover mode.
LAUNCH AND RECOVERY: Not applicable. The Spähplattform is vehicle-mounted, and tethered to its control vehicle by an umbilical cable, via which drive from the parent vehicle is transmitted to spin up the four-blade flywheel rotor to 4,000 rpm for take-off. The blade-tips of the rotor are attached to the upper gyroscopic ring, in which the energy from spin-up is stored; the four control vanes, mounted on cruciform tubes within the stationary lower ring, can be actuated to control the platform in azimuth. A conventional cyclic-pitch control of the rotor determines the platform's position, and gyroscopic effect stabilises its attitude. The Spähplattform is started and reeled out from a transportation box with automatic covers, and hovers on the energy stored in the flywheel rotor.
GUIDANCE AND CONTROL: Control and sensor signals are transmitted via the tethering cable from the ground control vehicle.
MISSION EQUIPMENT: Still camera of 12.5 mm to 75 mm focal length, or TV camera, in mission equipment compartment.
DIMENSION:
Rotor diameter   1.20 m (3 ft 11.25 in)
WEIGHTS:
Weight of twin-ring assembly   20 kg (44 lb)
Weight of complete vehicle, without mission load
                                                         30 kg (66 lb)
Mission equipment load   2–5 kg (4.4–11 lb)
Max T-O weight   35 kg (77 lb)
PERFORMANCE (A: with 2 kg; B: with 5 kg payload):
Reel-in/reel-out speed: A, B   5 m (16.4 ft)/s
Operating altitude:
A   100 m (330 ft)
B   50 m (165 ft)
Endurance at operating altitude:
A   55 s
B   40 s
Max endurance   1 min 10 s

DORNIER MTC II

First flown on 21 March 1981, the MTC II (Mini Tele-Copter Two) was tested initially within a limited flight envelope in hovering flight, and at forward speeds of up to 13.5 knots (25 km/h; 15.5 mph) and flight altitudes of 25 m (82 ft). For these tests it was controlled from a console via a control cable approx 60 m (200 ft) in length. Conversion to remote radio control was introduced later. Development has been completed.

Possible applications of MTC II derivatives include battlefield reconnaissance, target acquisition and fire control, mine detection, detection of NBC contaminated areas, communication link jamming, and decoy of anti-ship missiles.

TYPE: Experimental unmanned helicopter.
AIRFRAME: Two coaxial, contra-rotating three-blade rotors, driven by a single-stage coaxial bevel gear governed by a centrifugal clutch. Constant chord blades, of mixed wood and glassfibre construction, attached to hub by blade holders and flapping hinges. Clutch disengages immediately in the event of engine failure, to permit autorotation. Main airframe consists of a torsionally rigid tube on which the power plant, fuel tanks, gearbox, rotors and mission equipment are mounted, and rests on a four-leg 'spider' type sprung landing gear.
POWER PLANT: One 30 kW (40 hp) Hirth O28-276-RO-3E two-cylinder two-stroke engine, with electric starting. Two laterally mounted fuel tanks, with combined capacity of 30 litres (6.6 Imp gallons; 7.9 US gallons).
LAUNCH AND RECOVERY: Conventional vertical take-off and landing.
GUIDANCE AND CONTROL: See introductory text. Aircraft fully stabilised by an attitude controller and equipped with a yaw damping circuit. Four control interventions possible, each independent of the others. Control commands linear in character, giving very little cross-influencing even with multiple overriding. Heading controlled by changing torque balance of rotors.
EQUIPMENT: Electrical power supplied by one 300W three-phase generator. Other equipment, according to mission, could include stabilised TV camera (or FLIR) with autotrack capability, laser designator, high resolution thermal imager, ECM jammers or decoy transmitters.

Dornier MTC II during tethered trials

DIMENSIONS:

Rotor diameter (each)	3.20 m (10 ft 6 in)
Rotor separation	0.305 m (1 ft)
Length overall (excl rotors)	1.505 m (4 ft 11.25 in)
Width of fuselage	0.48 m (1 ft 7 in)
Height overall	1.15 m (3 ft 9.25 in)
Landing gear track (c/l of feet)	0.80 m (2 ft 7.5 in)
Landing gear base (c/l of feet)	1.20 m (3 ft 11.25 in)

WEIGHTS:

Max equipment load	60 kg (132 lb)
Max T-O weight	190 kg (419 lb)

PERFORMANCE:

Max level speed	75.5 knots (140 km/h; 87 mph)
Max endurance	approx 2 h

DORNIER PRIAMOS

The Argus I (see Do 34 entry) was cancelled following French withdrawal, but Dornier has proposed a successor known as Priamos (originally Argus II), based on its experience with the experimental MTC II free-flying drone helicopter and equipped with a battlefield radar and radio downlink.

In 1986 integration work began on a demonstrator, which was due to fly in 1987. This will use a modified Gyrodyne QH-50D drone helicopter airframe (see US section), fitted with a French LCT Orphée II radar and powered by a 246 kW (330 shp) Boeing T50-BO-12 turboshaft engine, and will serve as a test vehicle for an advanced standoff battlefield surveillance system known as Priamos (Primäraufklärungsmittel und Ortungssystem: primary reconnaissance and detection system).

Dornier Argus II/Priamos battlefield RPH

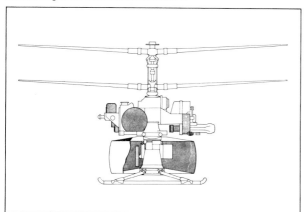

DIMENSIONS (demonstrator): As for QH-50D

WEIGHTS (Priamos):

Weight empty	458 kg (1,010 lb)
Payload	272 kg (600 lb)
Fuel	327 kg (720 lb)
Max T-O weight	1,057 kg (2,330 lb)

PERFORMANCE (Priamos, estimated):

Time to 2,000 m (6,560 ft)	approx 5 min
Max operating altitude	4,000 m (13,125 ft)
Radar sensor range	32–43 nm (60–80 km; 37–50 miles)
Endurance	approx 1 h 30 min

DORNIER TACTICAL MINI-DRONES

In addition to its involvement in the US Army's Aquila programme (see under LMSC in the US section), Dornier has

Early prototype Dornier mini-drones

pursued the development of delta-winged mini-RPVs of its own design since the mid-1970s, first exhibiting an example of such a drone at the 1977 Paris Air Show. Typical missions for which the basic mini has been considered, or is suitable, include electro-optical reconnaissance, target acquisition and fire control, anti-radar operations, anti-tank or point target attack, or training target presentations.

Although not yet selected for series production, the design has figured in a number of major competitive study programmes, beginning in 1978 when it was considered for joint Luftwaffe (anti-radar) and Bundeswehr (target acquisition/fire control) requirements and full scale prototypes were test flown for the first time. This requirement then became linked for a time with the USAF's **Locust** programme for an anti-radar drone. For this, Dornier teamed with Texas Instruments (as payload partner) in offering a **KDAR** version (Kleindrohne Anti-Radar) featuring wingtip fins and rudders, side-force panels above and below the wing roots, a payload of 30 kg (66 lb) and launch weight of 80 kg (176 lb). When the German government withdrew from this bi-national programme in 1981 for budgetary reasons, Dornier refocused its attention on target acquisition as the primary role until 1983, when it displayed an attack version known as the **Hornisse** (hornet) at that year's Paris Air Show. This was in response to a Defence Ministry contract to develop a version primarily for anti-tank duties, with only a secondary capability for anti-radar and electronic warfare missions. However, in 1984 the KDAR anti-radar requirement (now renamed **DAR**) became the front runner again. Both DAR and the parallel **DAT** anti-tank drone programme were still in the competitive phase in 1987.

Dornier mini-drone in 1986–87 DAR configuration

It is difficult to resist the conclusion that, had the German Army and Air Force defined their requirements sooner (and stuck to them), and had consistent budgetary support been forthcoming, at least one system of those explored could well have been in service before now.

Exact configuration of the Dornier minis varies according to role, but the following description is fairly typical:

TYPE: Expendable or recoverable mini-drone.

AIRFRAME: Consists essentially of two glassfibre half-shells, with some plywood and aluminium components. Wings built integrally with fuselage, and fitted with elevons on trailing edges. High aspect ratio retractable side-force panel above and below each wing, near root, deployed to stabilise drone in terminal dive stages of expendable mission. Small fin and rudder at each wingtip, plus central underfin to protect propeller during landing.

POWER PLANT: One 19.4 kW (26 hp) Fichtel & Sachs two-cylinder two-stroke engine, mounted in rear of fuselage and driving a two-blade pusher propeller. Fuel in two wing leading edge tanks; provision to install a third tank in centre of fuselage instead of main recovery parachute. Provision for booster engine for launch.

LAUNCH AND RECOVERY: During initial flight tests, drone was launched by catapult from hydraulically operated launching sled. When required for re-use, it is fitted with an electro-mechanically deployed parachute recovery system (main parachute in centre-fuselage), activated by radio command, with automatic activation in the event of onboard systems failure. Inflatable airbags to absorb landing impact. For expendable missions, parachute can be replaced by an additional fuel tank or other equipment.

GUIDANCE AND CONTROL: Automatic or remote radio command guidance system. Aerodynamic control by elevons and rudders.

MISSION EQUIPMENT: For reconnaissance and target acquisition and fire control missions, the sensor package could comprise a stabilised TV camera, possibly with autotrack facility coupled with a laser illuminator. The DAR version would have a Texas Instruments passive radar seeker. Anti-radar missions and attacks on tanks or point targets would be 'kamikaze' missions in which the vehicle would home on to and attack the target after a search flight using, for example, passive or active radar and/or infra-red seeker heads. For target missions it could be fitted with various augmentation devices, including smoke cartridges, flares or Luneberg lenses. It could also be used to test missile proximity fuses or homing heads.

DIMENSIONS:

Wing span:	
standard mini	2.10 m (6 ft 10.5 in)
DAR version	2 m (6 ft 6.75 in)
Length overall:	
standard mini	2 m (6 ft 6.75 in)
DAR version	2.25 m (7 ft 4.5 in)
Height overall: DAR version	0.35 m (1 ft 1.75 in)
Payload compartment (standard mini):	
Length	0.60 m (1 ft 11.5 in)
Diameter	0.20 m (8 in)

WEIGHTS:

Mission payload	15 kg (33 lb)
Max launching weight:	
standard	70 kg (154 lb)
DAR version	110 kg (242.5 lb)

PERFORMANCE (standard and DAR):

Max diving speed	194 knots (360 km/h; 223 mph)
Max level speed at S/L, ISA	135 knots (250 km/h; 155 mph)
Max operating height	3,000 m (9,850 ft)
Max endurance	3 h

DORNIER KZO

The KZO (Kleinfluggerät für Zielortung) is intended as an all-weather day/night surveillance and target designation mini-RPV for the West German Army. The competitive phase, in which MBB is also a contender, was still under way in 1987.

Dornier's contender is based on the Israeli Mazlat Pioneer (which see), equipped with the relevant mission subsystems for navigation, sensing, launch and recovery. The overall system includes a sophisticated ground control station for mission planning, air vehicle guidance, and imagery interpretation.

No other details were received before going to press.

MESSERSCHMITT-BÖLKOW-BLOHM GmbH (MBB) (Defence Systems Group)
Postfach 801149, 8000 München 80

Before their merger on 1 January 1981, MBB and VFW (Vereinigte Flugtechnische Werke) had both been engaged in RPV development since the latter half of the 1970s. Each produced, independently, designs to meet a joint Luftwaffe (anti-radar) and Bundeswehr (target acquisition and fire control) drone requirement. Following the merger, VFW's Tucan design has been the subject of continuing development by MBB's Defence Systems Group.

In addition to developing derivations of the Tucan for various operational applications, MBB has an agreement with Matra of France for joint development of a new RPV known as the Brevel.

MBB KDAR/HARASSMENT DRONE

Not to be confused with the more recent DAR programme, MBB's original KDAR (Kleindrohne Anti-Radar) harassment drone was a missile-configuration, ground-launched vehicle (catapult or booster) powered by a 7.5–10 kW (10–15 hp) piston engine. Design, which began in 1978, had been modified by 1979 to that of a container-launched vehicle with flip-out wings, developed in conjunction with Teledyne Brown Engineering and fitted with a Motorola terminal guidance system.

The KDAR was launched, by means of a solid propellant booster motor, directly from its storage and transport container. When inside the container the wings, tail control surfaces and propeller were folded, flipping out for use immediately upon launch. First launch was made in the spring of 1980.

DIMENSIONS:

Wing span (deployed)	2.60 m (8 ft 6.5 in)
Length	2.20 m (7 ft 2.5 in)
Body diameter	0.183 m (7.25 in)

WEIGHTS AND PERFORMANCE:
Not known

Early model MBB KDAR harassment drone, with flip-out propeller, wings and tail fins

Zero-length launch of an MBB Tucan test vehicle

VFW-Fokker predecessor of Tucan (wind tunnel model)

MBB Tucan air vehicles: full size in foreground, scale flight test models on the walls

MBB RT-900 TUCAN (TOUCAN)

To meet a German Defence Ministry requirement, VFW-Fokker (as VFW was then known) began developing a catapult-launched mini-RPV of canard configuration in about 1977–78. A subscale first prototype, designed in association with Northrop, had tapered wings and was powered by a 1.5 kW (2 hp) piston engine mounted at the tail to drive a two-blade pusher propeller. It carried no telemetry, and weighed only 5 kg (11 lb). After a period of training for the pilot, with the model in a wind tunnel, it made free flights at up to 52 knots (96 km/h; 60 mph) after take-off from a moving motorcar.

The larger second prototype, displayed at the 1978 Hanover Air Show as 'Mini-RPV 2012', had constant chord wings of Wortmann section, fitted with spoilers, a 4.5 kW (6 hp) single-cylinder engine and onboard telemetry, increasing the take-off weight to 20 kg (44 lb). It had foreplane elevators, and a tail fin but no rudder.

The RT-900 Tucan, which first flew in November 1979, was a pre-production follow-on to these prototypes. The later RT-910 (first flight 1 April 1980) was a contender for the joint USAF/German Locust programme, from which Germany withdrew in 1981.

The Tucan has, however, since been used to test, on behalf of the Federal Ministry of Defence, various payloads for reconnaissance, target location and other tasks. Sensor testing started in 1983, and by 1985, when development flying ended, some 300 test flights had been made (about 50 with 12 full size air vehicles, the rest with two-thirds scale models). Operational derivatives currently being proposed are the **KZO**, **KDH** and **DAR**, described separately.

The following description applies to the Tucan:

TYPE: Recoverable multi-purpose mini-RPV.

AIRFRAME: Low-wing monoplane, with medium aspect ratio wings. Modular construction, made of glassfibre for low radar cross-section. Outer wing panels are folded downwards for storage in launch container.

POWER PLANT: One 16.5 kW (22 hp) Fichtel & Sachs SF 2/330 rear-mounted two-stroke flat-twin engine, with two-blade pusher propeller. Fuel capacity 15 litres (3.3 Imp gallons; 4 US gallons). Booster motor for launch.

LAUNCH AND RECOVERY: Launched by booster motor from starting ramp or from static or vehicle-mounted container.

Parachute and airbag recovery system with autonomous emergency mode, independent of ground equipment.

GUIDANCE AND CONTROL: Autonomous onboard navigation system, which can be updated by radio command. Three-axis aerodynamic control (elevons and rudders). Ground control system comprises mission planning and control, air vehicle status control, and real-time observation.

MISSION EQUIPMENT: Nose-integrated stabilisation platform with TV or FLIR camera, tracker, forward/rearward/downward/side-looking capability, and command, telemetry and video data link equipment. Can also be fitted with infra-red linescanner, low light level TV or other sensors.

DIMENSIONS:

Wing span	3.30 m (10 ft 10 in)
Length overall	2.055 m (6 ft 9 in)
Body diameter	0.35 m (1 ft 1.75 in)

WEIGHTS:

Payload	30–50 kg (66–110 lb)
Launching weight	100–140 kg (220–308 lb)

PERFORMANCE (at launch weight of 100 kg (220 lb)):

Max level speed	135 knots (250 km/h; 155 mph)
Max operating height	3,000 m (9,850 ft)
Operational radius (incl 30 min hold)	38 nm (70 km; 43 miles)
Max endurance	4 h 30 min

MBB expendable combat drone in KDH anti-tank form, with wings folded

MBB EXPENDABLE COMBAT DRONE

MBB is continuing to develop from the Tucan a combat weapon system to fulfil two main tasks. One version, known as **KDH** (Kleindrohne Heer), is for an anti-tank role; the other, for defence suppression missions, is known as **DAR** (Drohne Anti-Radar). The latter is the current designation for the former USAF/German Locust programme, which was revived as a purely national programme by the German Ministry of Defence in 1984. MBB's KDH and DAR proposals were competing in 1986–87 for production contracts from the West German Army and Luftwaffe respectively. A definition phase for the DAR was due to begin in mid-1987, with the concept phase to follow in 1988. The MBB proposal suggests launching swarms of DARs from a container to attack heavy artillery belts and other strongly defended targets. In the current DAR

System concept of MBB's DAR proposal, based on Tucan *(Jane's/Mike Keep)*

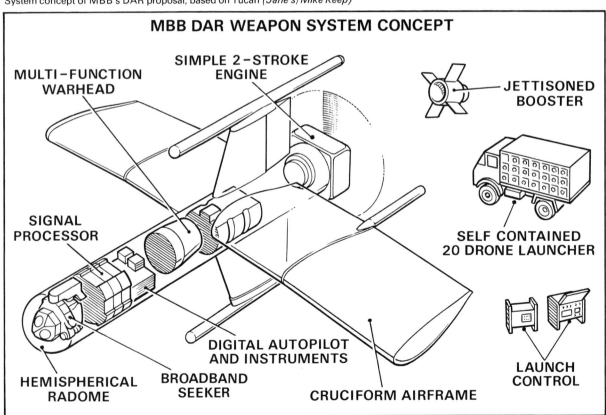

MBB DAR WEAPON SYSTEM CONCEPT

MULTI-FUNCTION WARHEAD

SIMPLE 2-STROKE ENGINE

JETTISONED BOOSTER

SIGNAL PROCESSOR

SELF CONTAINED 20 DRONE LAUNCHER

HEMISPHERICAL RADOME

DIGITAL AUTOPILOT AND INSTRUMENTS

BROADBAND SEEKER

CRUCIFORM AIRFRAME

LAUNCH CONTROL

competition, MBB's proposed RPV would carry a simplified version, by Marconi Defence Systems, of the seeker head fitted to the ALARM missile.

The combat drone was developed as a tail-less cruciform wing configuration with direct force capability, to provide terminal phase accuracy comparable to that of a missile during a high-speed diving approach to its target. By folding the wings, 20 drones can be stored in a single 6.10 m (20 ft) standard container which serves as the storage, transport and launch unit. Zero launch is effected by a booster which detaches from the drone automatically after burnout when the wings of the drone have unfolded after leaving the container. No special separation mechanism is required. The container launch and satisfactory flight characteristics (no banking required for turns and steep dives) have been demonstrated successfully in Tucan test flights.

The attack drone fulfils many important tactical requirements, including high mobility; rapid deployment and operational readiness; low personnel requirements; all-weather capability; long-duration search phase/deep penetration range; high survivability; autonomous target acquisition; automatic target attack; and economical operation (attack is abandoned if target not confirmed as genuine by terminal guidance sensor). To these advantages can be added low system costs and low logistic support requirements: low production costs, storage as ammunition (containerised drones can be stored for up to 15 years, in the open if necessary), no periodical maintenance necessary, and deployment by all military and civil road, rail, sea and air means of container transport.

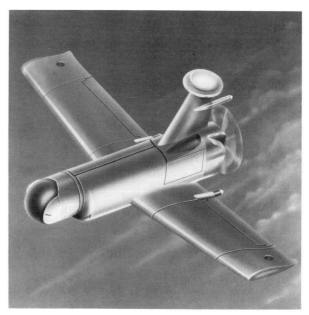

Model of the MBB/Matra Brevel/KZO

DIMENSIONS:

Wing span	2.26 m (7 ft 5 in)
Length overall	1.81 m (5 ft 11.25 in)
Body diameter	0.25 m (9.75 in)
Height overall	1.03 m (3 ft 4.5 in)

WEIGHTS:

Weight empty, equipped	100 kg (220 lb)
Payload plus fuel	50 kg (110 lb)

PERFORMANCE:

Speed	75–135 knots (140–250 km/h; 87–155 mph)
Cruise altitude	up to 3,000 m (9,850 ft)
Endurance	several hours

MBB KZO

The Tucan system provides a suitable hardware basis for the MBB proposal for an operational target acquisition and location RPV known as KZO (Kleinfluggerät für Zielortung: small flight vehicle for target location), designed especially to meet the stringent requirements of bad weather capability together with high operational readiness under adverse mid-European environmental conditions.

Powered by a two-cylinder two-stroke engine, mounted in the rear of the fuselage driving a two-blade pusher propeller, the KZO has a high lift-drag ratio and is fitted with a programmable autopilot. It is launched automatically by booster from a truck-mounted and transportable short ramp, recovery being by parachute to an airbag landing. Real-time data acquisition is by stabilised high-resolution FLIR with electronic image processing (onboard recorder optional); target location is by Rho/Theta radio navigation with map/image correlation. The data link is resistant to jamming. Other sensors, such as IR linescanners or LLL TV cameras, can be substituted without difficulty.

Intended in-service date for the KZO is 1993. A government go-ahead for the development phase was still awaited in mid-1987.

DIMENSIONS:

Not known	

WEIGHT:

Max launching weight	100–150 kg (220–330 lb)

PERFORMANCE:

Speed range	75–135 knots (140–250 km/h; 87–155 mph)
Operating height range	300–3,000 m (985–9,850 ft)
Range	27–43 nm (50–80 km; 31–50 miles)
Max endurance	more than 3 h 30 min

MBB/MATRA BREVEL

Under the name Brevel (coined from their companies' locations at Bremen and Vélizy), MBB of West Germany and Matra of France agreed in April 1983 to develop a new reconnaissance RPV capable of being organised in rapidly deployable mobile batteries with one or more launching vehicles and a single command, control and communications vehicle. MBB is responsible for the air vehicle and Matra for the ground system.

The Brevel, which also fulfils the KZO requirements, is in the 100–150 kg (220–330 lb) weight class, with a penetration range of 27–43 nm (50–80 km; 31–50 miles) and an endurance of several hours. It can accommodate a TV or FLIR sensor, and a playback recorder for deferred in-flight transmission, allowing data storage in cases where real-time transmission would not be possible.

Brevel combines the two companies' experience with, respectively, the MBB Tucan and Matra Scorpion (which see). In 1987 both companies were awaiting a government decision to proceed beyond the concept definition phase. Intended in-service date is 1993.

MW Electronic Telecopter MW 2

MW ELECTRONIC GmbH & Co KG

Attersee 9 (Postfach 3005), 4500 Osnabrück

MW ELECTRONIC TELECOPTER MW 2

Displayed at the 1986 Hanover Air Show, the MW 2 is a small surveillance RPH, carrying a Rolleiflex camera, for aerial survey, pollution monitoring, traffic control, forestry watch and similar applications. It has been test flown in winds of up to about 12 knots (22 km/h; 14 mph). The West German police and border forces have reportedly shown interest.

TYPE: Surveillance mini-RPH.

AIRFRAME: Two-blade rigid main rotor and two-blade tail rotor. Skeletal fuselage frame, mainly of steel tube, with some duralumin in engine mount and rotor head. Skid landing gear. Main and tail rotor blades, and landing gear, are of carbonfibre reinforced GfK. Vibration damping for engine, landing gear and camera mount.

POWER PLANT: One 2.8 kW (3.8 hp) 54 cc single-cylinder two-stroke engine (type not known). Standard fuel capacity 1.5 litres (0.33 Imp gallons; 0.4 US gallons).

LAUNCH AND RECOVERY: Conventional helicopter take-off and landing.

GUIDANCE AND CONTROL: Normally by real-time video link, using an onboard MW Electronic CCD camera, but this can hand over to a small onboard computer for automatic control in the event of signal interference.

MISSION EQUIPMENT: Rolleiflex SLX reflex camera, controlled by ground operator. 6V battery.

DIMENSIONS:

Main rotor diameter	2.002 m (6 ft 6.8 in)
Tail rotor diameter	0.47 m (1 ft 6.5 in)
Fuselage: Length	1.764 m (5 ft 9.5 in)
Max width	0.26 m (10.25 in)
Height overall	0.72 m (2 ft 4.25 in)
Width over skids	0.71 m (2 ft 4 in)

WEIGHTS:

Weight empty	approx 14 kg (30.9 lb)
Payload (Rolleiflex camera)	4 kg (8.8 lb)
Max T-O weight	19.5 kg (43 lb)

PERFORMANCE (approx):

Max level speed at S/L	43 knots (80 km/h; 50 mph)
Max rate of climb at S/L	300 m (984 ft)/min
Operating height range (normal)	60–200 m (200–660 ft)
Ceiling	5,000 m (16,400 ft)
Mission radius	27 nm (50 km; 31 miles)
Endurance with standard fuel	1 h 30 min

Greece

HELLENIC AEROSPACE INDUSTRY (HAI)

Athens Tower, Messogion 2-4, GR-115 270 Athens

HAI PEGASUS

Developed initially for use by the Greek Air Force, the Pegasus surveillance RPV was first displayed publicly at the Defendory International defence exhibition in Athens in October 1986, at which time a production order was said to be imminent. A Greek Army order is also anticipated.

Pegasus was designed by the KETA military aviation research establishment, the prototype being built and flight tested by HAI. The pod-and-twin-tailboom airframe has a non-retractable tricycle landing gear, is powered by a single piston engine with a two-blade pusher propeller, and is equipped with a nose-mounted video camera providing real-time data to a ground control station.

DIMENSIONS:

Wing span	5 m (16 ft 4.75 in)
Fuselage: Length	2.07 m (6 ft 9.5 in)
Diameter	0.34 m (1 ft 1.5 in)
Tail unit span (over fins)	1.67 m (5 ft 5.75 in)

WEIGHT:

Max T-O weight	130 kg (286 lb)

PERFORMANCE:

Max cruising speed at 2,100 m (6,890 ft)	
	86 knots (160 km/h; 99 mph)
Loiter speed at S/L	40 knots (75 km/h; 46 mph)
Time to 2,100 m (6,890 ft)	8 min
Endurance at max cruising speed at 2,100 m (6,890 ft)	
	3 h 30 min

HAI (NORTHROP) TELAMON

The result of an agreement signed in October 1986, Telamon (television area monitor) is a reconnaissance/surveillance version of the Northrop BQM-74C Chukar III (see US section), and was due to enter flight test in mid-1987. Initial in-service roles will be those of real-time and OTH surveillance, under pre-programmed autopilot control, with capability for air, ground or at-sea launch. Later, the Telamon may be adapted to perform jamming and other electronic warfare duties. Maximum speed and range have been quoted as 499 knots (925 km/h; 575 mph) and 405 nm (750 km; 466 miles) respectively. Onboard equipment will include a navigation computer, GPS satellite navigation receiver, air data computer, and a low light level video camera with a transmission range of 100 nm (185 km; 115 miles).

India

AERONAUTICAL DEVELOPMENT ESTABLISHMENT (ADE)
Ministry of Defence, Jeevanbimanagar, Bangalore 560075

The ADE's first mini-drone, tested in 1976, was little more than a radio controlled model aircraft powered by a motorcycle engine, and was unsuccessful.

ADE EXPERIMENTAL MINI-RPV

Work on developing this low-cost experimental mini-RPV, with the specific objective of gaining an insight into vehicle technology, remote control and flying, began in 1981–82. Design requirements specified a lightweight, easily transportable airframe of wood and GRP composites, powered by a two-cylinder piston engine and capable of carrying 10–15 kg (22–33 lb) of fuel and a 10–15 kg payload.

The Indian ADE's first (unsuccessful) mini-RPV of 1976

ADE experimental mini-RPV with increased wing area and raised tailplane

A need to shorten the take-off run was met by adding fixed trailing edge flaps (increasing wing area by 30 per cent) and, later, spanwise extensions to the original 3.80 m (12 ft 5.5 in) wings. The tailplane was relocated on top of the tailbooms (instead of between them) and increased in area.

Development was continuing in early 1984. A new lightweight wing was built in 1983, and by early 1984 other programmes were in hand to develop assisted launch, net recovery, weight reduction and lower engine noise levels. No later news has been received.

TYPE: Experimental mini-RPV.

AIRFRAME: High-wing monoplane with central fuselage nacelle, twin tailbooms bridged by tailplane/elevator, and single central fin and rudder. Constant chord wings, extended by fixed trailing edge flaps; conventional ailerons. Wings have wooden spars and ribs with GRP skin, and are attached to fuselage by four bolts. Rectangular section fuselage is an all-GRP structure (longerons, bulkheads and skin), with a moulded GRP nosecone. Elliptical section detachable tailbooms are of filament-wound GRP, reinforced at wing attachment by wood inserts and stiffened overall by epoxy resin impregnated glasscloth. Non-retractable tricycle landing gear, with 160 mm diameter wheels on all units. Mainwheel legs are cantilever units of self-sprung glassfibre; sprung nose unit has twin wheels.

POWER PLANT: One 13.4 kW (18 hp) NGL WAM 274-6 two-cylinder two-stroke engine, driving a two-blade wooden pusher propeller turning within an annular shroud. Fuel capacity depends on amount of payload carried.

LAUNCH AND RECOVERY: Designed for conventional take-off and landing using short runways or highways. Net assistance used to arrest landing after some test flights. Two-stage parachute (controlled automatically or from ground) for emergency recovery.

GUIDANCE AND CONTROL: UHF-FM/FDM/FM uplink system, with four proportional channels (throttle, ailerons, elevator and rudder) and four discrete. Downlink data telemetry is four-channel (engine rpm, altitude, pitch/roll angle and direction heading indication) VHF-FM/FM.

ONBOARD EQUIPMENT: Analog autopilot, vertical gyro, heading sensor, height hold and air data transducers, and airborne camera.

DIMENSIONS: Not known

WEIGHTS:

Payload	10–15 kg (22–33 lb)
Fuel	10–15 kg (22–33 lb)
Max T-O weight	70 kg (154 lb)

Experimental launch vehicle (ELV) for the ADE Pilotless Target Aircraft

PERFORMANCE (designed):
Max level speed	100 knots (185 km/h; 115 mph)
Max endurance	2 h

ADE PTA

The PTA (Pilotless Target Aircraft) is a re-usable, ship or ground-launched variable speed subsonic target drone, developed by the ADE for use by all three Indian armed services. A small batch of experimental launch vehicles (ELVs), one of which is illustrated, have been completed. Test launches from a ground launcher began in 1983, using a Bharat Dynamics JATO bottle for launch assistance. These vehicles, and the two prototype PTAs (first flight of which was due in December 1985), are powered by a Microturbo TRI 60 turbojet engine.

The production PTA will be manufactured by Hindustan Aeronautics Ltd at Bangalore, and will be powered by a 3.43 kN (771 lb st) PTAE-7 expendable turbojet engine (PTA Engine 7) currently being developed by HAL. This engine is intended to have an operating life of 25 hours. The PTA is designed to tow two HAL infra-red or radar augmented targets, each on a 1,500 m (4,920 ft) cable, and to have an onboard digital data link through which information from the towed targets will be relayed back to the ground controller in real time. A programmable flight computer will provide the PTA with navigation information; recovery is by parachute, with a crushable nosecone to absorb ground impact.

Series production of the PTA was planned to begin in 1987. Although intended primarily for target duties, the design could be adapted for battlefield reconnaissance, coastguard or environmental control, and/or offensive military roles.

DIMENSION:
Length overall	approx 6 m (19 ft 8 in)

WEIGHTS:
Not known

PERFORMANCE:
Speed range	Mach 0.4 to 0.85
	265–563 knots (491–1,043 km/h; 305–648 mph)
Operating height range	300–9,000 m (985–29,525 ft)
Range	54 nm (100 km; 62 miles)
Endurance at 400 knots (741 km/h; 460 mph)	
at 7,000 m (22,965 ft)	1 h

ADE MT

The MT is an air-launched, expendable target for evaluating surface-to-air missiles. Flight development and evaluation trials have been completed.

AIRFRAME: Long cylindrical body, with tapered nosecone having small movable canard surfaces near tip. Rear-mounted delta wings, with ailerons. Small 'arrowhead' endplate fin at each wingtip. Ventral fin under rear fuselage.

POWER PLANT: Two rocket motors in tandem (booster and sustainer).

MISSION EQUIPMENT: Altitude sensor; vertical, roll rate and yaw rate gyros. Two batteries and APU. Luneberg lens in underbody pod. Optional equipment includes fixed target/miss distance indicator and transponder/control display unit.

DIMENSIONS AND WEIGHTS:
Not known

PERFORMANCE:
Speed range	Mach 0.7 to 1.4
Operating height range	100–13,000 m (330–42,650 ft)
Range	19–38 nm (35–70 km; 22–44 miles)
Endurance	2.5 to 5 min

MT expendable target produced by the ADE

Indonesia

LEMBAGA PENERBANGAN DAN ANTARIKSA NASIONAL (National Aeronautics and Space Institute) (LAPAN)

This Institute, established in 1963, designed and built an experimental mini-RPV known as the XTG-01.

LAPAN XTG-01

Test-flown for the first time at Rumpin airfield in FY 1977, the XTG-01 was evaluated for such possible applications as aerial photography, emergency transmitter aerial, and flight research. Development ended in about 1979.

Lapan XTG-01 prototype

TYPE: Experimental mini-RPV.

AIRFRAME: High-wing monoplane configuration, built basically of balsa wood; wings given 2° dihedral, 2° incidence, and a flat-bottomed section. Balsa fuselage, laminated with synthetic fibres.

POWER PLANT: One 1.28 kW (1.71 hp) Hirtenberger HP 61 FS single-cylinder aircooled piston engine, driving a two-blade fixed-pitch wooden propeller. Fuel capacity 2.5 litres (0.55 Imp gallon; 0.66 US gallon).

LAUNCH AND RECOVERY: Conventional T-O and landing.

GUIDANCE AND CONTROL: Futaba FP-6FN six-channel radio command flight control system; transmitter and receiver operating in 27 MHz band. Aerodynamic control by ailerons, elevators and rudder.

EQUIPMENT: 9.6 V battery.

DIMENSIONS:

Wing span	2.43 m (7 ft 11.75 in)
Wing area	0.814 m² (8.76 sq ft)
Length overall	1.60 m (5 ft 3 in)
Height overall	0.575 m (1 ft 10.75 in)

WEIGHTS:

Weight empty	5.3 kg (11.7 lb)
Max payload	2 kg (4.4 lb)
Max T-O weight	7 kg (15.4 lb)

PERFORMANCE:

Speed	60 knots (112 km/h; 70 mph)
Endurance	1 h

Israel

MAZLAT LTD (Mini-RPV Systems)

20 Eliahu Eitan Street, New Industrial Zone, Rishon Le-Zion 75750

Mazlat was formed in September 1984, when Israel Aircraft Industries and Tadiran established it as a subsidiary company to consolidate their efforts in the mini-RPV business. Mazlat is now the sole source of the IAI Scout and Tadiran Mastiff Mk III mini-RPVs in Israel, and has developed the new generation Pioneer mini to combine the best elements of the two earlier systems.

MAZLAT (TADIRAN) MASTIFF Mk III

Details of the earlier Mastiff Mks I and II can be found under the Tadiran heading. The major production version, the Mk III, is an RPV of conventional miniature aircraft configuration for use in reconnaissance, surveillance, target designation and

Mastiff III multi-role tactical mini-RPV *(Brian M. Service)*

Short distance landing system for the Mastiff III

artillery spotting roles. The payload compartment can carry a variety of sensors, including still or TV cameras mounted on gyro stabilised gimbals, and high survivability is ensured by the aircraft's small radar cross-section, negligible infra-red signature, and low visibility and noise levels.

The Israeli Army has acquired considerable battlefield experience with the Mastiff system. It has also been produced for export, including eight Mastiff Mk IIIs supplied to the US Navy in 1984–85. These equip the 1st RPV Platoon of the US Marine Corps at Camp Lejeune, North Carolina; their evaluation led to the requirement for the Pioneer mini-RPV (which see).

TYPE: Tactical mini-RPV.

AIRFRAME: High-wing braced monoplane, with high-mounted tailplane and twin tailfins, supported by two slender tailbooms. Single wing bracing strut each side. Non-retractable tricycle landing gear. Nacelle-type fuselage, in which power plant and mission equipment are mounted. Modular construction, with wings, booms and tail detachable to facilitate transportation.

POWER PLANT: One 16.4 kW (22 hp) two-cylinder two-stroke engine, driving a two-blade pusher propeller. Fuel capacity 35 litres (7.7 Imp gallons; 9.25 US gallons).

LAUNCH AND RECOVERY: Non-retractable tricycle gear for conventional take-off and landing. Vehicle-mounted hydraulic launcher, activated and controlled automatically by

Mastiff III vehicle mounted GCS shelter

an electronic system, is optional. Recovery by means of arrester wire stretched at near ground level between two energy absorbers. On landing, RPV engages wire with tailhook.

GUIDANCE AND CONTROL: Remotely controlled from ground control station (GCS) or portable control station (PCS). The GCS is housed in a standard S-250 type shelter which is normally carried on a 2 ½ ton military vehicle. The functions of this unit are mainly those of air vehicle and payload control, RPV tracking, video and telemetry data reception, with mini-computer processing of received data for real-time or subsequent analysis. There is a PCS that permits RPV take-off and landing at a site remote from the GCS; this is used when the latter is located in terrain unsuitable for launch and recovery, and/or when extended mission range is required. All mission phases are under autopilot control. Aerodynamic control by ailerons and elevator.

MISSION EQUIPMENT: The Mastiff III generates up to 1 kW of electrical power, of which some 400W is available for various payloads, depending upon customer requirements. These can include: (1) TV camera on stabilised gimbals, operable in yaw (360°) and pitch (−88° to +5°) movements, with remote control of camera lens viewing angle and 1:10 zoom; (2) gimbal-mounted TV camera and miniature panoramic film camera for detail photography; (3) various electronic warfare and ECM packages (GFE); (4) certain other electro-optical payloads such as laser designator and miniature FLIR, to suit specific missions (GFE).

DIMENSIONS:

Wing span	4.25 m (13 ft 11.25 in)
Wing area	2.27 m² (24.4 sq ft)
Length overall	3.30 m (10 ft 10 in)

A dismantled Mazlat (IAI) Scout with its shipping crate

Scout mini-RPV prepared for launch

Mazlat (IAI) Scout with wheel landing gear

Height overall	0.89 m (2 ft 11 in)
Propeller diameter	0.72 m (2 ft 4.25 in)
WEIGHTS:	
Weight empty	77 kg (170 lb)
Max mission equipment	37 kg (81 lb)
Max fuel	24 kg (53 lb)
Max T-O/launching weight	138 kg (304 lb)
PERFORMANCE (at 115 kg; 253.5 lb T-O/launching weight):	
Max level speed at S/L	
	100 knots (185 km/h; 115 mph)
Cruising speed	53 knots (98 km/h; 61 mph)
Stalling speed	46 knots (86 km/h; 53 mph)
Max rate of climb at S/L	305 m (1,000 ft)/min
Max operating altitude	4,480 m (14,700 ft)
Landing run (arrested)	within 25 m (82 ft)
Range: without PCS	73 nm (135 km; 84 miles)
with PCS	108 nm (200 km; 124 miles)
Endurance	7 h 30 min

MAZLAT (IAI) SCOUT

The Scout mini-RPV system, developed originally by Israel Aircraft Industries, is employed primarily for real-time battlefield reconnaissance and surveillance, and is designed for operation by ground troops after only minimum training. The complete system, operated by a crew of 12, comprises up to eight Scout aircraft, ground control station, launcher and retrieval net. The current version is designated **Scout 800**.

Scout in recovery net

Military and civil applications include missile site reconnaissance, battlefield control, target identification, strike force control, artillery targeting, border patrol, coastal and waterway control, and damage assessment.

Scouts are in service with the Israeli Army and Air Force, which have used them operationally with considerable success, and have also been supplied to a number of export customers, including South Africa and Switzerland (one system for evaluation). Many of the TV pictures of the Lebanon crisis have been filmed from Scout RPVs.

TYPE: Tactical mini-RPV.

AIRFRAME: Cantilever high-wing monoplane. Fuselage is a rectangular section aluminium nacelle; twin inward-canted fins and rudders, supported by twin tailbooms extending from wings outboard of fuselage. Wings, tailbooms and tail unit are of glassfibre. Aircraft can be delivered with undercarriage and arrester hook for wheeled take-off and landing, and/or 'launching legs' for catapult take-off and net retrieval. Modular construction, with large access panels; wings, booms and tail unit detachable for transportation. Low detection signatures.

POWER PLANT: One 16.4 kW (22 hp) two-cylinder two-stroke engine, installed in rear of fuselage nacelle, driving a specially designed two-blade pusher propeller. Fuel capacity (20:1 petrol/oil mixture) 33 litres (7.25 Imp gallons; 8.7 US gallons).

LAUNCH AND RECOVERY: Catapult launch from a truck-mounted ramp. Recovered by flying into retrieval net set up at ground station.

GUIDANCE AND CONTROL: Pre-programmed or ground controlled, as situation requires. Control system is organised so that operator has merely to transmit flight path demands to the RPV, rather than using link between RPV and ground station to convey signals for direct operation of air vehicle's aerodynamic control surfaces. Instead, demands transmitted to air vehicle are fed to autopilot, which embodies necessary control logic to translate these demands into appropriate movements of control surfaces. Advantage of this method is that transmission is required only when a fresh flight demand (e.g. change of altitude or heading) has to be passed to the air vehicle, eliminating the almost continuous ground-to-air use of the command link that would be needed to pilot the air vehicle under full remote control. For recovery, aircraft is guided semi-automatically by an optical device into centre of retrieval net.

MISSION EQUIPMENT: Tamam TV camera, with telephoto lens, mounted in belly on gyro stabilised platform servo-controlled for vibration damping. Large transparent hemispherical blister under centre of fuselage nacelle. Camera can be controlled remotely by ground operator, and can rotate and scan through 360° in azimuth and 0–90° in pitch. Two payloads are available, differing in field of view adjustment range: Mk I (47.5° to 3.4°) and Mk II (23.8° to 1.7°). Pictures obtained are relayed back to ground station by data link for real-time display. The RPV can also be fitted with a panoramic camera to scan an area within 60° on each side of flight path. Configuration permits installation of other mission equipment packages, such as laser designator/ rangefinder and thermal imaging camera, to customer's requirements. Ground control station essentially similar to that for Mastiff (which see), housed in one of a variety of standard military shelters.

DIMENSIONS:
Wing span	4.96 m (16 ft 3.25 in)
Length overall	3.68 m (12 ft 1 in)
Height	0.94 m (3 ft 1 in)
Propeller diameter	0.74 m (2 ft 5 in)

WEIGHTS:
Weight empty	96 kg (211 lb)
Max mission equipment	38 kg (84 lb)
Max fuel	25 kg (55 lb)
Max launching weight	159 kg (350 lb)

PERFORMANCE (typical):
Max level speed	95 knots (176 km/h; 109 mph)
Speed for max range	55 knots (102 km/h; 63 mph)
Stalling speed	42 knots (78 km/h; 49 mph)
Rate of climb at S/L	244 m (800 ft)/min
Max operating altitude	4,575 m (15,000 ft)
*Control range	54 nm (100 km; 62 miles)
Max flight endurance	7 h

*Can be doubled if RPV is handed over to a second GCS

MAZLAT PIONEER

Pioneer is the next generation of mini-RPV systems developed by Mazlat to satisfy future military and civilian requirements. It incorporates the accumulated battlefield and technical experience of the IAI Scout and Tadiran Mastiff systems, which between them have logged more than 10,000 flight hours in about 2,000 sorties, most of them over hostile territory.

The complete Pioneer system consists of a few basic elements, plus additional subsystems that may be used to upgrade the basic system to the specific requirements of the user. The basic system includes the air vehicles; MKD-200 stabilised TV payload; Elta GCS-2000 ground control station (GCS); portable control station (PCS); MRU-2000 mobile receiving unit (MRU); a pneumatic launcher or rocket booster; and

Prototype Mazlat Pioneer surveillance and targeting RPV

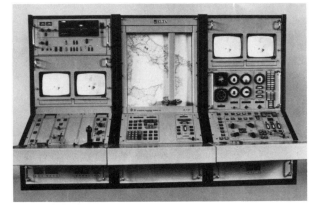

Elta GCS-2000 ground control station for the Mazlat Pioneer

recovery system(s). An integrated support provides all necessary logistics to allow independent storage, operation and maintenance of the system by users in the field, and includes training (maintenance and operation), complete set of manuals, spare parts allocation, special test equipment, and maintenance shelters.

After a 1985 fly-off competition against the Pacific Aerosystem Heron 26 (see US section), the US Naval Air Systems Command placed an order on 7 January 1986 for three Pioneer short range RPV systems: two for shipboard use by the US Navy and one to form a US Marine Corps land based RPV platoon. This contract called for 21 drones (five to eight per system), ground control stations, portable control stations, remote data receiving stations, and launch and recovery equipment. Deliveries began in June 1986. The initial contract included options for two more complete systems in 1987 (ordered in February) and four in 1988. Mazlat's partner in the US Navy programme is AAI Corporation (see US section).

Preliminary tests and extensive shore testing of the Pioneer's take-off and landing controls were carried out in 1986 by Squadron VC-6 at the Naval Air Test Center, Patuxent River, Maryland, followed in December of that year by successful at-sea tests off the Virginia Capes on board the battleship USS *Iowa*. In January 1987 the Pioneer system was deployed, in *Iowa*, for operations off the east coast of Central America. In use, it provides basic gunfire support, with OTH targeting and reconnaissance out to more than 87 nm (161 km; 100 miles) from the ship's surface action group. Of the five Pioneers carried during the January 1987 deployment, one was lost at sea and three others during the retrieval phase. Despite this, the system was expected to achieve IOC with the US Navy in mid-1987.

TYPE: Recoverable reconnaissance/surveillance mini-RPV.

AIRFRAME: Shoulder-wing monoplane with constant chord wings, of similar general configuration to Scout. Central fuselage nacelle of mainly rectangular cross-section, tapered at each end. Slender tailboom extending from each wing, outboard of fuselage, supporting twin inward-canted fins and rudders connected by a central tailplane with elevator. Wings, booms and tail unit detachable to simplify dismantling and assembly in the field and facilitate prompt despatch of several vehicles at one time. Airframe built mainly of composite materials to minimise radar signature. Non-retractable tricycle landing gear, plus arrester hook.

POWER PLANT: One 19.4 kW (26 hp) Sachs two-cylinder two-stroke engine, driving a two-blade pusher propeller. Fuel capacity 42 litres (9.2 Imp gallons; 11.1 US gallons).

LAUNCH AND RECOVERY: Conventional wheeled take-off from short, improvised strips; or catapult launch from pneumatically operated twin-rail launcher, compressed air tank for which is charged by truck's or ship's air compressors. Recovery by wheel landing, using short distance landing system (SDLS) of arrester cable, secured by two energy absorbers, to engage ventral hook; or by retrieval in vertically strung net attached to an energy absorbing system. Retrieval can be carried out from within GCS.

GUIDANCE AND CONTROL: Autopilot control in all mission phases, from take-off to landing, ensures platform stability and ease of control. Programmed emergency manoeuvres allow for extreme flight situations. Elta GCS-2000 ground control station operates and controls the aircraft and its payloads, and receives, computes and displays real-time data from the aircraft, including TV pictures of the target area, via an automatic tracking antenna and secure two-way data link. Target co-ordinates are computed for display on the TV screen; alpha-numeric and graphic displays allow artillery fire adjustment and improve the commander's control of the battlefield situation. The GCS-2000 is compact enough to be housed in small shelters such as the S-250, or in an armoured personnel carrier, giving it mobility under the most severe environmental conditions. It requires only a two-person crew (aircraft operator and observer), and operation and maintenance are simplified by the intensive use of microprocessors and software.

MISSION EQUIPMENT: Main payload compartment in centre fuselage, with volume of 0.1 m³ (3.6 cu ft). Up to 500W of electrical power available for mission payloads which can include day (TV) or night (FLIR) sensors in transparent under-fuselage dome, EW, ECM, decoy, communications relay, and laser target designator and/or rangefinder.

DIMENSIONS:

Wing span	5.15 m (16 ft 10.75 in)
Length overall	4.26 m (13 ft 11.75 in)
Height overall	1 m (3 ft 3.25 in)

WEIGHTS:

Mission payload	up to 45 kg (100 lb)
Max T-O weight	195 kg (430 lb)

PERFORMANCE:

Max level speed (typical)	100 knots (185 km/h; 115 mph)
Cruising speed (typical)	48–70 knots (90–130 km/h; 56–81 mph)
Max rate of climb at S/L	244 m (800 ft)/min
Ceiling	4,575 m (15,000 ft)
Landing distance with SDLS	within 70 m (230 ft)
Mission radius	100 nm (185 km; 115 miles)
Endurance (typical)	6–9 h

TADIRAN LTD

11 Ben-Gurion Street (PO Box 648), Givat Shmuel, 61006 Tel Aviv

Tadiran began developing the Mastiff series of mini-RPVs in the latter half of the 1970s. Major version is the Mastiff Mk III; this has been marketed since late 1984 by the IAI/Tadiran subsidiary Mazlat Ltd, and is described under the Mazlat entry.

TADIRAN MASTIFF Mk I

Unlike the later versions of Mastiff, this initial version was of tractor-engined 'mini-lightplane' configuration, as shown in

Tadiran Mastiff Mk I

the accompanying photograph. First flown in about 1978, it made more than 100 successful test flights.

TYPE: Recoverable mini-RPV.

AIRFRAME: High-wing monoplane, with low-set tailplane, non-retractable tailwheel landing gear, and a ventral payload compartment within the centre fuselage. Very low radar signature.

POWER PLANT: One 10.4 kW (14 hp) two-cylinder piston engine, driving a two-blade propeller. Fuel capacity 22.7 litres (5 Imp gallons; 6 US gallons).

LAUNCH AND RECOVERY: Conventional take-off and landing.

GUIDANCE AND CONTROL: Remotely controlled from ground radio control station or, independently, by a pre-programmed airborne autopilot controller. Onboard avionics included autopilot, vertical gyro, barometric altitude transducer and magnetic compass. Aerodynamic control by ailerons, elevators and rudder.

MISSION EQUIPMENT: Electrical power system supplied by alternator and standby battery. Standard payload of TV camera, with 7° to 35° zoom lens, mounted on a bi-axial platform capable of motion in pitch and roll of up to 45° to each side of vertical axis. Ground controller controlled camera pitch and roll angles by joystick or by potentiometer dialling to required angle relative to RPV. He could also control viewing angle of zoom lens. Camera angles controlled directly by payload servo-actuators and a zoom servo system.

DIMENSIONS:

Wing span	4.20 m (13 ft 9.5 in)
Wing area	2.00 m² (21.53 sq ft)
Length overall	2.60 m (8 ft 6.25 in)
Height overall	1 m (3 ft 3.25 in)

WEIGHTS:

Weight empty	52 kg (114.5 lb)
Max payload	15 kg (33 lb)
Max T-O weight	80 kg (36.3 lb)

Tadiran Mastiff Mk II

PERFORMANCE:

Max level speed	80 knots (148 km/h; 92 mph)
Typical cruising speed	
	40–60 knots (74–111 km/h; 46–69 mph)
Stalling speed	35 knots (65 km/h; 41 mph)
Max operating altitude	3,050 m (10,000 ft)
T-O and landing run	150 m (492 ft)
Range	38 nm (70 km; 43.5 miles)
Endurance	4 h

TADIRAN MASTIFF Mk II

The Mk II was an interim model of the Mastiff, marking the first change from the tractor-engined Mk I to the twin-boom pusher-engined layout seen also on the later Mk III. It entered production in about 1980–81, being replaced by the Mk III about a year later.

TYPE: Tactical mini-RPV.

AIRFRAME: High-wing braced monoplane, with high-mounted tailplane and single central fin and rudder, supported by two slender tailbooms. Non-retractable tricycle landing gear. Nacelle type fuselage, in which power plant and mission equipment are mounted. Modular construction, with wings and tailplane detachable to facilitate transportation. Low radar and infra-red signatures; low visibility and noise levels.

POWER PLANT: One 10.4 kW (14 hp) Kolbo Korp two-cylinder piston engine, driving a two-blade pusher propeller. Fuel capacity 22.7 litres (5 Imp gallons; 6 US gallons).

LAUNCH AND RECOVERY: Vehicle-mounted pneumatic launcher activated by a compressor and controlled automatically by an electronic system. Recovery by means of arrester wire stretched at near ground level between energy absorbers. On landing, RPV engages wire with tailhook.

GUIDANCE AND CONTROL: Remotely controlled by radio from ground control station (GCS) or, independently, by a portable control station (PCS). (For functions, see Mastiff Mk III description.) Use of PCS permits T-O and landing at sites distant from GCS when terrain near GCS is unusable for RPV T-O and landing; and/or when extended mission range is required. All mission phases are under autopilot control. Aerodynamic control by ailerons, elevators and rudder.

MISSION EQUIPMENT: Up to 350W of electrical power available for variety of mission equipment, such as: (1) TV camera on stabilised gimbals, operable in yaw (360°) and pitch (90° down, 10° up) movements, with controllable angle of view of camera lenses; (2) gimbal-mounted TV camera and miniature panoramic film camera for detail photography; (3) various electronic warfare and ECM packages; (4) customer-ordered items such as laser designator and miniature FLIR. The Mastiff can also deliver explosive charges, and simulate larger aircraft or ships by means of radar lenses.

DIMENSIONS:

Wing span	4.30 m (14 ft 1.25 in)
Wing area	2 m² (21.53 sq ft)
Length overall	2.60 m (8 ft 6.25 in)
Height overall	1 m (3 ft 3.25 in)

WEIGHTS:

Weight empty	52 kg (114.5 lb)
Max mission equipment load	15 kg (33 lb)
Max launching weight	75 kg (165 lb)

PERFORMANCE:

Max level speed	70 knots (130 km/h; 80.5 mph)

Typical cruising speed

	40–60 knots (74–111 km/h; 46–69 mph)
Stalling speed	30 knots (56 km/h; 35 mph)
Max rate of climb at S/L	more than 152 m (500 ft)/min
Max operating altitude	3,050 m (10,000 ft)

Range:

without PCS	38 nm (70 km; 43.5 miles)
with PCS	75.5 nm (140 km; 87 miles)
Endurance	more than 4 h

TAMNAR AVIATION TECHNOLOGY

62 Hailanot Street, Gat Rimon, 49920 Petah Tikva

Tamnar develops and produces training aids for air defence forces, and has been the exclusive supplier of target drones to the Israeli Defence Forces since 1972. Its latest target drone is the EDO; it also produces half-scale and full-scale target versions of the Mazlat (IAI) Scout mini-RPV for training operating crews, and a scale target version of the Soviet MiG-27.

TAMNAR TM-105 EDO

Approved for use by air, ground and naval anti-aircraft units of the IDF, the EDO 'model aircraft' target drone permits realistic AA unit training with guns or missiles. The target can simulate various aircraft attack modes and manoeuvres, and is extremely low-cost and easy to operate. Its name is derived from the initials of the Hebrew names of three anti-aircraft soldiers killed in Lebanon in 1982.

Design of the EDO began in February 1982, and the first flight was made in September 1983. Production began in December of that year, and by the beginning of 1986 had totalled 540 (including exports), of 800 then on order.

Tamnar half-scale training version of the Scout

Tamnar EDO air defence training target

TYPE: Air defence target drone.

AIRFRAME: Shoulder-wing monoplane. Wings have a birch plywood skin with polystyrene core; fuselage is of impact absorbing glassfibre and epoxy, tail unit of balsa wood. Steel landing skid standard; can also be fitted with tricycle landing gear.

POWER PLANT: One 3 kW (4 hp) Quadra Q-50, Q-82 or 7.1 kW (9.5 hp) Q-100 single-cylinder two-stroke engine, driving a Clark two-blade wooden propeller. Fuel capacity 4.5 litres (1 Imp gallon; 1.2 US gallons) standard; extended range tank optional.

LAUNCH AND RECOVERY: By catapult from Tamnar rail launcher, returning to land (if not shot down during mission) on underfuselage skid. Alternatively, can be fitted with tricycle gear (jettisoned after take-off) for conventional T-O from any suitable 50–80 m (164–262 ft) length of roadway, track or grass. At sea, can be platform-launched from any vessel of patrol boat size or larger, and recovered in retrieval net installed at stern.

GUIDANCE AND CONTROL: Radio-controlled by operator located within unit training area, using a Kraft 10W transmitter able to control two drones simultaneously. During each exercise, instructions can be transmitted to both AA battery crew and EDO operator. Commander thus remains in control throughout training session, and can initiate or alter strategic situations within seconds.

MISSION EQUIPMENT: Includes hit counter which relays results in real time to ground control display. For use as missile target, can be equipped with devices to activate missile's infra-red homing.

DIMENSIONS:

Wing span	2.50 m (8 ft 2.5 in)
Length overall	2.31 m (7 ft 7 in)
Propeller diameter:	
Q-50	0.46 m (1 ft 6 in)
Q-82	0.51 m (1 ft 8 in)
Q-100	0.56 m (1 ft 10 in)

WEIGHTS:

Weight empty	13.5 kg (29.8 lb)
Max payload (incl fuel)	4.5 kg (9.9 lb)
Max T-O/launching weight	18 kg (39.7 lb)

PERFORMANCE:

Max level speed	162 knots (300 km/h; 186 mph)

Tamnar 'Flogger' hand launched target

Min flying speed	19 knots (35 km/h; 22 mph)
Radio control range	3.2 nm (6 km; 3.7 miles)
Endurance: standard fuel	1 h 30 min
optional fuel	2 h

TAMNAR 'FLOGGER' and 'FROGFOOT'

Target representations of the MiG-27 'Flogger' and Su-25 'Frogfoot' entered production in 1986, the latter (which is no longer being built) varying only slightly in appearance from the EDO. The 'Flogger' target has a deeper fuselage, and altogether resembles the real Soviet aircraft more closely than does the 'Frogfoot' drone. Both are constructed, like the EDO, of impact absorbing glassfibre, have a 7.1 kW (9.5 hp) Quadra Q-100 engine, and are similarly launched and recovered.

DIMENSIONS (both):

Wing span	3.30 m (10 ft 10 in)
Length overall	3.05 m (10 ft)

WEIGHT (both):

Max T-O/launching weight	18 kg (39.7 lb)

PERFORMANCE (both):

Endurance: standard fuel	1 h
optional fuel	1 h 30 min

Italy

METEOR COSTRUZIONI AERONAUTICHE ED ELETTRONICHE SpA
146 Via Nomentana, 00162 Rome

Meteor was established in Trieste in 1947. It produces various propeller-driven and turbojet-powered radio-controlled and/or automatic navigating drones for the Italian and foreign armed forces, at its Monfalcone factory near Trieste; a facility at Villaputzu, Sardinia, is equipped for flight operations and to provide technical assistance to users of the tri-service range at Salto di Quirra.

In addition to RPVs and targets of its own design, Meteor co-produces the Northrop-Ventura KD2R-5 (as the NVM-1 Meteor 1), MQM-74A (NVM-2 Meteor 2) and USD-1 (SD-1(M)); and Beechcraft AQM-37A (BM-1). Under licence from Canadair, it also produces 50 per cent of the AN/USD-501 (CL-89) reconnaissance systems for the Italian Army.

METEOR P.1

The Meteor P.1 is a subsonic target drone for training with anti-aircraft batteries of medium and large calibre and with ground-to-air missiles. It was produced in two versions, both usable for in-sight and out-of-sight operation. The **P.1/100** has a 74.5 kW (100 hp) Meteor Alfa 1 four-cylinder X-type two-stroke aircooled engine for operation at heights up to 8,000 m (26,250 ft). The **P.1/120** has a Meteor Alfa 1AQ engine, giving 89.5 kW (120 hp) constant up to 6,500 m (21,325 ft) and permitting operation at heights up to 13,000 m (42,000 ft). Production ended in 1976.

TYPE: Recoverable target drone.

AIRFRAME: Largely of glassfibre-reinforced polyester resin. Engine manufactured from anti-corrosive and special steel and aluminium, with extensive chromium plating, to permit recovery from salt water and re-use. Flotation ensured by blocks of expanded resin inside the structure.

LAUNCH AND RECOVERY: Launched normally with engine running at peak rpm, assisted by jettisonable solid propellant rockets. Alternatively, catapult can be used, or targets can be air-launched.

GUIDANCE AND CONTROL: For out-of-sight radio control, over ranges up to 54–86 nm (100–160 km; 62–100 miles), operator uses control levers linked to UHF ground transmitter which emits a five-tone modulated carrier signal. Receiver in target transforms signals into seven distinct control operations. Two tones control elevator, two the ailerons, and fifth is used to stop engine and deploy recovery parachute at end of flight. Ailerons and elevators operated by electrical servo controls, those for ailerons being combined with a gyro which stabilises target laterally. Onboard equipment also includes two-axis automatic stabilisation system. Target's track and altitude are plotted normally by radar of gun or missile battery using it, and wingtip reflectors can be fitted to amplify echoes from target. Alternatively, a UHF tracking and telecontrol system can be used, in conjunction with lightweight transponder in target.

DIMENSIONS:
Wing span without wingtip containers

	3.68 m (12 ft 1 in)
Length overall	3.39 m (11 ft 1.5 in)
Height overall	0.65 m (2 ft 1.5 in)

WEIGHTS (out-of-sight versions):
Weight without fuel and electronics:

P.1/100, P.1/120	133 kg (293 lb)

Electronic and gyro guidance equipment:

P.1/100, P.1/120	25 kg (55 lb)

Launching weight (one-hour flight):

P.1/100	195 kg (425 lb)
P.1/120	202 kg (444 lb)

Max launching weight:

P.1/100	220 kg (484 lb)
P.1/120	225 kg (495 lb)

PERFORMANCE:
Max level speed at 6,500 m (21,325 ft):

P.1/100	178 knots (330 km/h; 202 mph)
P.1/120	296 knots (550 km/h; 342 mph)

Stalling speed:

P.1/100, P.1/120	62 knots (115 km/h; 71 mph)

Max rate of climb at S/L:

P.1/100	900 m (2,950 ft)/min
P.1/120	1,200 m (3,940 ft)/min

Time to 6,100 m (20,000 ft):

P.1/100	10 min
P.1/120	5 min

METEOR P.1/R

This reconnaissance version of the P.1, first displayed publicly in 1966, was powered by an 82 kW (110 hp) Meteor Alfa 1 engine driving a constant-speed propeller, and launched from a zero-length ramp by a 17.65 kN (3,968 lb st) Meteor 8785/Z solid propellant booster rocket. Control was partly by radio command signal and partly by a pre-programmed guidance system set up prior to take-off. The latter was housed in a pylon-mounted container under the starboard wing, and was ECM resistant. A similar container under the port wing housed the reconnaissance camera, and could be released in flight for separate parachute recovery.

The P.1/R was radar tracked in flight, using the coded response of a transponder supplemented by the onboard TV camera. Drone recovery was by a conventional parachute system.

A small number of P.1/Rs was produced for the Italian armed forces, production ending in about 1975.

DIMENSIONS: As for P.1
WEIGHTS:

Useful load	30 kg (66 lb)
Max launching weight	250 kg (551 lb)

PERFORMANCE:

Max level speed	270 knots (500 km/h; 310 mph)
Ceiling	9,150 m (30,000 ft)
Operational radius	54 nm (100 km; 62 miles)
Endurance	1 h

METEOR P.2

The P.2 was generally similar to the P.1 in configuration, construction and method of operation, but was larger and intended primarily for out-of-sight flying. A TV camera and transmitter could be fitted for battlefield surveillance duties.

Production, which ended in about 1974, was in two versions, powered respectively by a Meteor Alfa 3AQ four-cylinder two-stroke engine rated at 119 kW (160 hp) constant up to 6,000 m (19,685 ft) for operation at altitudes up to 13,000 m (42,000 ft); or a 238 kW (320 hp) Alfa 5 eight-cylinder two-row engine for operation up to 8,000 m (26,250 ft).

DIMENSIONS:

Wing span	3.72 m (12 ft 2 in)

Meteor P.1 on launch rail

Length overall:	
P.2/160	4 m (13 ft 1.5 in)
P.2/320	4.42 m (14 ft 6 in)
Height overall	0.68 m (2 ft 3 in)

WEIGHTS:

Weight empty, equipped:	
P.2/160	210 kg (463 lb)
P.2/320	252 kg (555 lb)
Launching weight for 1 h flight:	
P.2/160	270 kg (594 lb)
P.2/320	372 kg (818 lb)
Max launching weight:	
P.2/160	400 kg (882 lb)
P.2/320	500 kg (1,102 lb)

PERFORMANCE:

Max level speed at S/L at launch weight for 1 h flight:	
P.2/160	242 knots (450 km/h; 279 mph)
P.2/320	323 knots (600 km/h; 372 mph)
Max level speed at 6,500 m (21,325 ft):	
P.2/160	296 knots (550 km/h; 342 mph)
P.2/320	270 knots (500 km/h; 315 mph)
Stalling speed:	
P.2/160	70 knots (130 km/h; 80 mph)
P.2/320	86 knots (160 km/h; 99 mph)
Max rate of climb at S/L:	
P.2/160	1,200 m (3,940 ft)/min
P.2/320	900 m (2,950 ft)/min
Time to 6,000 m (19,685 ft):	
P.2/160	4 min 5 s
P.2/320	10 min

METEOR P.X

The P.X basic training drone is generally similar in layout to earlier Meteor drones, but is lighter and has a lower powered engine.

P.X systems were produced for the armed forces of Italy and other countries; production ended in about 1978.

TYPE: Re-usable training drone.
AIRFRAME: Mainly of glassfibre-reinforced polyester resin.
POWER PLANT: One 53.7 kW (72 hp) flat-four engine, driving a two-blade propeller; Meteor 8785 solid propellant booster rocket.
LAUNCH AND RECOVERY: Zero-length launch, using jettisonable booster rocket. Recovery by parachute, deployed automatically or on receipt of ground signal.
GUIDANCE AND CONTROL: Radio control, via Meteor RSS 529 fully transistorised two-axis autopilot, with radar tracking.

Meteor P.X basic training drone

MISSION EQUIPMENT: No details known.
DIMENSIONS:

Wing span without wingtip containers	
	3.56 m (11 ft 8 in)
Length overall	3.46 m (11 ft 4.25 in)
Body diameter	0.40 m (1 ft 3.75 in)
Span of tail unit	1.21 m (3 ft 11.5 in)

WEIGHT:

Max launching weight	165 kg (363 lb)

PERFORMANCE (at max launching weight):

Max level speed	194 knots (360 km/h; 224 mph)
Time to 6,100 m (20,000 ft)	10 min
Ceiling	8,000 m (26,250 ft)
Radius of action	86 nm (160 km; 100 miles)
Endurance	1 h

METEOR GUFONE (OWL)

Meteor developed the Gufo tactical reconnaissance system in the 1970s to meet anticipated military requirements into the 1980s. In operational form the Gufo was intended to enable up to 27 kg (60 lb) of sensors to be carried at 400 knots (740 km/h; 460 mph) to target areas up to 110 nm (200 km; 125 miles) from the launch site.

The drone part of the system, known as the **Gufone (Owl)**, was proposed in three versions, the standard air vehicle being based on the American Northrop Chukar I (MQM-74A) target drone modified by Meteor to carry new guidance equipment and sensors, together with inflatable bags to cushion the landing shock. Equipment could include various infra-red sensors and cameras. For night operations, the Gufone could carry 14 wingtip flares to be dropped at preselected time intervals. At take-off, the 0.54 kN (121 lb st) turbojet engine was supplemented by two Meteor 8785/CNS solid propellant jettisonable boosters, providing a total thrust of 25.5 kN (5,730 lb) for 0.7 seconds.

A complete Gufo system was intended to comprise a launching section; a guidance and control section; a sensor recovery, interpretation and headquarters section; and a vehicle recovery and preparation section. The Gufone drone could be launched in any direction and would normally make the first part of its flight under guidance over friendly territory. Subsequently it could be directed very precisely on to the first

Gufone drone on its launch trailer, towed by launch truck

stage of a programmed flight to the target. Once put on course, it became 'deaf' to all friendly or enemy electronic signals until approaching the end of its return flight and coming under command guidance for recovery.

Provision was also made for an intermediate pre-programmed guidance phase between the guided and 'deaf' phases. In such case, the drone would accept only specially coded commands of very short duration, for the sole purpose of correcting its course.

Although extensively and successfully tested, the Gufo system did not go into production, but much of the experience gained was later built into the Andromeda system and Mirach air vehicles described in the next two entries.

DIMENSIONS:

Wing span	1.69 m (5 ft 6.75 in)
Length overall	3.61 m (11 ft 10 in)
Height overall	0.73 m (2 ft 5 in)

WEIGHTS:

Sensors (max)	27 kg (60 lb)
Max launching weight	136 kg (300 lb)

PERFORMANCE:

Max level speed	400 knots (740 km/h; 460 mph)
Max cruising altitude	10,670 m (35,000 ft)

METEOR ANDROMEDA SYSTEM

Andromeda is a multi-role system equipped with various types of RPV for combat or training use by air, land and naval forces. Now in operation with many armed forces around the world, it is characterised by completely independent operation, maximum utilisation and considerable mobility. It is composed of the following subsystems:

1st Subsystem (Alamak/Sirah). Ground station for controlling the mission by ground crew (Standard and RID (Reduced) versions) and equipment which keeps air vehicle automatically on a pre-programmed flight.

2nd Subsystem. Equipment for launch, recovery and maintenance of the air vehicles.

3rd Subsystem. Equipment for preparation, recovery, maintenance and operation and/or evaluation of the payload and/or its results.

4th Subsystem. Part of the air vehicle system, comprising five different types of vehicle, all known as **Mirach**. The

Andromeda system can be adapted to use other types of air vehicle which a customer may already have in his inventory.

METEOR MIRACH

Three propeller driven and three turbojet powered types of Mirach air vehicle have been built or projected, as follows:

Mirach-10. Small delta-winged, twin-finned RPV for target acquisition/location/designation, surveillance, 'kamikaze' missions and enemy defence saturation. Powered by single 16.4 kW (22 hp) piston engine with pusher propeller. Meteor radio command guidance system. Real-time TV, photo-reconnaissance camera or laser designator payloads. Developed for foreign customers; superseded in about 1980–81 by Mirach-20.

Mirach-20 Condor and Pelican. Mini-RPV for target acquisition, location and designation; surveillance; and defence saturation. Powered by single 19.5 kW (26 hp) Herbrandson Dyad two-stroke flat-twin engine driving a two-blade wooden pusher propeller. Twin-boom, twin-tail configuration, with central fuselage nacelle. Skid landing gear. Airframe built mainly of Kevlar and synthetic expanded resin, with minimal use of metal; can remain afloat after ditching for up to 24 hours. Shoulder-mounted wings are detachable. Booster rocket fitted under rear of fuselage, for assisted take-off from zero-length launcher, provides 10.79 kN (2,425 lb) of thrust for 0.7 s and is then jettisoned. Fuel load for piston engine is 23 kg (51 lb). Recovery by parachute stored in dorsal compartment forward

Mirach-20 on truck mounted zero-length launcher

Onboard equipment of Mirach-20 Pelican naval version

MIRACH 20 · PELICAN ONBOARD EQUIPMENT

1. Flux gate
2. Throttle servo
3. Elevator servo
4. Rudder servo
5. Rate gyro
6. Directional gyro
7. Amplifier
8. Vertical gyro
9. Autopilot, Target position computer and Data converter unit
10. Recovery parachute
11. Parachute door actuator
12. Power supply
13. Downlink TX
14. Downlink antenna
15. Uplink antenna
16. Aileron servo
17. Altitude sensor
18. Speed sensor
19. FLIR
20. Cooling pack
21. Acquisition radar
22. Pitot tube
23. Alternator
24. Engine
25. Telemetry TX
26. Telemetry antenna

of engine bay. Ground controlled (radio command) or pre-programmed automatic Omega/VLF navigation, with real-time data uplink and downlink and four-channel hybrid autopilot. Aerodynamic control via ailerons, elevator and rudders. Onboard sensors and other avionics can include over-the-horizon acquisition radar (radius 50 nm; 93 km; 57.5 miles at 915 m; 3,000 ft), TV camera, FLIR, target position computer and data conversion unit, vertical/directional/rate gyros (one of each), speed/altitude/rpm sensors (one of each), emergency locator transmitter, and flux gate. Electrical power (28V DC) from 1.7 kW generator. Alternative sensors can include IRLS, photo-reconnaissance cameras and laser designator. In production for Italian Army (Condor) and Navy (Pelican). Fully pre-programmed versions of Condor and Pelican, requiring no GCS, are known respectively as **Raven** (for day or night reconnaissance) and **Parrot** (for communications relay, jamming or ESM missions). Modified versions produced in USA by Pacific Aerosystem (which see) as the **Heron 26**, and in Argentina by Quimar as the **MQ-4 Agilucho**.

Shipboard launch of a Mirach-70

Mirach-70. Target drone, or electronic warfare or decoy RPV, similar in appearance to Meteor P.X. Powered by single 52 kW (70 hp) piston engine. Radio command guidance system. Various combat or training payloads. Also produced under licence in Argentina by Quimar (which see) as the **MQ-1 Chimango**.

Mirach-100. Target drone, or RPV for surveillance; reconnaissance; target location and acquisition; electronic warfare; defence saturation; and strike. Powered by single 1.78 kN (400 lb st) NPT 401 turbojet. Ground control or automatic navigation with real-time data transmission. Various combat or training payloads. In production for Italy and foreign countries (over 150 built by early 1987), with customers reported to include Iraq and Libya; further contract placed in January 1987 to supply 15–20 of this version to NAMFI missile range on Crete during 1988–90. Mirach-100 is

Mirach-100 (target version) being launched at sea

Reconnaissance RPV versions of the Mirach-100 on an Agusta A 109A

also produced under licence in Argentina by Quimar (which see) as the **MQ-2 Bigua**. Normal one-way penetration range of 485 nm (900 km; 560 miles). An extended range **Mirach-100ER**, equipped with BAe MIRLS 4000 linescanner and Pacific Aerosystem Mizar avionics data link and ground equipment, was entered in 1986 to bid for the US Navy's mid-range RPV requirement. The Agusta A 109/Meteor Mirach-100 combination, consisting of the transport, release and recovery by helicopter of one or two Mirach-100 RPVs, has been delivered to various customers and is now operational. With Quimar, Meteor has developed a mounting enabling a Bigua to be carried underfuselage by the IA 58A Pucará, and flight trials with such an aircraft were continuing in 1987. The Mirach-100 is equipped with an automatic navigation subsystem called Sirah. With this system installed, the RPV can be programmed to loiter over a battlefield for surveillance purposes. It also has potential applications as a tactical cruise missile, launched from an Aeritalia G222 'mother' aircraft carrying six Mirach-100s.

Mirach-300. Target drone, or RPV for surveillance, reconnaissance, target location and acquisition, electronic warfare, strike, and defence saturation. Powered by single 3.70 kN (832 lb st) turbojet engine. Guidance and automatic

Mirach-300 target/RPV on launching ramp

navigation as for Mirach-100. Various combat or training payloads. Still under development.

Mirach-600. RPV for area reconnaissance, electronic warfare, strike, and defence suppression. Powered by two 3.70 kN (832 lb st) turbojet engines. Guidance and automatic navigation as for Mirach-100. Various combat or evaluation payloads. Not yet built.

DIMENSIONS:

Span overall (wings or fins):

10	2.71 m (8 ft 10.75 in)
20	3.83 m (12 ft 6.75 in)
70	3.57 m (11 ft 8.5 in)
100	1.80 m (5 ft 11 in)
300	2.83 m (9 ft 3.5 in)
600	3.60 m (11 ft 9.75 in)

Length overall:

10	2.25 m (7 ft 4.5 in)
20	3.62 m (11 ft 10.5 in)
70	3.66 m (12 ft)
100	3.94 m (12 ft 11 in)
300	5 m (16 ft 4.75 in)
600	6.10 m (20 ft)

Height overall: 20   1.12 m (3 ft 8 in)

WEIGHTS:

Weight empty:

10	50 kg (110 lb)
20	95 kg (210 lb)
70	200 kg (441 lb)
100	210 kg (463 lb)
*300	400 kg (882 lb)
*600	680 kg (1,499 lb)

Combat load (internal):

20	25 kg (55 lb)
70	20 kg (44 lb)
100	70 kg (154 lb)
300	150 kg (330 lb)
600	300–500 kg (661–1,102 lb)

Max launching weight (incl booster where applicable):

10	70 kg (154 lb)
20	197 kg (434 lb)
70	260 kg (573 lb)
100	310 kg (683 lb)
*300	800 kg (1,763 lb)
*600	1,000 kg (2,204 lb)

estimated

PERFORMANCE:

Max level speed:

10	97 knots (180 km/h; 112 mph)
20	108 knots (200 km/h; 124 mph)
70	194 knots (360 km/h; 224 mph)
100	458 knots (850 km/h; 528 mph)
*300, 600	Mach 0.92

estimated

Max rate of climb at 1,000 m (3,280 ft):

20	240 m (787 ft)/min

Ceiling: 20   3,000 m (9,850 ft)

Max endurance:

10	3 h
20	3 h
70, 100	1 h
*300, 600	2 h

estimated

Japan

FUJI HEAVY INDUSTRIES LTD (Fuji Jukogyo Kabushiki Kaisha)

Subaru Building, 7-2, Nishi-Shinjuku, 1-chome, Shinjuku-ku, Tokyo 160

Under contract from the Japan Defence Agency, Fuji builds Teledyne Ryan BQM-34A Firebee I subsonic target drones (see US section) for use in training Tartar missile and gunnery crews, and for evaluation of air-to-air missile systems and Japanese-built F-15Js. The first shipboard launch of a Fuji-built drone was carried out in 1970, and about 390 flights had been made by the beginning of 1987.

By the end of March 1987 a total of 51 Fuji-built BQM-34AJs had been delivered to the JMSDF and 20 to the JASDF. These include four fitted with RALACS (radar altimeter low altitude control system) for training the crews of defensive weapons against attack by anti-shipping missiles.

FUJI RESEARCH MINI-RPV

The Technical Research and Development Institute of the Japan Defence Agency authorised the design, development and

Fuji research mini-RPV on a 1986 test flight

construction of the first all-Japanese RPV, a research mini-RPV for JGSDF surveillance and reconnaissance missions.

As the accompanying photograph shows, the air vehicle has a pod shaped fuselage, with high-mounted sweptback wings on which twin fins and rudders are fitted at the trailing edge at just

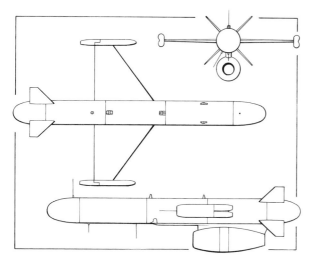

Fuji Model 820 XJ/AQM-1 *(Michael A. Badrocke)*

over mid-span. Power plant is a 13.4 kW (18 hp) DH Enterprises (Herbrandson) Dyad 220 engine, driving a two-blade pusher propeller. Launch is from a mobile ramp, the aircraft being accelerated to flying speed by a JATO booster rocket.

Fuji was prime contractor, with Nippon Avionics providing the onboard guidance equipment, Hitachi the TV camera, and Hitachi and Nippon Electric the ground control equipment. Other Japanese participants were Japan Aviation Electronics and Daicel.

DIMENSIONS:
Wing span	3.50 m (11 ft 5.75 in)
Length overall	2.30 m (7 ft 6.5 in)

WEIGHT:
Basic operating weight empty	90 kg (198 lb)

PERFORMANCE:
Max level speed at S/L	
	120 knots (222 km/h; 138 mph)
Service ceiling	above 2,500 m (8,200 ft)
Endurance	1 h

FUJI MODEL 820

JASDF designation: XJ/AQM-1

This is an expendable air-launched target drone currently being developed for the JASDF under Japan Defence Agency contract. Fuji was selected by the JDA in July 1983 as prime contractor, and the first of 11 prototypes made its initial flight in March 1986. The flight test programme was completed successfully in December 1986, and production for the JASDF was due to begin in FY 1987.

General configuration of the XJ/AQM-1 is shown in the accompanying three-view drawing. Construction is virtually all-metal (steel and aluminium).

TYPE: Expendable target drone.

AIRFRAME: Mid-wing monoplane, with clipped-delta wings which are interchangeable left/right. Four tail fins, of similar planform, indexed in X configuration at 45° to vertical and horizontal axes. Cylindrical metal body, with glassfibre nosecone and tailcone. Engine suspended on centreline pylon beneath rear of fuselage. No landing gear.

POWER PLANT: One 1.96 kN (441 lb st) Mitsubishi Heavy Industries TJM3 turbojet in underslung nacelle. Pressurised fuel tank in centre of fuselage, capacity 47 litres (10.3 Imp gallons; 12.4 US gallons).

LAUNCH AND RECOVERY: Can be air-launched from underwing pylon (one under each wing) of JASDF McDonnell Douglas F-4EJ Phantom or F-15J/DJ Eagle. Non-recoverable.

GUIDANCE AND CONTROL: Pre-programmed guidance system, which can be overridden by radio command from either the launch aircraft or a surface station. Digital flight control system, including engine throttle control.

MISSION EQUIPMENT: X-band reflector in fore and aft body compartments. Smoke or infra-red generators can be attached to wingtips. Miss distance indicator can be installed in forward section of fuselage.

DIMENSIONS:
Wing span (over smoke generator pods)	2.07 m (6 ft 9.5 in)
Wing area	1.20 m² (12.92 sq ft)
Length overall	3.65 m (11 ft 11.75 in)
Height overall	0.92 m (3 ft 0.25 in)
Body diameter (max)	0.35 m (1 ft 1.75 in)
Span over tail fins	0.98 m (3 ft 2.5 in)

WEIGHTS:
Max mission payload	42.2 kg (93.5 lb)
Fuel	32 kg (70.5 lb)
Max launching weight	235.5 kg (519 lb)

PERFORMANCE:
Max level speed at 9,150 m (30,000 ft)	Mach 0.95
Max sustained turn at 9,150 m (30,000 ft)	3.2g
Operating height: min	660 m (2,000 ft)
max	9,150 m (30,000 ft)
Endurance at Mach 0.9 at 9,150 m (30,000 ft)	18 min
g limits	+5/−2

FUJI MANUFACTURING CO LTD

16 Hotoku-cho, Kita-ku, Nagoya

FUJI MODEL 500 AERO-SHIP

The origin of this craft lay in a small remotely controlled pilotless research airship known as the **Flying Submarine Model 503**, powered by two 0.47 kW (0.63 hp) engines and built by members of the Japan Experimental Aircraft Association in about 1973–74. The airship was 7.80 m (25 ft 7 in) long, and an unusual feature was the attachment, to the lower surface of the gondola, of a horizontal lifting surface with

Fuji Model 500 Aero-Ship

a fixed centre section and movable outer panels, its purpose being to assist with vertical control as well as to provide lift. Gross weight of the Flying Submarine was 18.6 kg (41 lb), and successful flight testing included a cruising speed of 11 knots (20 km/h; 12.5 mph).

Leaders of the JEAA team were Daisaku Okamoto and Kikuo Koizumi of Fuji Manufacturing, and the first full size version of their design (c/n 2), known as the **Model 500 Aero-Ship**, was built in the autumn of 1974, making its first flight on 23 December that year. A slightly modified third airship followed on 28 July 1975. Both had a helium filled envelope made of plastics, the gondola, wing and tail surfaces being constructed from Japanese cypress, balsa and plywood with a covering of silk. Power plant comprised two ENYA 60 IIIB air-cooled engines, each developing 0.97 kW (1.3 hp), mounted at the rear of the gondola at each end of an outrigger. The forward part of the gondola could house a camera or other specialised equipment; radio control equipment and batteries were accommodated in the centre portion, and a fuel tank in the rear section. Proposed applications of the Aero-Ship included aerial photography, meteorological and pollution monitoring, seed/fertiliser/pesticide distribution, and advertising.

Limited range of the radio control equipment used in the early stages of the programme prevented full evaluation of the Aero-Ship's performance, but a speed range of 5.4–43 knots (10–80 km/h; 6.2–50 mph) and ceiling of 1,000 m (3,280 ft) were demonstrated. Construction numbers up to 12 were allocated to subsequent Aero-Ships, although it is not known for certain whether all 12 were completed. No. 7, which first flew on 21 November 1975, had an overall length of 6 m (19 ft 7.5 in) and was supplied to Tohoku University Geographical Laboratory. No. 8 was built in 1976 for the Tasei Construction Company, and No. 12 (to which the following data apply) was under test at the end of 1978, after which the Aero-Ship programme appears to have ended.

DIMENSIONS:

Wing span	3.26 m (10 ft 8.5 in)
Wing area	1.01 m² (10.87 sq ft)

Length overall	8 m (26 ft 3 in)
Envelope diameter (max)	1.90 m (6 ft 2.75 in)
Envelope volume, gross	18.28 m³ (645 cu ft)

WEIGHTS:

Weight empty, equipped	22.7 kg (50 lb)
Weight, helium filled	4 kg (8.8 lb)
Max T-O weight	6 kg (13.2 lb)

PERFORMANCE:
See text

MITSUBISHI HEAVY INDUSTRIES LTD (Mitsubishi Jukogyo Kabushiki Kaisha)
5-1, Marunouchi 2-chome, Chiyoda-ku, Tokyo 100

MITSUBISHI QF-104J

Approval was given in the 1985 defence budget for the storage of retired JASDF F-104J Starfighters with a view to their eventual modification into QF-104 target drones, for use in air-to-air combat training and domestically developed missile tests, and possibly also to investigate ECM or decoy RPV technology. Current plans are for two prototype modifications, with 29 more QF-104J conversions to follow.

NEC CORPORATION (Nippon Denki Kabushiki Kaisha)
33-1, Shiba 5-chome, Minato-ku, Tokyo 108

Under licence from Northrop Corporation, USA, NEC is responsible for production and repair of Northrop KD2R-5 Basic Training Target and Chukar II high-speed target drones for the Japan Defence Agency.

Deliveries of the KD2R-5 and Chukar II began in 1961 and 1982 respectively. By the beginning of 1987 a total of 367 KD2R-5s and 86 Chukar IIs had been delivered to the JDA.

Saudi Arabia

MID-CONTINENT SCIENTIFIC COMPANY (MCS)
PO Box 3603, Riyadh

MCS PL-60

Design of this twin-engined mini-RPV began in the USA in 1971; a prototype was flown in 1972, and series production began in the same year. By March 1979 a total of 1,580 had been ordered and built in two versions, designated **PL-60A** and **PL-60B**, the latter having a strengthened structure to carry a heavier payload. Production was then transferred to Saudi Arabia, but no news of it has been received since that time.

Applications described for the PL-60 include surveillance

Mid-Continent PL-60

and other military duties, border patrol, forest fire surveillance, aerial photography, traffic patrol, air pollution and weather monitoring. It is claimed to be virtually undetectable by radar.

POWER PLANT: Two 1.4 kW (1.9 hp) piston engines, mounted in overwing nacelles and each driving a two-blade propeller. Fuel capacity 1.9 litres (0.4 Imp gallon; 0.5 US gallon) standard, 7.6 litres (1.7 Imp gallons; 2 US gallons) optional.
LAUNCH AND RECOVERY: Conventional T-O, using tailwheel type fixed landing gear. Wire recovery.
GUIDANCE AND CONTROL: No details known.
MISSION EQUIPMENT: Automatic navigation system, TV or other camera installations, optional.
DIMENSIONS:

Wing span	3.30 m (10 ft 10 in)
Wing area	1.57 m² (16.94 sq ft)
Length overall	1.96 m (6 ft 5 in)
Height overall	0.58 m (1 ft 11 in)

WEIGHTS:

Payload: PL-60A	11.3 kg (25 lb)
PL-60B	21.8 kg (48 lb)
Max T-O weight (both)	27.2 kg (60 lb)

PERFORMANCE:

Max level speed	65–87 knots (121–161 km/h; 75–100 mph)
Cruising speed	56 knots (105 km/h; 65 mph)
Max operating altitude	3,050 m (10,000 ft)
T-O run (hard surface)	99 m (325 ft)
Range: standard fuel	30 nm (56 km; 35 miles)
max optional fuel	121 nm (225 km; 140 miles)

South Africa

NATIONAL DYNAMICS (PTY) LTD
RCA Division, PO Box 2804, Durban 4000, Natal

NATIONAL DYNAMICS ND-100 OBSERVER

The Observer prototype was built as a private venture low-cost multi-purpose mini-RPV for various military and civil applications, including real-time forest surveillance; aerial photography; search missions; flood, wildlife and shoreline pollution detection and mapping; powerline, pipeline and highway traffic observation and patrol; air sampling and storm research; fishing law enforcement and fishery spotting; and aerial survey.

Design began in 1974, and it flew for the first time in October 1975. However, its 'flying wing' configuration was not considered ideal from the stability point of view, and the rear-mounted engine location presented a relatively high infra-red signature. These considerations led to the choice of a rhomboid wing configuration for its successor, the Eyrie.

TYPE: Experimental multi-purpose mini-RPV.
AIRFRAME: High-wing monoplane, of near-delta planform, with special aerofoil section. Dihedral 0°. Sweepback 30° on leading edges. Trailing edge elevons, actuated by radio-controlled servos, functioning as both ailerons and elevators. NASA (Whitcomb) fixed 'winglet' at each wingtip; no vertical moving surfaces. Cylindrical fuselage, with wooden bulkheads, glassfibre/epoxy skin, and transparent hemispherical nose-cap. Low-density styrofoam and plywood also used in construction, to provide corrosion-resistant structure.
POWER PLANT: One 15 kW (20 hp) Herbrandson Dyad 280 piston engine, with electronic ignition, driving a four-blade fixed-pitch wooden pusher propeller. Single fuselage fuel tank, capacity 42.5 litres (9.35 Imp gallons; 11.2 US gallons).
LAUNCH AND RECOVERY: Self-powered launch from vehicle-mounted, controllable (in T-O speed and direction) rotary arm launcher acting also as boom for low-speed parafoil/boom recovery. Alternative launch by catapult, with net recovery.
GUIDANCE AND CONTROL: Tracking by onboard transponder and forward-looking video tracking subsystem, with associated X-Y plotter and TV monitor in two-man mobile ground control station. Target designation by separate downward-looking video subsystem. Guidance and control based upon command uplink plus antennae, command receiver, control servos, electrostatic autopilot with ionising units, telemetry channels to monitor airframe/engine states and RPV equipment, and data link and video transmitters. Landing, after deployment of parafoil in response to command signal from ground, by standard non-tracking radio control link, using a portable transmitter. Rotating beacon fitted to assist recovery in poor visibility.
EQUIPMENT: Engine-driven alternator, rectifier/regulator and twin-battery pack providing electrical power to operate onboard receiver, servos, lightweight autopilot, telemetry and video equipment, and transmitters. Space for ample equipment payload, according to mission.
DIMENSIONS:

Wing span	4.34 m (14 ft 3 in)
Wing area	4.13 m² (44.5 sq ft)
Length overall	2.54 m (8 ft 4 in)
Height overall	1.12 m (3 ft 8 in)

National Dynamics ND-100 Observer

Eyrie Mk 1

Eyrie Mk 3 prototype with extended chord low-speed wingtips to facilitate recovery at sea

Production Eyrie 6A-60 multi-role recoverable mini-RPV

Body diameter	0.46 m (1 ft 6 in)
Propeller diameter	0.61 m (2 ft)
WEIGHTS:	
Weight empty, equipped	50 kg (110 lb)
Max fuel load	32 kg (70 lb)
Max payload (avionics)	36 kg (80 lb)
Max launching weight	118 kg (260 lb)
PERFORMANCE (at max T-O weight at S/L):	
Max level speed	95 knots (177 km/h; 110 mph)
Cruising speed	65 knots (120 km/h; 75 mph)
Stalling speed	38 knots (69 km/h; 43 mph)
Max rate of climb	533 m (1,750 ft)/min
Service ceiling	approx 4,575 m (15,000 ft)
Range	Radio line-of-sight (or, out-of-line-of-sight, by use of two RPVs: one sensor and one relay)
Endurance	more than 6 h

NATIONAL DYNAMICS EYRIE TD 110

The Eyrie is a miniature unmanned aircraft of sturdy construction and low observable signatures, utilising a Warren-Young type rhomboid wing configuration. The rhomboid wing is inherently stable and unstallable, yet very manoeuvrable, with no control surface movement restrictions, and it can be assembled quickly. Production is from precision moulds, enabling a packaged system to be delivered promptly. The standard system comprises five or six air vehicles, a ground control station, launch and recovery subsystems, antenna group, a GPU, film processing unit, a test/service shelter, and storage/crew shelter, transported on five trucks and five trailers. The system is designed for rapid emplacement and displacement, high availability, and ease of operation and maintenance.

Design of the Eyrie **Mk 1** began in May 1978, and the first of three prototypes made its initial flight in April 1980. These were followed by six prototypes of the **Mk 2** (first flight June 1981), three of the **Mk 3** (first flight March 1984), and series production of the Mk 3 (first flight September 1984). The subsequent availability of suitable four-stroke engines, with twin electronic ignition and fuel injection, has enabled National Dynamics to offer two current production models covering a wide spectrum of target and RPV applications. These are the **Eyrie TD 110** basic training target drone, to which the following description applies, and the **6A-60** mini-RPV, which is described separately. Details of customers and production quantities are classified.

TYPE: Radio controlled recoverable aerial target.

AIRFRAME: As described for RPV version.

POWER PLANT: One 82 kW (110 hp) two-cylinder four-stroke turbocharged engine, with twin ignition driving a two-blade Kevlar pusher propeller with remotely controlled variable and reverse pitch. Fuel capacity 55 litres (12 Imp gallons; 14.5 US gallons).

LAUNCH AND RECOVERY: Surface launch from land or ship by conventional wheeled take-off or by zero length launcher (one JATO rocket). Recovery by wheel landing, plus reverse thrust braking, with truck supported vertical ribbon net for backup.

GUIDANCE AND CONTROL: Radio command guidance system, available with or without standard tracking control station to control drone via autopilot at distances up to 87 nm (161 km; 100 miles). Radar/transponder link provides accurate positioning, transmission of commands to drone, and transmission of telemetry data from drone. Command and telemetry data are encoded into a PPC (pulse position coded) format. Aerodynamic control via ailerons, elevators, and rudder.

MISSION EQUIPMENT: Electrical power provided by 1.2 kW alternator, rectifier/regulator and 28V battery pack. Equipment includes strobe light, remotely controlled smoke generator, recovery guidance aid, and various ECM options.

DIMENSIONS:	
Wing span	5.03 m (16 ft 6 in)
Wing area	3.53 m² (38.0 sq ft)
Length overall	3.81 m (12 ft 6 in)
Height overall	1.07 m (3 ft 6 in)
Body diameter (max)	0.55 m (1 ft 9.75 in)
Nosecone volume	0.212 m³ (7.5 cu ft)
Propeller diameter	1.22 m (4 ft)
WEIGHTS:	
Basic operating weight empty	123 kg (272 lb)
Fuel	40 kg (88 lb)
Electrical payload	36 kg (80 lb)
Max launching weight	200 kg (440 lb)
PERFORMANCE:	
Max level speed at S/L	204 knots (378 km/h; 235 mph)

Min flying speed	47 knots (87 km/h; 54 mph)
Max rate of climb at S/L	1,554 m (5,100 ft)/min
Ceiling	8,230 m (27,000 ft)
Range at S/L with max fuel	295 nm (547 km; 340 miles)

NATIONAL DYNAMICS EYRIE 6A-60

As indicated in the preceding entry, a mini-RPV version of the Eyrie is currently available, as the 6A-60.

TYPE: All weather, day/night, recoverable mini-RPV for multi-mission land and sea roles.

AIRFRAME: Warren-Young type rhomboid wing configuration, with mid-wing front wing and low-wing rear wing/stabiliser. No control surfaces on front wing; rear wing fitted with inboard elevators and outboard ailerons, both operated by electric servos. Ailerons and elevators mass and aerodynamically balanced internally. Streamlined fuselage, of circular cross-section, with sweptback fin and electric servo operated rudder, plus ventral fin and skid. Entire structure of Kevlar, rigid PVC foam, glassfibre and polyester resin.

POWER PLANT: One 44.7 kW (60 hp) two-cylinder four-stroke engine, with twin ignition, driving a two-blade variable-pitch Kevlar pusher propeller via a large diameter torsion-damped hollow shaft. Engine speed controlled remotely by electric servo-operated throttle; propeller pitch varied remotely by electric servo motor. Single fuel cell in fuselage, capacity 44 litres (9.7 Imp gallons; 11.6 US gallons).

LAUNCH AND RECOVERY: Can be launched from aircraft, zero-length launcher or moving truck. Recovery by (a) short-stroke travelling net, (b) parafoil and tined gantry, or (c) skids and short-stroke vertical barrier net. All three systems are suitable for land and shipboard recovery.

GUIDANCE AND CONTROL: Radio command with radar tracking, as described for target version. Ground control by crew of three (mission commander, flight controller and terrain analyst) with target control transponder and TV target group set for two TV cameras. Flight controller in GCS is in full control of air vehicle at all times, operating RPV manually according to telemetry and real-time TV imagery and overriding the autopilot, or in supervisory mode with autopilot engaged. Autopilot has magnetic heading sensor and automatic 'return to base' mode. Jamming resistant telemetry of essential data. Aerodynamic control by ailerons, elevators and rudder.

MISSION EQUIPMENT: Electrical power provided by 1.68 kW onboard alternator with rectifier/regulator and battery pack. Two gimballed TV cameras (one forward-looking for navigation and strike, under forward top canopy, and one sideways-looking and slewing for target identification, retractable in belly). Nose-mounted remotely controlled mini-panoramic camera. Ample volume in forward fuselage for optional electronic warfare equipment.

ARMAMENT: Rails for four 2.75-in rockets.

DIMENSIONS: As for target version

WEIGHTS:

Basic operating weight empty	138 kg (305 lb)
Fuel	32 kg (70 lb)
Electrical payload	52 kg (115 lb)
Max launching weight	222 kg (490 lb)

PERFORMANCE:

Max level speed at S/L	163 knots (302 km/h; 188 mph)
Max cruising speed at S/L	148 knots (273 km/h; 170 mph)
Min flying speed	40 knots (74 km/h; 46 mph)
Max rate of climb at S/L	692 m (2,270 ft)/min
Ceiling	6,765 m (22,200 ft)
Range with max fuel, no reserves	946 nm (1,754 km; 1,090 miles)
Max endurance	13 h

Sweden

FÖRSVARETS FORSKNINGSANSTALT (FOA)
(National Defence Research Institute)
Applied Electronics Department (FOA 3), Box 1165, S-581 121, Linköping

FOA SKATAN (MAGPIE)

The Skatan system was designed to study the possibility of using a cheap and simple flying platform for short-range daylight-only reconnaissance and surveillance over zones immediately behind the forward edge of the battle area (FEBA). The complete system comprised miniature aircraft, a radio transmitter and telescopic antenna, two pairs of binoculars, and a case for cameras and film processing equipment. The first (feasibility) phase of the programme had been demonstrated by 1979, and in 1982 a second phase began, to study the use of miniaturised real-time optical sensors. It was, however, suspended a year or two later due to the presence on the market of existing systems of similar type.

TYPE: Experimental short-range battlefield reconnaissance mini-RPV.

AIRFRAME: Strut-braced shoulder-wing monoplane, with constant chord wings and square fuselage. Construction of balsa wood. Non-retractable tailwheel landing gear. Small radar signature; not affected by ECM in programmed flight.

POWER PLANT: One 1.2 kW (1.6 hp) O.S. Max H80/RC 13.23 cc single-cylinder glow-plug engine, driving a two-blade propeller. Fuel tank capacity 0.5 litre (0.11 Imp gallon; 0.13 US gallon).

LAUNCH AND RECOVERY: Conventional T-O and landing, under radio control; alternative parachute recovery system optional.

GUIDANCE AND CONTROL: Radio command guidance. Manual control throughout flight, controlled in line-of-sight by use of two pairs of binoculars (one of low magnification for very close range control, and a higher magnification pair for use at longer range), mounted coaxially; manual guidance could also be possible by use of radar data and triangulation

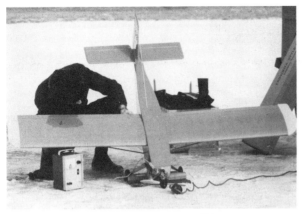

FOA Skatan experimental battlefield mini-RPV

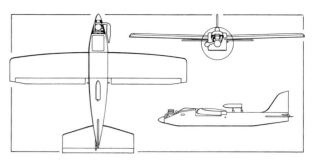

Norabel Ripan anti-aircraft gunnery target *(Jane's/Mike Keep)*

instead of binoculars. (Distance/calculation method proved the most effective.) Alternatively, drone could be fitted with automatic flight control system for pre-programmed flight. Aneroid altimeter was linked to onboard control to maintain operating altitude within accuracy of 20 m (66 ft). Course controlled by special device based on magnetic terrain compass. Using this system, onboard radio receiver could be switched off over surveillance area, avoiding ECM while aircraft photographed area below. Aerodynamic control by conventional ailerons and tail control surfaces.

MISSION EQUIPMENT: Several onboard camera systems tested. Best results were obtained with Hasselblad 500 EL (70 frames) and Nikon F (36 frames), both having electric motor to advance film. Various lenses, depending on mission configuration, also tested. Other potential payloads included radio relay equipment, jammers, smoke generators, laser target designator, TV camera, radar reflector, or (in 'kamikaze' role) small attack weapons.

DIMENSIONS:

Wing span	2.14 m (7 ft 0.25 in)
Length overall	1.61 m (5 ft 3.5 in)

WEIGHTS:

Weight without camera	4.4 kg (9.7 lb)
T-O weight with 0.4 litre (0.09 Imp gallon: 0.11 US gallon) fuel:	
with Canomatic M70 camera	6 kg (13.2 lb)
with Nikon F camera	7.4 kg (16.8 lb)

PERFORMANCE:

Max level speed	54 knots (100 km/h; 62 mph)
Optimum operating height	300–500 m (985–1,640 ft)
T-O run (on tarmac, zero wind)	7 m (23 ft)
Landing run	20 m (66 ft)
Line-of-sight control range	2.7 nm (5 km; 3.1 miles)
Typical mission times:	
briefing and preparation	5-10 min
out and back flight	7-10 min
film removal and processing	5-10 min
total time	17–30 min

NORABEL AB (MILITARY PRODUCTS)

PO Box 803, S-713 00 Nora

NORABEL RIPAN

Ten prototypes of this very small target drone had been completed by the beginning of 1986.

TYPE: Re-usable anti-aircraft gunnery target.

AIRFRAME: Shoulder-wing monoplane with conventional tail unit. Wings are of symmetrical profile, and have a plywood skin with an expanded polystyrene core. Ailerons and tail surfaces are of balsa wood. Prototypes have a fuselage box structure of plywood, balsa and expanded polystyrene; this would be entirely of polystyrene in production version. No landing gear.

POWER PLANT: One 1.9 kW (2.5 hp) 15 cc Super Tigre piston engine, driving a two-blade propeller. Fuel capacity 0.45 litre (0.10 Imp gallon; 0.12 US gallon).

LAUNCH AND RECOVERY: Hand-launched; recovery by belly landing.

GUIDANCE AND CONTROL: Radio command guidance system. Aerodynamic control by full span ailerons, rudder and one-piece elevator.

MISSION EQUIPMENT: Three-element hit indicator system comprising dorsally mounted acoustic sensor (microphone), hit recorder and indicator. Microphone can be preset for either 7.62 mm or 5.52 mm ammunition, and six sensitivity levels corresponding to radii from 2 m (6.6 ft) to 12 m (39.4 ft) can be preselected to represent different hit zones (i.e. target sizes). Sound of passing projectile is registered by microphone, and signals processed electronically by hit recorder. Sensor computer, in centre fuselage, can be set at different numbers of registered hits (up to 15) required to produce a 'kill'. When required number is reached, computer signals to adjacent indicator unit, which activates a pyrotechnic cartridge, producing a vivid flash that is visible up to at least 0.5 nm (1 km; 0.6 mile) away, indicating to gunners that target has been 'killed'. Hit recorder is powered by 8.4V nickel-cadmium batteries; indicator is a rechargeable cassette containing ten disposable flash cartridges.

DIMENSIONS:

Wing span	1.77 m (5 ft 9.75 in)
Length overall	1.40 m (4 ft 7 in)
Height overall	0.15 m (6 in)

WEIGHTS:

Payload	1.5 kg (3.3 lb)
Max launching weight	4 kg (8.8 lb)

PERFORMANCE:

Max level speed	108 knots (200 km/h; 124 mph)
Stalling speed	22 knots (40 km/h; 25 mph)
Range	0.5 nm (1 km; 0.6 mile)
Endurance	10–15 min

Switzerland

FARNER AIR SERVICE AG

Grenchen Airport, CH-2540 Grenchen

One of Switzerland's leading aircraft maintenance companies, Farner Air Service AG overhauls Swiss Air Force training aircraft and helicopters, and performs similar work on piston- and turbine-engined civil aircraft. With the Federal Aircraft Factory, it is also producing AATS Topaz target drones for the Swiss Army.

FARNER/F + W AATS TOPAZ

AATS (anti-aircraft training system) Topaz is the current (1987) version of the KZD-85 (Kleinzieldrohne: small target drone), of which 60 were produced jointly by Farner Air Service and the Swiss Federal Aircraft Factory (F + W) for the Swiss Army. Farner produces the airframe, launcher and ground support equipment; F + W supplies the remote control system and acts as prime contractor to the military procurement authority for the total system.

Normally, the system is operated by one aircraft controller and one handler, and can be made ready for use within 20 minutes by a trained crew. Two or more target aircraft can be operated simultaneously, and the Topaz system is designed to work independently in the field for at least 12 hours per day, away from runways, roads and general infrastructure. The current version is available in two aircraft sizes.

TYPE: Re-usable or expendable small target drone.
AIRFRAME: Shoulder-wing monoplane, with Kevlar reinforced GRP sandwich wings and tail and a frames and stringers aluminium alloy fuselage, to the underside of which is bonded a foam rubber strip to cushion the landing impact.

Farner KZD-85 Topaz anti-aircraft gunnery target on its launch ramp

Wing and tail surfaces detach to simplify transportation. No landing gear.
POWER PLANT: One 100–300 cc two-stroke engine, driving a two-blade propeller. Electronic ignition. Fuel capacity (20:1 petrol/oil mixture) is 2 litres (0.4 Imp gallon; 0.5 US gallon).
LAUNCH AND RECOVERY: Catapult-launched from trailer-mounted 6.5 m (21.3 ft) ramp. Recovery by 11 m (36 ft) diameter cruciform parachute or by belly landing on ventral rubber skid.
GUIDANCE AND CONTROL: PCM radio command guidance transceiver (R/F output 1W) for line-of-sight operation, powered by 1.8 Ah rechargeable battery. If command link is lost, engine shuts down automatically after 0.5 s and recovery parachute is deployed. Aerodynamic control by conventional wing and tail control surfaces.
MISSION EQUIPMENT: Topaz can be produced in a cheap version as an expendable target for live anti-aircraft firing practice. In re-usable form, it can carry a hit indicator and give active reflected signals of hits on a towed target; or a miss distance indicator with active signalling when Topaz itself is the target; or it can emit a radar beam giving a passive reflected signal.

DIMENSIONS:

Wing span:	
A	2.50 m (8 ft 2.5 in)
B	3.50 m (11 ft 5.75 in)
Wing area: A	0.875 m² (9.42 sq ft)
Length overall:	
A	2 m (6 ft 6.75 in)
B	2.40 m (7 ft 10.5 in)
Height overall: A, B	0.62 m (2 ft 0.5 in)
Propeller diameter: A, B	0.51 m (1 ft 8 in)

WEIGHTS:

Weight empty, equipped: A	20.9 kg (46.1 lb)
Fuel: A	1.6 kg (3.5 lb)
Max launching weight:	
A	23 kg (50.7 lb)
B	30 kg (66.1 lb)

PERFORMANCE:

Max diving speed	135 knots (250 km/h; 155 mph)
Max level speed	108 knots (200 km/h; 124 mph)
Min flying speed	43 knots (80 km/h; 50 mph)
Max operating altitude	2,500 m (8,200 ft)
Max range: line-of-sight	1.1 nm (2 km; 1.25 miles)
with binoculars	2.2 nm (4 km; 2.5 miles)
Max endurance	30 min
g limit	+7

Union of Soviet Socialist Republics

Despite the fact that their development began as early as 1950, the use of drones for target and RPV roles by the USSR is still very largely a 'grey' area so far as reliable information is concerned, and is undoubtedly more widespread than the size of this section would suggest. Most of the known Soviet UMAs have until recently resulted from the adaptation of obsolete full size aircraft and large missiles, but signs are now emerging that the lesson of successes achieved elsewhere by smaller, dedicated tactical RPVs has not been lost on the Soviets, and more up to date designs have now begun to enter service.

LAVOCHKIN La-17

Probably the USSR's first genuine UMA to be designed as such, the La-17 was developed by the Lavochkin OKB (design bureau) between 1950–53 and subsequently entered production as a standard target drone for use by the Warsaw Pact nations, primarily for air-to-air weapons training of jet fighter pilots and surface-to-air missile crews. Production probably ended with the closure of the bureau after Lavochkin's death in 1960, or even earlier, but some La-17s may still be in service.

Detailed data have not been possible to confirm officially, but the following description is thought to be substantially correct. The La-17 also appears to have inspired the Chinese Nanjing CK1C (which see).

TYPE: Recoverable jet-powered target drone; may also have had some early tactical applications.
AIRFRAME: All-metal mid-wing monoplane, with constant chord non-swept wings. Slim cylindrical fuselage, tapered at each end. Rectangular fin and rudder, with constant chord non-swept tailplane and elevators mounted part-way up fin.
POWER PLANT: One 8.83 kN (1,984 lb st) Tumansky RU-19-300 turbojet engine, mounted in pod under centre of fuselage.
LAUNCH AND RECOVERY: Ramp-launched using two jettisonable JATO type solid propellant booster rockets mounted under wings near roots. Recovery method not known.
GUIDANCE AND CONTROL: Radio command guidance system. Aerodynamic control by conventional wing and tail control surfaces.

Launch photograph of an La-17 with the boosters firing

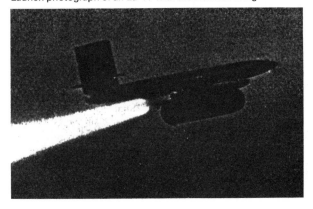

DIMENSIONS:	
Wing span	6.95 m (22 ft 9.5 in)
Length overall	7.10 m (23 ft 3.5 in)
Height overall	2.53 m (8 ft 3.5 in)
Body diameter (max)	0.50 m (1 ft 7.75 in)
WEIGHTS:	
Weight empty	1,200 kg (2,645 lb)
Max launching weight	1,800 kg (3,968 lb)
PERFORMANCE:	
Max level speed:	
at high altitude	485 knots (900 km/h; 559 mph)
at low altitude	464 knots (860 km/h; 534 mph)
Service ceiling	14,000 m (45,925 ft)
Max endurance	1 h

SUKHOI Su-9/Su-11

NATO reporting name: Fishpot

The Su-9 initial production version of 'Fishpot' became operational as a single-seat fighter in 1959 and the later Su-11 remained in service until about 1981. After their withdrawal (or much earlier, according to one report) some were modified as radio controlled target drones for testing anti-aircraft missiles.

The following brief description applies to the piloted version of the Su-9:

AIRFRAME: All-metal monoplane, with mid-mounted delta wings, circular section fuselage, sweptback fin and rudder and all-moving swept tailplane. Twin airbrakes on each side of rear fuselage. Wide track, inward-retracting mainwheels and forward-retracting nosewheel. Single-seat cockpit.
POWER PLANT: One 88.25 kN (19,841 lb st) Lyulka AL-7F afterburning turbojet engine. Internal fuel capacity in the order of 3,875 litres (852 Imp gallons; 1,023 US gallons).

DIMENSIONS (estimated):	
Wing span	8.43 m (27 ft 8 in)
Wing area	26.2 m² (282 sq ft)
Length overall, excl nose probe	16.50 m (54 ft 1.5 in)
Height overall	4.90 m (16 ft 1 in)
WEIGHTS (estimated):	
Weight empty, equipped	8,800 kg (19,400 lb)
Max internal fuel	3,000 kg (6,614 lb)
Max T-O weight ('clean')	12,000 kg (26,455 lb)
PERFORMANCE ('clean')	
Max level speed at 11,000 m (36,000 ft)	
	1,033 knots (1,915 km/h; 1,190 mph)
Service ceiling	17,000 m (55,775 ft)
Range with max internal fuel	
	593 nm (1,100 km; 683 miles)

YAKOVLEV Yak-25RD/RV

NATO reporting name: Mandrake

Production of the original Yak-25 'Flashlight' tandem two-seat fighter, which took place from about 1954 to 1958, is thought to have totalled somewhere in the order of 1,000. In later years

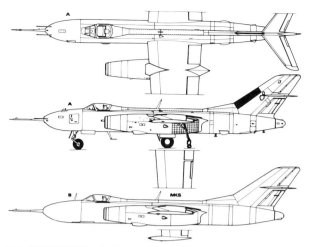

Yak-25RD/RV 'Mandrake': views A show reconnaissance version, view B the target version *(Martin Streetly)*

many derivatives were to appear, one of which was 'Mandrake', intended for photographic reconnaissance and other intelligence gathering missions similar to those undertaken by the West's Lockheed U-2. It was first reported operationally in the spring of 1963, and a substantial number are believed to have been produced. The necessary high altitude performance was achieved by exchanging the Yak-25's mid-mounted swept wings for new, non-swept surfaces of double the span and area, shoulder-mounted further aft to maintain the CG balance. Elimination of the need for a wing carry-through structure would have made more fuselage space available for additional internal fuel tankage. Except for a shorter nosecone, introduction of a single-seat cockpit and deletion of the strake under the tailcone, the shape and size of the standard 'Flashlight' fuselage and tail unit remained basically unchanged, although there is some evidence to support the view that their structural weight was reduced.

Until the mid-1970s 'Mandrake', in both piloted and unmanned versions, was one of the Soviet Union's principal reconnaissance and elint aircraft, being used on overflights of Central Europe, the Middle East, India, Pakistan and China; but by the end of the 1960s it had already begun to be relegated to use as a target drone, one appearing in a Soviet film of that time as a target for an SA-2 'Guideline' surface-to-air missile. This latter use may continue in the mid-1980s, but the aircraft is unlikely to be still operational as a reconnaissance RPV.

Despite the age of the design, few details of the Yak-25 family have been disclosed officially, and several of those quoted in Soviet or East European articles – even some basic dimensions – are open to question. Nor has 'Mandrake's' correct designation been established with any certainty. The obviously related 'RV' which set a number of payload-to-height records in 1959 is nowadays called Yak-25RV by the East European press, with RV said to indicate Rekord Vysoti (record height). Eight years later, however, when Marina Popovich set a women's international closed circuit *distance* record of 1,347.404 nm (2,497.009 km; 1,551.566 miles), the Soviet claim identified this aircraft also as an 'RV', powered by 39.23 kN (8,818 lb st) '37V' engines (now known to be the Tumansky R-11). The East European press now calls the latter aircraft Yak-25RD, the second suffix letter presumably standing for Dalnost (distance). In all probability neither of these record aircraft was completely identical with the operational reconnaissance 'Mandrake'. Another school of thought subscribes to Yak-25RM, which is suggested as Razvedchik Modifikatsirovanny (Reconnaissance, Modified); yet other sources, including some usually reliable US ones, opt for the entirely fresh designation Yak-26.

Subject to these provisos, however, the following description of 'Mandrake' is believed to be correct in most essentials:

TYPE: Manned aircraft or unmanned RPV and (latterly) target drone.

AIRFRAME: High aspect ratio equi-tapered wings, shoulder-mounted with slight anhedral; ailerons and slotted flaps on trailing edges. Circular section fuselage. Sweptback fin and split rudder, with dorsal fin faired into fuselage spine; sweptback variable incidence tailplane, with elevators, mounted mid-way up fin. Zero-track main landing gear, with single rearward-retracting front wheel and twin forward-retracting rear wheels. Rearward-retracting balancer wheel in each slim wingtip pod. Single-seat cockpit.

POWER PLANT: Two 25.5 kN (5,732 lb st) Tumansky RD-9 (ex-Mikulin AM-9) unaugmented turbojet engines in early examples; later aircraft powered by Tumansky R-11 (R-37) turbojets, each rated at 38.25 kN (8,598 lb st) dry and 50.01 kN (11,243 lb st) with afterburning. Internal fuel capacity in the order of 8,000 litres (1,760 Imp gallons; 2,113 US gallons). No known provision for external tanks.

LAUNCH AND RECOVERY: Conventional runway T-O and landing.

GUIDANCE AND CONTROL: Radio command system (no details known).

'Mandrake' drone used as a surface-to-air missile target

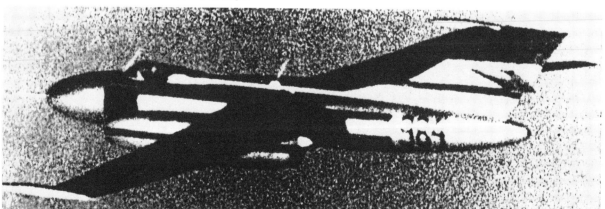

MISSION EQUIPMENT: No definite details known, but a US estimate has quoted a likely payload capacity of up to 295 kg (650 lb), most of which probably in nose and front fuselage bays vacated by fighter's radar, guns and ammunition. Other (varying) equipment installations, possibly including chaff dispenser, in tailcone. Manned reconnaissance version revealed dielectric panels on fin leading-edge and wingtip pods (absent from target version), plus blister fairings around nose/cockpit areas, and assorted antennae. No known provision for external stores.

DIMENSIONS (estimated):

Wing span	22 m (72 ft 2 in)
Wing area	55 m² (592 sq ft)
Length overall, excl nose probe	15.45 m (50 ft 8 in)
Height overall	4.32 m (14 ft 2 in)
Wheelbase	5.50 m (18 ft)

WEIGHTS (estimated):

Weight empty	8,000 kg (17,640 lb)
Max fuel	6,200 kg (13,670 lb)
Max mission payload	295 kg (650 lb)
Max T-O weight	14,600 kg (32,190 lb)

PERFORMANCE (estimated):

Max level speed at high altitude:

RD-9	405 knots (750 km/h; 466 mph)
R-11	445 knots (825 km/h; 513 mph)

Service ceiling:

RD-9	19,000 m (62,335 ft)
R-11	20,500 m (67,255 ft)

Range at high altitude with max fuel (either engine):

2,158 nm (4,000 km; 2,485 miles)

YASTREB (EAGLET)

Yastreb was a major Soviet reconnaissance and elint RPV in the European theatre from the mid-1960s to mid-1970s, but is nowadays deployed over Africa, the Near and Far East, and for target acquisition and ocean surveillance. Developed from the late 1940s T-4A supersonic cruise missile, it is launched atop a rocket booster and powered by a Tumansky R-31 turbojet, the engine that powers the MiG-25 interceptor. (This engine was originally qualified in about 1964 at a reheat rating of 98.1 kN; 22,045 lb st, and one report claims that it was developed initially *for* the Yastreb. Production R-31s have been rated successively at 107.9 kN/24,250 lb, 120.1 kN/27,005 lb and, in the R-31F, at 137.3 kN/30,865 lb thrust.)

The Yastreb can be either pre-programmed or remotely piloted under radio control. With a maximum speed of more than 1,890 knots (3,500 km/h; 2,175 mph), it has a ceiling of 27,500–30,000 m (90,225–98,425 ft) and a range of more than 540 nm (1,000 km; 620 miles).

SS-N-3

NATO reporting name: Shaddock

RPV versions of both 'Shaddock' and the related SS-C-1 'Sepal' transonic winged missiles entered service in the early 1970s. 'Sepal' is ground-launched, notably from fixed sites or trucks at Soviet coastal bases; 'Shaddock' is launched from surface vessels and from 'Echo II', 'Juliett' and 'Whiskey' class submarines. The missile is container-launched by two solid propellant rocket boosters, having hinged wings that flip out after it leaves the launch tube. Turbojet-powered, it can cruise at low altitude over water, and is radio-guided, possibly with active radar homing. The RPV version probably carries ballast

to make up any difference between its mission payload and the 1,000 kg (2,205 lb) warhead of the original missile.

A 'Shaddock' RPV launched from a Soviet submarine in the Barents Sea inadvertently violated Norwegian airspace in December 1984, subsequently crashing near a lake in Finland when its fuel was exhausted. This vehicle was tracked by radars at a speed of about Mach 1.1, and was flying at 'several thousand' feet when it entered Norwegian airspace.

DIMENSIONS (estimated):

Wing span	4 m (13 ft 1.5 in)
Length overall	10 m (32 ft 9.75 in)
Body diameter (max)	1 m (3 ft 3.25 in)

WEIGHT (estimated):

Max launching weight	4,700 kg (10,360 lb)

PERFORMANCE (estimated):

Max range	243 nm (450 km; 280 miles)

SS-N-12

NATO reporting name: Sandbox

An RPV version of the 'Sandbox' surface-to-surface missile reportedly entered service in the late 1970s, presumably intended as a replacement for the older and slower 'Shaddock' and 'Sepal', of which it is essentially an improved version. It has the advantage of being launchable from both land based and seaborne platforms, including 'Echo II' class submarines.

DIMENSIONS (estimated):

Wing span: folded	1.80 m (5 ft 11 in)
deployed	2.60 m (8 ft 6.5 in)
Length overall	10.80 m (35 ft 5.25 in)
Body diameter (max)	0.90 m (2 ft 11.5 in)

WEIGHT (estimated):

Max launching weight	5,250 kg (11,575 lb)

PERFORMANCE (estimated):

Max speed	Mach 1.7
Operational ceiling	10,700 m (35,100 ft)
Max range	297 nm (550 km; 342 miles)

UR-1

The Soviet UMA to which this designation applies is still something of an enigma, but is evidently of greater significance than was thought when it was first observed in the late 1970s. At that time it was known as a target drone employed during tests of late-model MiG-25 'Foxbat' interceptors equipped with AA-9 radar-guided air-to-air missiles. These tests were said to have been successful against UR-1s flying at low level, in ground clutter, and at altitudes up to approx 21,335 m (70,000 ft). The drones, used to simulate targets of some 25 m² (269 sq ft) gross area, are air-launched from Tu-16 'Badger' carrier aircraft. They are said to operate normally between 20,000 and 30,000 m (65,615–98,425 ft), but to be capable of flying as high as 40,000 m (131,230 ft). Other reports of the UR-1 have described it as being sophisticated, capable of high speed, and carrying remotely controlled subsystems such as a TV camera or electronic jammers for testing the latest Soviet airborne radars and air-to-air missiles. Its chief limitation is said to be a relatively short range.

More recently, it was stated that a Soviet-built reconnaissance/elint drone shot down by the Israeli Defence Forces near the Israel/Lebanon border on 13 June 1985 had been identified as a UR-1, and that at least one other Syrian-based UR-1 had been destroyed before this. The British

Ministry of Defence identifies those in Syrian service by the designation **YUR-1**.

Configuration of the UR-1 is still a matter for speculation, since no illustrations of the aircraft have yet been published openly. The Soviets are however known to have been particularly interested in the AQM-34 Firebee RPVs air-launched from DC-130 Hercules during the Vietnam war, and the UR-1 has been described as 'relatively large' and having a specification 'not unlike' the Firebee I. Given the Soviet predilection for adapting obsolescent missiles for RPV/target use, a possible basis for the UR-1 could be the AS-5 'Kelt' or AS-6 'Kingfish', each of which has a liquid propellant rocket motor and can be carried under the wings of the Tu-16.

DR-3

The DR-3 is the first known Soviet mini-RPV, its existence having been revealed by the conflict over Lebanon, where Syrian-based examples were first observed in the early part of 1984. Configuration is said to be similar to that of the Israeli Scout and Mastiff and the US Developmental Sciences SkyEye, with a twin-tailboom layout and sweptback wings. Main sensor is a non-gimballed reconnaissance camera with a fixed lens, but an improved version carrying a zoom lens TV camera on a stabilised mounting is also believed to have been developed in the USSR.

No other details were known at the time of going to press.

REMOTELY CONTROLLED AIRSHIPS

In late 1983 the Polish aviation press published a poor quality photograph of a small Soviet airship called the **Bumerang**. Unmanned and remotely controlled, it was designed by N. Bauman and built at the Moscow Polytechnic. It was said to be intended for atmospheric research; approximate dimensions include a length of 11.5 m (38 ft) and max diameter of 4.25 m (14 ft).

In the following year the USSR began flight testing a radio-controlled airship known as the **Angren-84**, reportedly as a small-scale prototype (length 9 m; 29.5 ft, diameter 3 m; 9.8 ft) for planned larger craft to transport freight to Siberia and the Soviet Far East. The production version was intended to be 45 m (147.6 ft) long, carry a 1,360 kg (3,000 lb) payload, and be powered by twin engines mounted on stub wings.

The Angren-84, named after the town in Uzbekhistan where it was developed, has a ventral gondola with mid-mounted stub wings and a non-retractable tricycle landing gear. The engines are mounted in rotatable nacelles near each wingtip; a wide-span horizontal tail surface, aft of the gondola and beneath the rear of the envelope, supports dependent endplate fins/rudders. Up to the end of 1984 the airship had been flight-tested at altitudes up to 100 m (330 ft) and distances of up to 2.7 nm (5 km; 3.1 miles) from the ground control station.

United Kingdom

ADMIRALTY RESEARCH ESTABLISHMENT (ARE)
Department XTW 1, Portsdown, Cosham, Hampshire PO6 4AA

The ARE has produced three small unmanned target aircraft known as **Alcat**, **Sigu** and **Bus**. At the time of going to press, details for this entry had been awaiting Ministry of Defence clearance for nearly two years.

AEL (RPV) LIMITED
Unit 4, North Heath Lane, Horsham, West Sussex RH12 4XA

AEL SMIDGE

The AEL 4560 Smidge small arms target drone is flown at a predetermined scaled distance, and this, coupled with its speed, enables it to simulate a full-size attacking aircraft. It can be flown directly at the trainee on a simulated attack profile. The radio equipment is normally recoverable for re-use in a new airframe. Production ended in about 1978.

TYPE: Small arms target drone.
AIRFRAME: Low-cost expendable airframe. Wings of veneer covered polystyrene foam, tail surfaces of balsa; fuselage of laminated hardwood with a paint finish.
POWER PLANT: One 10 cc piston engine, with glo-plug ignition. Fuel in fuselage tank of 170 g (6 oz) capacity.
LAUNCH: By hand.
GUIDANCE AND CONTROL: Radio command guidance system.
DIMENSIONS:
    Wing span   1.68 m (5 ft 6.25 in)
    Length overall   1.35 m (4 ft 5.25 in)
WEIGHT:
    Max launching weight   2.3 kg (5 lb)
PERFORMANCE:
    Max level speed   69.5 knots (129 km/h; 80 mph)
    Average flight endurance   10 min

AEL SNIPE MARKS I and II

The original AEL 4111 Snipe was produced as an international target system for air defence guns and close-range missiles. With the improved Mk II, it is in service with about 20 countries, and some Mk II customers have since upgraded to the larger Mk III (described separately).

The Mk II is designed to be engaged with 20–40 mm ammunition and man-portable surface-to-air missiles, and its high manoeuvrability enables it to simulate any attack profile normally executed by full size manned ground attack aircraft.

AEL Snipe Mk II on launch rail

It has many components in common with the Mk III, thus offering ease of operation and maintenance in the field.

The following description applies to both Marks except where indicated otherwise:

TYPE: Recoverable aerial target.

AIRFRAME: High-wing monoplane configuration, built of wood and plywood veneer covering a polystyrene foam core. Finish to customer's specification.

POWER PLANT: (Mk I) One 56 cc single-cylinder piston engine, with glo-plug ignition, driving a two-blade wooden propeller. (Mk II) One 6.6 kW (8.8 hp) Piper P.100 single-cylinder two-stroke engine. Fuel tank capacity (both versions) 2.3 litres (0.5 Imp gallon; 0.6 US gallon).

LAUNCH AND RECOVERY: Launch by simple rubber bungee catapult, mounted on two-wheel transporting trailer. Recovery normally by belly landing if space permits, or by Irvin (GB) 6.4 m (21 ft) diameter cruciform parachute. Fail-safe system closes throttle automatically after 1½ s and deploys parachute after a further 1½ s in event of loss of command signal or heavy radio interference. Independent auxiliary power supply automatically actuates fail-safe sequence in the event of main power failure or receiver malfunction.

GUIDANCE AND CONTROL: By specially developed radio control equipment operating in VHF or UHF bands. Aerodynamic control by ailerons and elevators.

MISSION EQUIPMENT: Standard RDF tracking system, with optional interface to plotting table. Autostabiliser and smoke enhancement flares.

DIMENSIONS:

Wing span: Mk I	2.50 m (8 ft 2.5 in)
Mk II	2.44 m (8 ft)
Wing area: Mk II	0.99 m² (10.64 sq ft)
Length overall: Mk I	2.10 m (6 ft 10.75 in)
Mk II	2.13 m (7 ft)

WEIGHTS:

Payload: Mk I	9 kg (20 lb)
Mk II	8 kg (17.5 lb)
Max launching weight: Mk I	24.5 kg (54 lb)
Mk II	19 kg (42 lb)

PERFORMANCE:

Max level speed:	
Mk I	111 knots (206 km/h; 128 mph)
Mk II	113 knots (209 km/h; 130 mph)
Max control range:	
Mk I	2.6 nm (4.8 km; 3 miles)
Mk II	4.3 nm (8 km; 5 miles)
Average sortie endurance:	
Mk I	25–40 min
Mk II	35 min

AEL SNIPE MARK III

Snipe Mark III (AEL 4700) is a larger, faster target aircraft than the Mark II, providing greater realism in tracking and live firing training. The Mark III can be deployed with the AEL tracking system giving range, bearing, height and heading. Together with the onboard autostabiliser, this gives an effective operational range in excess of 27 nm (50 km; 31 miles). A target aircraft can be prepared and launched within 15 min of the crew arriving at the range head; average turnround time between sorties is less than 10 min.

The Mark III is in service in four countries, and was ordered by the French Army in early 1986. Some users of the Mark II have upgraded their target systems to utilise the Mk III or later Snipes. Current versions of Snipe from 1986 are the Mks IV and V (described separately).

TYPE: Recoverable aerial target.

AIRFRAME: As described for Snipe I and II.

POWER PLANT: One 18.6 kW (25 hp) NGL WAEL 342 flat-twin engine, driving a two-blade propeller.

LAUNCH, RECOVERY, GUIDANCE AND CONTROL: As described for Snipe I and II.

MISSION EQUIPMENT: As for Snipe I and II.

DIMENSIONS:

Wing span	3.14 m (10 ft 3.5 in)
Length overall	2.50 m (8 ft 2.25 in)

WEIGHT:

Max launching weight	32 kg (70.5 lb)

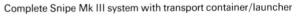

Complete Snipe Mk III system with transport container/launcher

PERFORMANCE:
Max in-service speed

    more than 162 knots (300 km/h; 186 mph)

Max range:

in-sight (binoculars)   4.9 nm (9 km; 5.6 miles)

tracking   more than 27 nm (50 km; 31 miles)

Average endurance   1 h

AEL SNIPE MARKS IV and V

These two new models of Snipe, introduced in 1986, are both developed from the Mk III to incorporate major improvements in airframe design and electronics, reduce turnround times and facilitate maintenance. The **Mark IV** has a high-lift wing section which allows high altitude operation even in high temperatures with a full payload; landing speeds are low. The **Mark V** has a high-speed wing section and is some 17 knots (32 km/h; 20 mph) faster, but remains a 'user-friendly' aircraft. Both versions are in customer service.

Both versions meet the target requirements for large calibre defence guns and medium-range missiles. They are considerably larger and faster than the now obsolete Mk II, and many of the latter have been upgraded to this standard by existing operators. Construction is similar to that of the Sparrowhawk (which see), and the same command link is used for both models.

The AEL autopilot gives the Mks IV and V a proven out-of-sight range of up to 27 nm (50 km; 31 miles), as required for range operation of medium-range weapon systems. It can be tracked with the AEL tracking unit, allowing deployment away from permanent installations. System reaction time is short, and a target can be launched within 15 minutes of crew arrival. Average turnround time between sorties is less than 10 minutes. Target recovery is by normal belly landing if there is sufficient space, or by parachute if not. A built-in fail-safe mechanism ensures that under conditions of lost command signal, severe interference, loss of main power or destruction of the receiver, the engine will be stopped and the parachute deployed automatically.

DIMENSIONS:

Wing span: IV   3.21 m (10 ft 6.5 in)

      V   3.06 m (10 ft 0.5 in)

Length overall (both)   2.77 m (9 ft 1 in)

WEIGHTS AND PERFORMANCE: See Addenda

Launch of a Snipe Mk IV

AEL SPARROWHAWK

The AEL 4800 Sparrowhawk surveillance system was designed for use in the field, to give real-time information from which commanders can make decisions. The basic air vehicle carries a TV camera and data downlink. Other more sophisticated payloads are available, such as still cameras, infra-red or thermal imaging packages, ESM/ECM, or chaff/flare dispensers. The complete system comprises the launcher, two RPVs, their control units and first line maintenance equipment, all of which can be carried by one wheeled or tracked vehicle and operated by a crew of three.

A number of Sparrowhawk systems was ordered by the French Army in early 1986, following trials which included control of the drone from Gazelle helicopters.

TYPE: Recoverable surveillance mini-RPV.

AIRFRAME: Glassfibre reinforced plastics fuselage; foam core marine ply wings.

POWER PLANT: One 18.6 kW (25 hp) NGL WAEL 342 flat-twin engine, driving a two-blade propeller.

LAUNCH AND RECOVERY: As described for Snipe I/II, but with larger recovery parachute.

GUIDANCE AND CONTROL: Radio command guidance system using long-range transmitter and control console to command RPV route or height changes and to operate onboard sensors. When fitted with tracking system, this provides continuous update of position for navigation and can be fed to monitors for target co-ordinates. AEL two-axis autostabiliser and digital proportional PCM command link standard.

MISSION EQUIPMENT: Basic Sparrowhawk carries TV camera and a data downlink, providing real-time surveillance capability. Other payload options include still cameras, low light IR or thermal imaging packages, electronic surveillance or countermeasures (ESM/ECM), or chaff/flare dispensers.

DIMENSIONS:

Wing span   3.21 m (10 ft 6.5 in)

Length overall   2.77 m (9 ft 1 in)

WEIGHT:

Max launching weight   59 kg (130 lb)

PERFORMANCE:

Max level speed   162 knots (300 km/h; 186 mph)

Max range   16 nm (30 km; 18.5 miles)

Endurance   1 h

AEL STREEK

The AEL 4600 Streek is a radio controlled trainer/all arms air defence drone that can serve as a cost-effective and realistic target for small arms and machine guns used in air defence roles. It is also used as an ab initio trainer for personnel using the larger Snipe aerial target systems; as such, Streek is in service with 15 armed forces worldwide, with production continuing in 1986.

TYPE: Small, re-usable target drone.

AIRFRAME: GRP fuselage, veneered polystyrene wings.

POWER PLANT: One Glo-fuel 10 cc piston engine, driving a two-blade propeller. Fuel capacity 2.5 litres (0.55 Imp gallon; 0.7 US gallon).

LAUNCH AND RECOVERY: Hand launched by operator or assistant. Recovered by belly landing on any reasonably level ground.

GUIDANCE AND CONTROL: VHF and UHF transmitter, to customer specifications.

AEL Streek

Asvec Merlin being readied for launch

GROUND SUPPORT EQUIPMENT (GSE): Comprises GRP box incorporating a fuel container, electric fuel pump, electric engine starter, ammeter, 12V battery to power equipment, and selection of hand tools.

DIMENSIONS:

Wing span	1.70 m (5 ft 7 in)
Length overall	1.385 m (4 ft 6.5 in)

WEIGHT:

Max launching weight	2.7 kg (6 lb)

PERFORMANCE:

Max level speed	76 knots (140 km/h; 87 mph)
Endurance	20 min

ASVEC (UK) LIMITED

Building 1, Blackwater Industrial Estate, Camberley, Surrey GU17 9XX

ASVEC MERLIN

The Merlin is a multi-role RPV designed for military or police type operations such as surveillance, artillery targeting, communications relay, ECM/decoy, payload delivery and NBC 'sniffing'. Individual RPVs can be supplied with specified slide-in mission pods, or the package varied to meet specific customer requirements. Two basic air vehicle models are available, depending upon mission and payload requirements.

In the surveillance role the standard system would comprise six Merlin RPS air vehicles fitted with video and still camera systems, plus a mobile ground station based on one of three available types of vehicle. The latter contains the control, guidance and navigation systems, tracking equipment, communications links, video surveillance and recording equipment, all housed in a desk console; plus the aircraft launcher and support facilities. Communication with command/HQ is provided by VHF/UHF and HF/SSB radio and 'slow scan' video transmission equipment. A range of options includes night vision equipment, mobile darkroom, facsimile link to command/HQ, speech encryption, teleprinter and other data processing equipment.

The two basic versions of the Merlin air vehicle are:

M100. With 10 kg (22 lb) payload and 50 cc engine.
M200. With 25 kg (55 lb) payload and 70 cc engine.

These are subdivided into the following mission variants:

RPL. Long-range surveillance version of M200 (up to 135 nm; 250 km; 155 mile range). Equipped as standard with auto-navigator, transponder, video system, still camera and dedicated digital autopilot system. Optional cameras as for RPS.

RPM. Short-range surveillance and gunnery target version of M100. Operated under manual control, using binoculars or video display monitor. Standard equipment comprises manual radio control unit, colour TV camera and transmitter; options include SIT (silicon intensifier target) camera.

RPR. 'Repeater' version of either M100 or M200, designed to operate in conjunction with RPL by relaying transmissions between surveillance RPV and mobile ground station. Equipped with stabilised autopilot, auto-navigator and radar transponder, video and command transmitters and receivers.

RPS. Medium-range surveillance version of M200 (up to 54 nm; 100 km; 62 mile range). Equipped as standard with stabilised autopilot system, auto-navigator, radar transponder, colour TV camera with 90 mm lens, video/telemetry transmitter and 35 mm still camera. Options include thermal imaging, infra-red and SIT cameras.

RPT. Training version, for use with Asvec pilot training programme. Slightly smaller than M100. Normally fitted with radio control equipment only, but video system can be installed for more advanced operator training. Also available, with minimal avionics, as low-cost decoy RPV.

RPX. Low-cost expendable version of M100, operated under manual control. Payload comprises monochrome TV camera with two-lens head units, positioned at different angles, plus a container for explosives and an impact detonator. Aircraft is flown manually via video display until target is sighted, then switched to sighting lens and flown directly into target.

The following description applies generally to all Merlin variants, except where a specific model is indicated:

TYPE: Multi-role recoverable (except RPX) mini-RPV.

AIRFRAME: High-wing monoplane with central fuselage nacelle, twin tailbooms, and twin fins and rudders bridged at top by tailplane with one-piece elevator. Manufactured from double-skinned GRP with a honeycomb core; wings have a foam infill. Main wing comprises centre section and two outer panels, and can be bolted to fuselage at one of several positions to cater for CG changes caused by different payloads. Fuselage consists of nosecone, main body and engine cowling. Nosecone incorporates optically ground clear plastics windows to permit undistorted video images, and its removal provides access to slide-in tray on which avionics and mission equipment are mounted. Further optical window, for still camera, in underside of main fuselage section. Reinforced skids beneath fuselage for attaching to launching platform and for conventional landings.

POWER PLANT: (M100) One 2.7 kW (3.6 hp) 50 cc Quadra single-cylinder two-stroke engine, mounted in rear of fuselage and driving a two-blade wooden pusher propeller. (M200) One 5.8 kW (7.75 hp) 70 cc Horner two-cylinder two-stroke engine, driving a two-blade propeller. Electronic ignition on both engines. Standard fuel capacity 2.5 litres (0.55 Imp gallon; 0.66 US gallon) in all versions; RPL version of M200 has provision for two underwing auxiliary tanks, doubling total capacity to 5 litres (1.1 Imp gallons; 1.4 US gallons).

LAUNCH AND RECOVERY: Can be launched either by WL 25 pneumatic launcher supplied with system or, in suitable terrain, from wheeled trolley. Recovered by manual radio-controlled skid landing, initiated within 2.7 nm (5 km; 3.1 miles) of transmitter to avoid radiation detection. Recovery parachute can be fitted optionally, at expense of some payload capacity.

GUIDANCE AND CONTROL: PCM telecommand guidance system (VHF or UHF). Normally pre-programmed by feeding in predetermined waypoints, airspeeds, heights and bearings from ground based navigation computer to onboard stabilised digital autopilot and auto-navigator. Several areas can be visited on one mission, with pre-programmed loiter time over each target (extendable by manual override if required). Final waypoint is location of ground station. Radar tracking, via onboard transponder to ground station telemetry display unit and computer map plotter. Mission progress supervised via TVR 10 video receiver with colour monitor and video recorder. Alternatively, aircraft can be flown entirely under manual radio control, either visually using binoculars or via the onboard video camera and TV surveillance monitor. If RPV is required to operate beyond normal control or video transmission range, a 'repeater' RPV can be launched, programmed to fly a holding pattern at about 3,000 m (9,850 ft). This aircraft then acts as airborne relay for telecommand, telemetry and video surveillance systems.

MISSION EQUIPMENT: Multi-role capability, using interchangeable slide-in mission pods. Engine driven alternator provides 28V DC power for avionics, surveillance and other systems; standby rechargeable battery pack is carried to power control systems. Standard equipment in surveillance versions comprises solid state colour TV camera with 90 mm zoom lens (RPL, RPM and RPS); TVX 20 UHF real-time video/telemetry transmitter (RPL, RPM and RPS); and 100-frame 35 mm still camera for high quality photography of target area (RPL and RPS). Optional cameras as detailed under model listing; monochrome TV camera in RPX. All video cameras, their lens options and positioning can be varied to suit specific locations or targets. At customer's option other mission pods and systems, including ECM, radar jamming, chaff, flares, NBC and other 'sniffing' equipment, can be installed in either M100 or M200.

DIMENSIONS (M200):

Wing span	3.45 m (11 ft 4 in)
Wing area	1.78 m² (19.2 sq ft)
Length overall	3.05 m (10 ft)
Height overall	1.02 m (3 ft 4 in)
Propeller diameter	0.51 m (1 ft 8 in)

WEIGHTS:

Weight empty:	
M100	15 kg (33 lb)
M200	20 kg (44 lb)
Payload (incl fuel):	
M100	10 kg (22 lb)
M200	25 kg (55 lb)
Max launching weight:	
M100	25 kg (55 lb)
M200	45 kg (99 lb)

PERFORMANCE (M100 and M200 except where indicated):

Operating speed range	51–97 knots (95–180 km/h; 59–112 mph)
Stalling speed	30 knots (55 km/h; 35 mph)
Typical rate of climb at S/L	244 m (800 ft)/min
Normal operating height range	250–1,525 m (820–5,000 ft)
Ceiling	4,575 m (15,000 ft)
Range with max fuel:	
M200 RPS	54 nm (100 km; 62 miles)
M200 RPL	135 nm (250 km; 155 miles)
Endurance:	
M100 and M200, standard fuel	2 h
*M200 RPL, auxiliary fuel	4 h

*with reduced payload

ASVEC SWIFT

Developed from the Merlin, the Swift is a low-cost aerial target designed to UK MoD specifications for use with ground-to-air missile and anti-aircraft systems. Chief recognition differences are the circular section fuselage and tractor propeller. Swift can also be deployed on non-target missions such as ECM, artillery ranging, decoy/chaff dispensing and surveillance.

TYPE: Recoverable target or RPV.

AIRFRAME: Generally similar to Merlin except for shape of fuselage. Modular construction, using composite materials.

POWER PLANT: One 7.5 kW (10 hp) Horner 100 cc two-cylinder two-stroke engine, driving a two-blade tractor propeller. Fuel tank in centre of fuselage, capacity 5.34 litres (1.17 Imp gallons; 1.41 US gallons).

LAUNCH AND RECOVERY: Can be launched by Asvec pneumatic launcher, or adapted for other suitable existing launch systems. Slow stalling speed permits recovery either by radio-controlled landing on reinforced under-fuselage skids

Asvec Swift twin-boom target/RPV *(Michael A. Badrocke)*

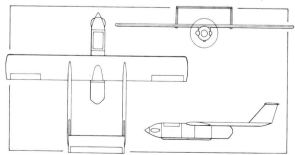

or by deploying onboard emergency parachute housed in forward fuselage.

GUIDANCE AND CONTROL: Manual radio system, with autopilot optional. Ailerons and one-piece elevator for aerodynamic control. Manual or automatic control ground stations available, including telemetry and video display monitors. Also available is a binocular system enabling the aircraft to be flown manually over a distance of approx 5.4 nm (10 km; 6.2 miles).

MISSION EQUIPMENT: Can be fitted with 16 sequentially switched smoke canisters, in pod forming rear compartment of fuselage, or with various infra-red flares in the interchangeable pod, to enable it to be used as a target for most types of ground-to-air missile. Safety circuits prevent accidental firing of smoke or infra-red burners. Racal miss distance indicator system can be installed as an option, complete with telemetry downlink and ground display equipment.

DIMENSIONS:

Wing span	2.74 m (9 ft)
Length overall	2.29 m (7 ft 6 in)
Propeller diameter	0.46 m (1 ft 6 in)

WEIGHT:

Max launching weight	33.6 kg (74 lb)

PERFORMANCE:

Max level speed	140 knots (259 km/h; 161 mph)
Stalling speed	39 knots (73 km/h; 45 mph)
Max rate of climb at S/L	588 m (1,930 ft)/min
Ceiling	2,970 m (9,750 ft)
Endurance	1 h 30 min

BEN BUCKLE RPV

9 Islay Crescent, Highworth, Wiltshire SN6 7HL

As an engineer and model aircraft hobbyist, Mr Buckle has over 30 years of experience of particular value in the design and manufacture of small remotely piloted aircraft, and formed a company in 1982 to exploit this capability. His first production mini-RPVs are the PR 21 and Owl.

BUCKLE PR 21

This small pilotless aircraft is intended for such applications as aerial photography, air sampling and cropspraying, and can be dismantled and packed into a transit case 3.20 × 0.65 × 0.65 m (10 ft 6 in × 2 ft 1.5 in square) for easy transportation to remote areas. Five, all for export, had been delivered by April 1984, in various configurations including a twin-engined version, with production then continuing. No later information received.

TYPE: Remotely controlled unmanned aircraft.

AIRFRAME: High-wing monoplane of pod and boom configuration. The wing, constructed on a rigid foam core and covered with plywood and nylon, has a specially developed aerofoil section combining high lift with exceptional longitudinal stability. Trailing edge flaps aid very short take-off and, when extended fully to 90°, serve as effective airbrakes for landing in confined spaces. Load-carrying fuselage pod is a laminated wood box, upswept sharply at nose to enable a camera to look forward as well as obliquely and vertically. Tailboom is a detachable aluminium tube

Ben Buckle PR 21

supporting the cruciform tail surfaces. Underfuselage landing skid.

POWER PLANT: For operation at MTOGW and above 1,220 m (4,000 ft), aircraft is powered by a Quadra 50 cc single-cylinder two-stroke engine with a two-blade pusher propeller. A 2.1 kW (2.8 hp) 44 cc Tartan two-cylinder two-stroke, with methanol fuel, can be used for less demanding operations.

LAUNCH AND RECOVERY: Takes off from small wheeled trolley; lands on underfuselage skid.

GUIDANCE AND CONTROL: Radio command guidance system.

SYSTEMS AND EQUIPMENT: To customer's requirement.

DIMENSIONS:

Wing span	3.05 m (10 ft)
Wing area (nominal)	1.54 m² (16.6 sq ft)
Length overall	2.03 m (6 ft 8 in)

WEIGHTS:

Payload (nominal, depending on fuel capacity and engine)	8.2 kg (18 lb)
Max T-O weight	31.8 kg (70 lb)

PERFORMANCE (at max T-O weight except where indicated):

Max level speed	81 knots (150 km/h; 93 mph)
Stalling speed	22 knots (40 km/h; 25 mph)
Min level speed at 25 kg (55 lb) AUW	11 knots (20 km/h; 13 mph)

BUCKLE PR 13 OWL

The Owl was designed and prototyped to a customer requirement for a quiet, stable, easy to control air vehicle capable of carrying two standard 35 mm cameras and having a 20 min endurance. Initial trials with a scaled-down PR 21 were superseded by a conventional tractor monoplane design with 'taildragger' landing gear, which proved more satisfactory for engine starting and camera location. Three different wings were tested (with flaps and ailerons, without flaps, and without either). Fuselage and tailplane proved entirely satisfactory, and the twin fins and rudders, when combined with 9° of wing dihedral, resulted in an aircraft characteristically incapable of spinning, and very slow flying was demonstrated.

The prototype programme was completed to the original customer's satisfaction, and preparations for production were started in spring 1984. No other or later details have been forthcoming.

BRITISH AEROSPACE PLC (BAe)

Naval and Electronic Systems Division, PO Box 5, Filton, Bristol BS12 7QW

BAe's Naval and Electronic Systems Division, and predecessor companies on the Filton site, have a long and established involvement with RPV and target aircraft. This work has included design, development, manufacture and operation of aircraft in both categories. BAe experience includes a long association with UK Jindivik activities (see ATA in Australian section), and the company is the UK co-ordinating design authority for the latest Mk 4A version of this aircraft.

Since the early 1970s, effort has been devoted to the development of surveillance RPVs, funded from both company and MoD contract resources. The work has covered several distinct families of airframes, investigation of payloads which include IR, optical and elint sensors, in addition to active EW and decoy packages. In several cases complete system evaluation has been undertaken, and offers based on these systems have been made to potential customers.

BAe (BAC) TAILWIND

Begun in 1976 by the Guided Weapons Division of British Aircraft Corporation, the Tailwind was intended to provide missile operators with a realistic full size target aircraft, with a view to possible use with the Rapier air defence system. Prototype development was undertaken using a proprietary light aircraft, the AJEP Tailwind 2, a British development of the original US Wittman design.

This aircraft (G-AYDU) was used to evaluate UMA sensor flight control and servo equipment. It was employed extensively on a variety of trials, and was fully equipped and checked for autonomous unmanned flight, but because of approval and flight clearance problems was never flown without a pilot on board. At one stage, serious consideration was given to the possibility of using production versions as surface-to-air weapon targets in support of a weapon system sale to an overseas customer.

POWER PLANT: One 75 kW (100 hp) Continental PC60 flat-four piston engine, driving a two-blade propeller.
LAUNCH AND RECOVERY: Conventional T-O and landing on non-retractable tricycle landing gear.
GUIDANCE AND CONTROL: Radio command guidance system; manual controls retained, for normal piloted operations when required.
MISSION EQUIPMENT: Autopilot and radio command link.
DIMENSIONS:

Wing span	6.86 m (22 ft 6 in)
Wing area	8.36 m² (90 sq ft)
Length overall	6.36 m (20 ft 10.5 in)

The BAC/AJEP (modified Wittman) Tailwind

WEIGHT:

Max T-O and landing weight	635 kg (1,400 lb)

PERFORMANCE:

Max level speed at S/L	152 knots (282 km/h; 175 mph)
Max cruising speed at S/L	143 knots (265 km/h; 165 mph)
Range, no reserves	534 nm (990 km; 615 miles)

BAe FLYBAC

This family of small experimental air vehicles was used by the Royal Aircraft Establishment and BAe for early RPV experiments, particularly with autopilot and sensor equipment, in the military applications of RPVs. They were instrumented to permit autonomous or remote pilot control, and carried telemetry and a range recovery parachute.

Between 10 and 20 Flybacs were built/rebuilt. The programme was regarded as a development exercise leading up to the Stabileye series.

POWER PLANT: One 1.3 kW (1.8 hp) 10 cc Webra single-cylinder engine, driving a two-blade propeller.
LAUNCH AND RECOVERY: Ramp launch; parachute recovery.
DIMENSIONS:

Wing span	1.83 m (6 ft)
Length overall	1.47 m (4 ft 9.75 in)
Height overall	0.41 m (1 ft 4.25 in)

WEIGHTS:

Payload	2 kg (4.4 lb)
Max launching weight	11 kg (24.2 lb)

PERFORMANCE:

Cruising speed	39 knots (72 km/h; 45 mph)
Max range	13 nm (24 km; 15 miles)
Max endurance	20 min

BAe STABILEYE Mks 1 and 2

The Stabileye family of mini-RPVs has been developed over a number of years for various Ministry of Defence and BAe research programmes. The initial concept was to produce a simple, robust mini-RPV, capable of flight testing a large variety of sensors and other mission payloads. A key feature of the airframe/autopilot design was the inclusion of a high level of inherent stability, so that acceptable surveillance images could be recovered from unstabilised sensor packages. The aircraft's

British Aerospace Flybac

BAe Stabileye Mk 2 in anechoic chamber

name was chosen to reflect the pursuit of this principle, and the concepts described governed the course of development through the early Mk 1 and 2 versions to the more advanced Stabileye Mk 3, which is described separately.

The first prototype **Mk 1** made its initial flight on 24 October 1974, powered by a 3 kW (4 hp) Rowena 60 cc piston engine. Twelve examples were built, remaining in almost continuous service until about 1981 in programmes to investigate the carriage of various potential payloads for military mini-RPVs.

The Stabileye **Mk 2**, which flew for the first time on 20 December 1979, retained the same basic aerodynamic configuration, but was strengthened structurally in order to carry test payloads of almost twice the weight. Built mainly of GRP and aluminium alloy, with a steel tube centre fuselage space-frame, it was powered by a 5.6 kW (7.5 hp) Weslake T-116 engine. The prototype was fitted with extended wingtips and used to demonstrate launch from a truck-mounted ramp; other examples carried a Luneberg lens in a 'thimble' nose.

DIMENSIONS:
Wing span:	
Mk 1	3.10 m (10 ft 2 in)
Mk 2	3.70 m (12 ft 1.75 in)
Wing area:	
Mk 1	1.65 m² (17.76 sq ft)
Mk 2	1.68 m² (18.08 sq ft)
Length overall (both)	2.60 m (8 ft 6.5 in)
Height overall (both)	0.89 m (2 ft 11 in)

WEIGHTS:
Max payload:	
Mk 1	8 kg (17.6 lb)
Mk 2	15 kg (33 lb)
Max launching weight:	
Mk 1	42 kg (92.5 lb)
Mk 2	55 kg (121 lb)

PERFORMANCE:
Max level speed:	
Mk 1	78 knots (144 km/h; 90 mph)
Mk 2	93 knots (173 km/h; 107 mph)
Cruising speed:	
Mk 1	68 knots (126 km/h; 78 mph)
Mk 2	83 knots (155 km/h; 96 mph)
Stalling speed:	
Mk 1	39 knots (72 km/h; 45 mph)
Mk 2	43 knots (79 km/h; 49 mph)

Max endurance:	
Mk 1	30 min
Mk 2	1 h

BAe STABILEYE Mk 3

Designed to carry a maximum payload of 25 kg, the Stabileye Mk 3 differs in some configuration details from its predecessors. The fuselage has a rectangular cross-section, and the wings have constant chord instead of the previous tapered planform. A single central fin, of greater area, replaces the twin fins of the earlier models.

The prototype Mk 3 flew for the first time on 24 September 1980, and a total of 20 was built, mostly under MoD contract; they continued in use in 1986 in a MoD flight trials programme. Later examples were delivered with improvements to the airframe and avionics. BAe development activities have included flight trials of digital autopilot systems with stored waypoint navigational capability, and advanced IRLS systems.

TYPE: Research mini-RPV.

AIRFRAME: Cantilever high-wing monoplane, with constant chord wings of NACA 4415 section. Twin tailboom configuration, with engine mounted at rear of rectangular section central nacelle. Single sheet of GRP/honeycomb core material is cut and folded to form bottom and sides of fuselage box. Bulkheads then cut from same material and bonded in position. GRP mouldings form nose and rear body fairings. Hinged 'lid' on top of fuselage allows access to payload bay and recovery parachute. Wings of foam core construction, fitted with conventional ailerons. Twin tailbooms, of square section GRP tube, attached by four bolts to undersurface of wings; another four bolts locate constant chord tailplane at rear end of booms. Single central fin, of honeycomb core, slotted on and bonded to tailplane. Elevator on each half of tailplane; provision for optional rudder. Complete wing, boom and tail assembly secured to top of fuselage by a single strap fastening; removal of this assembly gives access to flight control equipment bay. Configuration is chosen to allow large payload space with unobstructed views forward and downward.

POWER PLANT: Depending upon payload and mission requirements, various piston engines have been used. Generally, BAe has used the 18.6 kW (25 hp) NGL WAEL 342 two-cylinder two-stroke or the 200 cc counterpart from the same manufacturer; the latest fuel-injected version of the larger engine can be accommodated. In all cases the engine drives a pusher propeller.

Preparing a Stabileye Mk 3 for a mission

LAUNCH AND RECOVERY: Launch is from a pneumatic catapult. Recovery is by Irvin (GB) parachute, with an underfuselage airbag to cushion impact with the ground. Programme for recovery sequence (engine cut/deploy parachute/deploy airbag) is automatic. Sequence can be initiated on command from ground station or by emergence of preselected onboard conditions such as loss of radio contact.

GUIDANCE AND CONTROL: Onboard flight control equipment, interfacing with ground station via a pulse code modulated (PCM) telecommand system, includes digital flight control electronics, vertical gyro, yaw rate gyro, magnetometer, telemetry encoder, and command receiver/decoder. Semi-autonomous navigation is available by use of waypoint co-ordinate references stored in digital autopilot. Navigation options include tracking radar with transponder, or Omega, in conjunction with waypoint system. Ground equipment includes plotter unit showing position of RPV relative to a pre-printed map of the area of interest, and a colour TV screen on which the view seen by RPV can be displayed in real time.

MISSION EQUIPMENT: A variety of commercial TV and photographic cameras has been flown in Stabileye. Such equipment can be switched on or off, exposure sequences initiated, and lens movements controlled, either by onboard sequences or by ground control. One of the BAe series of IR Linescan equipments has also been flown successfully, and a selection of electronic warfare payloads has been evaluated for use on board. Power for onboard equipment is provided by a directly coupled alternator with regulator and backup batteries.

DIMENSIONS:
Wing span	3.66 m (12 ft)
Wing area	2.23 m² (24 sq ft)
Length overall	2.87 m (9 ft 5 in)
Height overall	1.03 m (3 ft 4.5 in)
Propeller diameter	0.56 m (1 ft 10 in)

WEIGHTS:
Max mission load	25 kg (55 lb)
Max launching weight	80 kg (176 lb)

PERFORMANCE:
Operating speed range	52–97 knots (96–180 km/h; 60–112 mph)
Max operating altitude	3,050 m (10,000 ft)
Endurance at 75 knots (140 km/h; 87 mph) with max payload	4 h

BAe STABILEYE Mk 4

Stabileye 4 was derived from a design prepared for the original British MoD Phoenix competition. This initial design incorporated flip-out wings, to permit launch directly from the storage box, but the version finally built was considerably enlarged to accommodate a stabilised IR imager, and dispensed with container launch in favour of a more conventional fixed-wing aircraft using a pneumatic rail launcher. In this form the aircraft retained a place in the Phoenix competition until the final contract award.

The aircraft was designed around the Lotus 225 four-stroke engine, but because of programme difficulties the prototype was flown using a two-stroke engine instead. Up to early 1986 only the one prototype had been flown, further work depending on a positive market assessment or on a specific enquiry for a vehicle having the capabilities offered by the Mk 4 version.

TYPE: Prototype mini-RPV.

AIRFRAME: Design philosophy of this air vehicle was to produce a stable flight platform with minimal radar, acoustic and IR signatures. The aircraft is shaped externally to minimise the radar cross-section as presented to a ground based radar system; this effect is achieved by use of a fuselage having a triangular cross-section, formed as a flat floor with two sloping sides. Fuselage is built from a heavy grade GRP

General arrangement of the Stabileye Mk 4 *(Jane's/Mike Keep)*

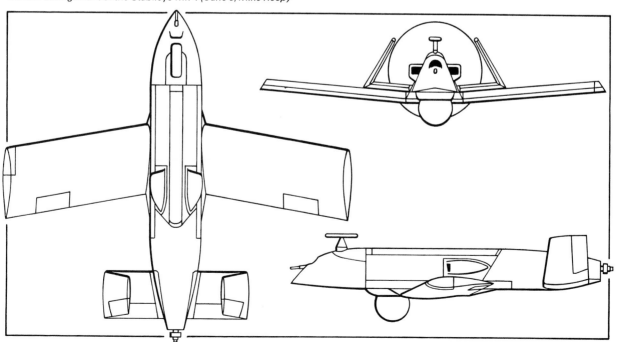

honeycomb material, metallised externally to be radar reflective. These features ensure specular reflection of impinging radar emanations away from the source, thus avoiding detectable reflections such as would be given by a metal box within a radar-transparent skin. Wings are mounted low, dihedralled and swept. Tailplane is also mounted low, with dihedral, and carries twin tail-fins canted inward to minimise radar signature. Prototype wings and tailplane were made of skinned plastics foam; those of production versions would be made as self-skinning foam mouldings.

POWER PLANT: Aircraft is configured to use 18.6 kW (25 hp) NGL WAEL 342 two-cylinder two-stroke engine (as originally flown), or the Lotus 225 two-cylinder four-stroke of the same rating, mounted in centre-section of fuselage above wing and driving a two-blade pusher propeller through a flexibly coupled shaft. Cooling air intakes are thus shrouded by wing, to minimise radar cross-section contribution from this source and to screen this area from IR detection. An engine-driven alternator is mounted on forward end of engine.

LAUNCH AND RECOVERY: Aircraft is designed to be launched from a pneumatic catapult, although a large motorcar fitted with a fixed cradle has been used for flight testing. Recovery is by parachute and airbag, as with Stabileye 3, but in case of Stabileye 4 air vehicle is inverted for recovery sequence. This recovery mode is intended to afford maximum protection on touchdown for relatively fragile payloads such as downward looking IR imagers.

GUIDANCE AND CONTROL: Versions of the equipment used with the Stabileye 3 system, with suitable software adjustments, are used in Stabileye 4.

MISSION EQUIPMENT: Entire range of sensors used in Stabileye 3 can be used in Stabileye 4. In addition, several different proprietary IR imagers can be accommodated.

DIMENSIONS:

Wing span	3.66 m (12 ft)
Wing area	2.69 m² (29 sq ft)
Length overall	3.40 m (11 ft 2 in)
Height over tail-fins	1.02 m (3 ft 4 in)

WEIGHTS:

Max mission load	50 kg (110 lb)
Max launching weight	131.5 kg (290 lb)

PERFORMANCE:

Operating speed range	68–87 knots (126–162 km/h; 78–101 mph)
Operational ceiling	3,960 m (13,000 ft)
Endurance, depending on engine and payload	4–7 h

BAe TARGETS and DECOYS

British Aerospace is involved in studies and experimental work for a number of target and decoy systems. Naval target activities have been influenced by budgetary constraints, but prototype testing work was in hand in 1986-87 for several off-board decoy systems.

The two most advanced projects at that time featured carrier vehicles designed to be launched from a standard 130 mm mortar. The first of these is an infra-red decoy system. The second, a wrap-round flexible (Rogallo) wing UMA known as **Plover**, is 1.70 m (5 ft 7 in) in overall length and has a wing span of 2.50 m (8 ft 2.5 in). It will carry a 20 kg (44 lb) payload, and is expected to have an endurance of several hours.

EYRIE ENTERPRISES
223 Bramhall Moor Lane, Hazel Grove, Stockport, Cheshire SK7 5JL

Eyrie Enterprises was formed by Mr Noel Falconer, originally to investigate the AX (Advanced eXpendable) flying wing RPV. When no immediate government interest was shown in this, attention was transferred to UMAC (UnManned Aircraft for Civil applications) which, although a much lighter and more limited vehicle, is still an exceptionally 'clean' flying wing.

EYRIE AX

The AX was an unusually clean flying wing RPV, with a design owing much to earlier Horten and Northrop approaches to this configuration. It was believed that expendables, without the weight and bulk of recovery systems, would be less vulnerable and last sufficiently longer against opposition to compensate for their loss at the end of a mission, on which basis it might take fewer expendables than recoverable RPVs to perform certain types of mission.

Hand-launched technology demonstrators were used to prove the basic flight characteristics of the all-wing configuration. Four versions were then planned, with wing spans of 1.5, 2, 2.5 and 3 metres, but only the 2 metre version was flown, as a lightweight aerodynamic prototype, before lack of official interest caused the project to be shelved. However, the choice of an electric power unit for this aircraft demonstrated a quietness, cleanliness, ease and safety of operation that could not have been matched by an internal combustion engine. Structural efficiency of the airframe was also highly satisfactory, despite having to carry large, heavy batteries.

TYPE: Expendable mini-RPV.

AIRFRAME: 'Flying wing' monoplane, without tail surfaces. Wings have an extensively modified Wortmann section (thickness/chord ratio 20%) and 10° sweepback at quarter-chord. No anhedral or dihedral. All-glassfibre construction, with aileron control by integral flexing skin; no other control surfaces. 'Fuselage' is no more than a bulge in centre of wing, extending from wing as necessary to accommodate a specific payload.

POWER PLANT: Technology demonstrators powered by Keller electric motors. Intention was to power later prototypes with various small four-stroke piston engines with selected fixed-pitch propellers.

LAUNCH AND RECOVERY: Technology demonstrators hand-launched like model aircraft.

MISSION EQUIPMENT: Battery for electrical power; video camera; downlink; modified Sanwa radio control system.

ARMAMENT: Able to carry warhead.

DIMENSIONS:

Wing span	2 m (6 ft 6.75 in)
Wing area	0.50 m² (5.38 sq ft)

WEIGHT (3 metre version, estimated):

Max launching weight (volume limited)	150 kg (331 lb)

PERFORMANCE (estimated):

Econ cruising speed at 500 m (1,640 ft)	108 knots (200 km/h; 124 mph)
Stalling speed	65 knots (120 km/h; 75 mph)
Max rate of climb at S/L	50–100 m (164–328 ft)/min
Ceiling	low
Range with max fuel, no reserves (3 metre version)	more than 1,080 nm (2,000 km; 1,243 miles)

EYRIE UMAC/MERLIN

The **UMAC I** first prototype (first flight December 1984) was flown initially as a glider, to investigate the aerodynamics of the design. By early 1986 the programme had utilised four prototypes, each reconfigured several times. **UMAC II**, which was then nearly ready to fly, has a slightly greater span than UMAC I, more sweep on the outer panels, and a larger centre section, to provide useful volume ahead of the CG so that the aircraft can be balanced without a nacelle. Tipsails take the place of the downturned wingtips of the UMAC I. Some sensor sets have been tested, cameras flown, and transfer of control while airborne achieved.

Roles for UMAC have been identified, and an economically viable aircraft is expected to result. This is subject to obtaining funding to 'productionise' the structure; the production version would be known as the **Merlin**.

UMAC is intended for such local operations as aerial photography or filming for television, where the brief endurance possible with primary electric power is acceptable. Radius of action is limited by control range to about 1.6 nm (3 km; 1.9 miles), although handover from one ground station to another has been demonstrated. Endurance is about 30 min on one battery and 70 min on two. The former is adequate for the typical 40 s run of a 16 mm film camera; the latter can be employed, for example, for direct surveillance of traffic or crowds. Moreover, because UMAC is so slow and light it will not cause major damage on landing, and so can be employed where a lightplane would not be acceptable.

TYPE: Experimental electric-powered mini-RPV.
AIRFRAME: 'Flying wing' monoplane, without tail surfaces. Current wings (1987) have Eppler E222/E230 instead of the earlier Wortmann aerofoil sections. Sweepback at quarter-chord 11° 36' on UMAC I, 18° 30' on UMAC II. No anhedral or dihedral. Downturned (Hoerner) wingtips on UMAC I, upturned Spillman tipsails on UMAC II. Construction is of glassfibre on a balsawood core. Two-axis control by elevons, with Futaba controls, hinged by flexing glassfibre skin; yaw control by differential throttle in twin-engined version. Combined de-spin parachute/drag brake. 'Fuselage', where applicable, achieved by bulging wing centre section as required by specific payloads.
POWER PLANT: One or two Unger 30 electric motors, each of 400 W (0.5 hp) input (single Unger 18 in UMAC II). Nylon two-blade pusher propeller.
LAUNCH AND RECOVERY: Launched by short bungee; recovery by belly landing on grass.

Eyrie (Falconer) UMAC II- prototype in 1986 configuration

GUIDANCE AND CONTROL: Futaba PCM radio control system with Colching II downlink.
MISSION EQUIPMENT: Sony XC 37 CCD-TV camera, Richer micro-16 mm film camera, or other payloads, fitted in centre section as required. One or two Sanyo SCR 1800 20-cell nickel-cadmium batteries installed immediately behind centre section leading edge to provide power for electric motors.
DIMENSIONS:

Wing span:	
UMAC I	2.29 m (7 ft 6 in)
UMAC II (excl tipsails):	
single engine	2.64 m (8 ft 8 in)
twin engines	3.30 m (10 ft 10 in)
Wing area:	
UMAC I	0.70 m² (7.50 sq ft)
UMAC II (excl tipsails):	
single engine	0.77 m² (8.25 sq ft)
Length overall: UMAC II	0.74 m (2 ft 5.25 in)
Height overall:	
wing only (excl tipsails)	5 cm (2 in)
with bulged (camera) 'fuselage'	10 cm (4 in)
Propeller diameter:	
current	25.4 cm (10 in)
planned	30.5 cm (12 in)

WEIGHTS (approx):

Flying wing (excl payload):	
single engine	4.1 kg (9 lb)
twin engines	5 kg (11 lb)
Max payload	2.5 kg (5.5 lb)
Batteries (each)	1.6 kg (3.5 lb)
Max launching weight	6.8 kg (15 lb)

PERFORMANCE (estimated):

Max level speed at S/L	72 knots (133 km/h; 83 mph)
Max cruising speed at S/L	48 knots (89 km/h; 55 mph)
Stalling speed	24 knots (45 km/h; 28 mph)
Max rate of climb at S/L (single engine)	100 m (328 ft)/min
Control limit ceiling	610 m (2,000 ft)
Launch to 15 m (50 ft)	15 m (50 ft)
Landing from 15 m (50 ft)	50 m (164 ft)
Landing run	10 m (33 ft)
Max range	22 nm (41 km; 25.3 miles)

FERRANTI DEFENCE SYSTEMS LTD (Electro-Optics Department)

St Andrew's Works, Robertson Avenue, Edinburgh EH11 1PX

Ferranti has worked on unmanned aircraft systems and subsystems since the late 1970s, and was one of the two finalists from whom prototypes were ordered in 1983–84 to compete for the British Army's requirement for a battlefield target acquisition and surveillance RPV system, known as Phoenix. The company is continuing to develop and market its own entry in that competition, now known as Firebird.

FERRANTI PHOENIX PROTOTYPES

The essential requirements for the Phoenix programme were for a low-observable, catapult-launched/parachute-recoverable mini-RPV, carrying a thermal imaging (infra-red) sensor package for day/night surveillance as the primary payload. Five Phoenix prototypes were built for the fly-off competition programme (first flight 1983), with early airframes provided by Slingsby Aviation.

TYPE: Recoverable reconnaissance RPV.

AIRFRAME: Generally as described for Firebird.

POWER PLANT: One 18.6 kW (25 hp) NGL WAEL 342 flat-twin engine, driving a two-blade propeller with spinner.

LAUNCH AND RECOVERY: Catapult launch from vehicle mounted ramp. Parachute recovery, using inflatable airbag to cushion landing. (Drone inverts during landing phase, to protect ventrally-mounted payload.)

GUIDANCE AND CONTROL: Radio command uplink from Ferranti Computer Systems ground control station (GCS), which received and processed telemetered infra-red signals via a jamming-resistant MEL downlink, shown on a Ferranti Navigation Systems display combining infra-red image with a moving map indicating location of RPV. Alternatively, IR signals could be transmitted to GCS via an airborne relay aircraft. Smiths Industries navigation system.

MISSION EQUIPMENT: Rank Pullin Controls thermal imaging sensor as primary payload, with a Ferranti stabilisation system, installed in a ventral ball mounting. Based on SPRITE (Signal PRocessing In The Element), with an RSRE coaxial scanner, this sensor has two separate fields of view: wide angle for target detection and narrow angle for identification; and can detect and identify a main battle tank at up to 1.08 nm (2 km; 1.25 miles) distance. Adequate space provision to add optional laser rangefinder.

DIMENSIONS:

Wing span	3.50 m (11 ft 5.75 in)
Length overall	2.83 m (9 ft 3.5 in)

WEIGHTS:

Max payload	44 kg (97 lb)
Max launching weight	137 kg (302 lb)

PERFORMANCE:

Max level speed	93 knots (172 km/h; 107 mph)
Cruising speed	68 knots (126 km/h; 78 mph)
Stalling speed	49 knots (90 km/h; 56 mph)
Range with max payload	340 nm (630 km; 391 miles)
Max endurance	more than 5 h

FERRANTI FIREBIRD

The complete Firebird system comprises the air vehicle, launcher, ground control station and support facilities, and is based on a compact, recoverable fixed-wing RPV carrying either a stabilised electro-optical sensor or stabilised daytime or low light level TV. Other payloads can be accommodated to meet specific customer requirements, the available range being able to provide real-time detection, location and identification of targets by day and night and in conditions of poor visibility.

TYPE: Recoverable reconnaissance RPV.

AIRFRAME: Low-wing monoplane, of all-glassfibre modular construction. Constant chord dihedral wings, with ailerons and spoilers. Trapezoidal section fuselage, to reflect radar away from transmitter. Engine module, at front of aircraft, is designed to minimise thermal radiation and engine noise levels. Removal of corner reflectors, where possible, also helps to reduce radar signature. Engine, fuel cell and payload are concentrated into small volumes to provide payload bays fore and aft, so allowing a variety of payloads to be accommodated. Anhedral tailplane, with elevators; inward canted endplate fins and rudders. Wings and tail unit detachable for transportation and storage. Retractable skids under fuselage.

POWER PLANT: One 19.4 kW (26 hp) NGL WAEL 342 flat-twin two-stroke engine, driving a two-blade propeller with spinner. (See under 'Weights' for fuel capacity.)

LAUNCH AND RECOVERY: Pneumatic catapult launch from vehicle-mounted ramp. Can be recovered by skid landing; or by parachute, using inflatable airbag to cushion landing. (Drone inverts during landing phase, to protect ventrally mounted payload.) Parachute can be deployed automatically by fuselage-mounted actuator in the event of a malfunction.

GUIDANCE AND CONTROL: Choice of uplinks and downlinks available; basic Firebird system uses a UHF uplink and VHF downlink in conjunction with a radar tracker. Flight control and navigation system is Ferranti Type 2001, using a Ferranti FS 60A vertical gyro. Basic two-man ground station uses an X-Y plotter for mission planning and progress; a Ferranti moving map display with a graphics overlay is available as an option. Air vehicle is normally pre-programmed using GCS computer to plan flight path by means of waypoints, but this can be overridden by GCS to carry out an en-route search mode in an area of interest. A manual flight mode is also available. Air vehicle will return to launch area if data or command link is lost.

MISSION EQUIPMENT: Basic Firebird payload is a Ferranti Type 233 daylight system, consisting of a TV camera with 10:1 zoom lens on a gyro stabilised platform contained in a

Ferranti Firebird reconnaissance RPV

Ferranti Phoenix prototype being test launched

transparent ventral dome with a full field of regard in the hemisphere beneath the aircraft. A variant of this equipment (Type 233A), fitted with an image intensifier, is available for low light applications. Other payloads which can be accommodated include a Ferranti Type 234 two- or four-gimbal stabilised platform containing a thermal imager and, if required, a boresighted laser; or a Type 237 two- or four-gimbal stabilised electro-optical platform carrying a thermal imager, TV camera, laser designator/rangefinder, or any combination of these. Electronic warfare, ESM and panoramic camera payloads are also available.

DIMENSIONS:
Wing span	4.40 m (14 ft 5.25 in)
Length overall	3.40 m (11 ft 1.75 in)
Fuselage: Max depth	0.28 m (11 in)
Propeller diameter	0.66 m (2 ft 2 in)

WEIGHTS:
Weight empty	75 kg (165 lb)
Max fuel	20 kg (44 lb)
Max payload	45 kg (99 lb)
Max launching weight	140 kg (308 lb)

PERFORMANCE:
Max level speed	93 knots (172 km/h; 107 mph)
Cruising speed	68 knots (126 km/h; 78 mph)
Stalling speed	49 knots (90 km/h; 56 mph)
Max rate of climb at S/L	360 m (1,181 ft)/min
Ceiling	3,000 m (9,850 ft)
Range with max payload	302 nm (560 km; 348 miles)
Max endurance	more than 4 h

FLIGHT REFUELLING LTD (FRL)
Brook Road, Wimborne, Dorset BH21 2BJ

For more than 25 years, Flight Refuelling has been engaged, inter alia, in the design and manufacture of control systems for pilotless aircraft. It was responsible for the conversion of more than 250 Gloster Meteor aircraft to pilotless or drone configuration. Some of these aircraft are still in service use for missile development trials and practice firings.

Flight Refuelling is continuing the development of RPVs and target drones, and is currently producing the ASAT and Raven vehicles for the UK Ministry of Defence. It is also teamed with GEC Avionics (which see) in developing the Phoenix surveillance RPV.

FRL UDP

The UDP (Universal Drone Pack) is a packaged system designed to enable most types of aircraft to be readily converted to drone or pilotless configuration with only minor modifications to their conventional flying control system inputs, and without degrading the aircraft's original manned performance envelope. The pack is designed for installation on the existing seat rail in the aircraft's cockpit, and was first fitted in the Hawker Siddeley Sea Vixen D. Mk 3. (The Sea Vixen drone programme was, however, abandoned for a number of reasons which included its untypical twin-boom configuration, the comparatively small number available for conversion, and low serviceability rate.)

FRL FR-500

The FR-500 was a variable speed multi-purpose target drone, developed in the late 1970s to meet a Royal Navy request for a vehicle capable of 500 knots (926 km/h; 575 mph) at sea level. The airframe was of modular construction, to facilitate rapid assembly, recovery, repair, refurbishing and storage. It did not go into production, but formed a development basis for the later ASAT.

TYPE: Variable speed multi-purpose target drone.

AIRFRAME: Low/mid-wing monoplane. Aluminium alloy stressed-skin structure, with circular section fuselage built in three modular units: forward, central and rear (parachute) section. Nose and tail fairings, and removable parachute bin, of glassfibre-reinforced plastics. Conventional all-metal tail unit. No landing gear.

POWER PLANT: One 1.33 kN (300 lb st) Noel Penny Turbines NPT 401 turbojet, mounted under fuselage in modular nacelle. Two-compartment integral fuel tank in central fuselage. Three standard JATO bottles, each giving 11.76 kN (2,645 lb st) for 0.7 s, attached beneath rear fuselage and jettisoned after launch.

LAUNCH AND RECOVERY: Launched by JATO booster rockets from zero-length cradle on land or ship platform. Automatic or command two-stage parachute system for recovery from sea. Fuel tanks sealed to contribute to flotation; forward fuselage shell also forms a buoyancy compartment.

GUIDANCE AND CONTROL: Radio command, guidance and tracking system, similar to that installed in Northrop MQM-74 targets currently in use by Royal Navy, using autopilot and VHF receiver/decoder. Provision to replace this with smaller and lighter Vega 656 system. Aerodynamic

Sea Vixen D. Mk 3, droned by FRL with universal drone pack

control by ailerons and elevators. 28V DC electrical system (engine-driven alternator-rectifier and nickel-cadmium battery) and recovery beacon.

MISSION EQUIPMENT: Operational equipment, according to mission, could include up to six infra-red/tracking flares on underwing pylons; nose and/or tail-mounted Luneberg lenses for radar augmentation; miss-distance and scoring equipment; radio altimeter; underwing towed targets, cable reel and brake; and reconnaissance/surveillance camera or other sensors.

DIMENSIONS:

Wing span	2.13 m (7 ft)
Length overall	4.27 m (14 ft)
Height overall	1.07 m (3 ft 6 in)
Payload volume	0.02 m² (0.75 cu ft)

WEIGHTS:

Basic operating weight empty	120 kg (265 lb)
Payload with full fuel	16 kg (35 lb)
Max fuel	86 kg (190 lb)
Max launching weight	222 kg (490 lb)

PERFORMANCE:

Max level speed at S/L	500 knots (926 km/h; 575 mph)
Max rate of climb at S/L	2,682 m (8,800 ft)/min
Time to 7,620 m (25,000 ft)	5 min
Service ceiling	12,200 m (40,000 ft)
Max range	more than 600 nm (1,112 km; 691 miles)
Endurance at S/L:	
at 300 knots (556 km/h; 345 mph)	more than 1 h
at 500 knots (926 km/h; 575 mph)	30 min
g limit	+6

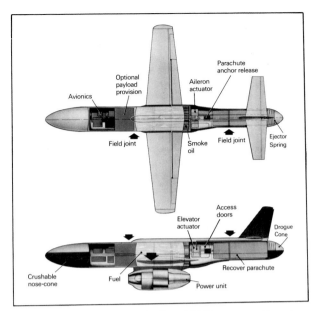

Main features of the Flight Refuelling ASAT jet powered target drone

FRL ASAT/Falconet, complete with rocket boosters, on zero-length launcher

FR ASAT

British Army name: Falconet

ASAT (advanced subsonic aerial target) was designed to meet a Ministry of Defence requirement. The first of eight prototypes began flight testing on 14 February 1982, and trials included launch and recovery in wind speeds up to 28 knots (52 km/h; 32 mph). Operation of the 'carousel' circular runway launch system, and stability and control of the air vehicle, have been established; a zero-length launch system, using JATO bottles, is also available, which allows the carriage of heavier payloads.

All eight development vehicles had flown by the beginning of 1984. Deliveries of Falconets to the British Army began in late 1983. A total of 105 had been delivered by December 1986, when a contract for a further 'substantial' number was announced.

Approach and intercept legs of a typical target mission total about 5.5 nm (10 km; 6.2 miles), over the whole of which the target vehicle may be flown at more than 400 knots (741 km/h; 461 mph) at S/L. Ten such circuits can be repeated at 4.5 min intervals. During less demanding operations, or where more time is required between presentations, the rate of fuel usage can be reduced by loiter at 3,000 m (9,850 ft) altitude.

Other possible applications for ASAT include the towing of banners or sub-targets, short/medium-range reconnaissance (with a suitable payload such as infra-red linescan), ECM, and decoy.

TYPE: Subsonic re-usable target drone or RPV.

AIRFRAME: Low/mid-wing monoplane. Wings, tailplane and elevators folded from flat aluminium alloy sheet, without compound forming. Wings are each attached to fuselage by four bolts, are fitted with plain ailerons, and are interchangeable port/starboard. Tailplane held in place by GRP fin, via two studs. Aluminium alloy stressed skin fuselage, of circular cross-section, with crushable nosecone to absorb nose-down ground impact. Nosecone attachment and body joints made by band clamps. Nosecone is expendable, and is replaced after each flight. Cylindrical canister in rear fuselage houses recovery parachute. Engine pod attached under fuselage by two bolts.

POWER PLANT: One 1.08 kN (242 lb st) Ames Industrial (Microturbo) TRS 18-075 turbojet, mounted in pod under centre of fuselage. Single integral fuel tank in centre of fuselage, between wings; this has a capacity of 77 litres (17 Imp gallons; 20.4 US gallons) and is pressurised at 1.0 bar (15 lb/sq in). Refuelling point on top of fuselage. Aft of fuel tank is a smaller tank for oil, which can be injected into jetpipe on command from ground to produce smoke for visual enhancement. Two jettisonable JATO boosters, each burning for 1.3 s, can be attached for zero-length launch.

LAUNCH AND RECOVERY: Production Falconet is configured for fixed base operations and takes off under own power from three-wheeled trolley, running clockwise on a circular track 115 m (377 ft) in diameter and tethered to a pylon in the centre. Aircraft reaches T-O speed in three laps of this track, equivalent to a straight line T-O run of 1,000 m (3,280 ft), and with this system can always be launched into wind. Alternative zero-length launcher also available, for mobile or shipboard operations. A phased release Irvin (GB) parachute recovery system, consisting of a drogue and single RPS/1 cruciform main canopy, is pre-loaded in a cylindrical pack and deployed by tailcone release. Can be recovered on land or from sea.

GUIDANCE AND CONTROL: Radio command PCM guidance system, with Skyleader receiver and GEC Avionics autopilot and ground control console. Programmable ground-based control option, using a microprocessor-based control station which utilises radar data as the basis for aircraft navigation and control functions. Aerodynamic control by ailerons and elevators, actuators for which are in rear fuselage, between fuel/oil tanks and parachute compartment.

SYSTEMS: Fuel and smoke/oil tanks pressurised by engine compressor bleed air. 400W direct drive alternator/PCU.

EQUIPMENT: Large bay in forward fuselage, aft of nosecone, for avionics and optional target equipment such as miss distance indicator and radio altimeter. Pylon provision for optical or infra-red flares, radar enhancement devices, subtargets, banners or other external stores. Capability, with suitable payload, for short/medium-range reconnaissance, ECM or decoy duties.

DIMENSIONS:

Wing span	3.05 m (10 ft)
Wing area	1.40 m² (15.1 sq ft)
Length overall	3.50 m (11 ft 6 in)
Body diameter (max)	0.387 m (1 ft 3.25 in)
Height overall	1.32 m (4 ft 4 in)
Tailplane span	1.32 m (4 ft 4 in)

WEIGHTS:

Basic weight empty	123 kg (271 lb)
Max fuel	60 kg (132 lb)
Payload (according to mission)	15–50 kg (33–110 lb)
Max launching weight	230 kg (507 lb)

PERFORMANCE:

Max level speed	450 knots (834 km/h; 518 mph)
Min loitering speed	150 knots (278 km/h; 173 mph)
Max rate of climb at S/L	2,600 m (8,530 ft)/min
Ceiling	3,000 m (9,850 ft)
Radius of action	13.5 nm (25 km; 15.5 miles)
Typical endurance	1 h
Max endurance	1 h 30 min
g limits	±6

FRL RAVEN 1

The Raven 1 is designed as a low-cost RPV surveillance system to provide real-time TV imagery and gathering of still photographs in daylight, and also the evaluation of alternative payloads and their roles. It was developed from the Royal Aircraft Establishment's XRAE series of equipment testbeds, the concept of which was purchased from RAE by Flight Refuelling in January 1983. First public showing of the Raven was at the Defence Exhibition in Changi, Singapore, in January 1984, and FRL initially developed it under MoD (PE) contract as an unmanned aircraft applications demonstrator.

Initial delivery, in May 1985, comprised one ground station, including radar tracker, and seven fully equipped air vehicles.

AIRFRAME: Mid-wing monoplane with pod and boom fuselage and cantilever T tail. Constant chord one-piece wing is of polystyrene foam cored GRP and obeche, bolted to fuselage. Tailplane, also attached by bolts, is of similar construction. Fuselage and integral fin are of GRP over a plywood internal structure. Wingtips and triple landing skids are frangible; wings, tailplane and propeller easily detachable.

POWER PLANT: One 1.9 kW (2.5 hp) 15 cc Webra 91 two-stroke engine, driving a two-blade pusher propeller. Max fuel capacity 2.3 litres (0.51 Imp gallon; 0.61 US gallon).

LAUNCH AND RECOVERY: Either by dedicated trailer-mounted elastic-powered rail launcher or, in suitable conditions, direct from ground by stretched elastic cable. Skid landing on smooth ground, net recovery in rough terrain.

GUIDANCE AND CONTROL: VHF or UHF radio command link via PCM (pulse code modulated) digital system using integrated autopilot. Air vehicle is continuously autostabilised, and commands can be input either manually or automatically (pre-programmed) via ground based microprocessor (HP 86 or equivalent) working co-operatively with suitable C-band or X-band tracking radar (Plessey WF3, Vega Cantley or similar). Automatic mode includes pre-programming of flight path through designated waypoints. Auto mode can be re-programmed during mission or can be interdicted manually. Three-axis aerodynamic control surfaces; outer aileron segments act as airbrakes.

Main features of the FRL Raven 1

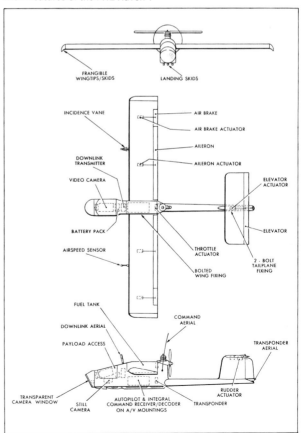

91

MISSION EQUIPMENT: Payload bay in nose contains real-time video camera, filming obliquely through nose transparency, and vertical Cosina Compact 35 mm still camera. Video downlink transmitter (1W) and telemetry operate in D band. Onboard receiver/decoder, radar transponder and nickel-cadmium battery pack. Alternative payloads can include an ECM or ESM package.

DIMENSIONS:

Wing span	2.70 m (8 ft 10.25 in)
Length overall	2.10 m (6 ft 10.75 in)
Height overall (over propeller)	0.50 m (1 ft 7.75 in)
Propeller diameter	0.36 m (1 ft 2 in)

WEIGHTS:

Typical payload	5 kg (11 lb)
Typical launching weight	15 kg (33.1 lb)

PERFORMANCE:

Normal operating speed range, ISA	40–68 knots (74–126 km/h; 46–78 mph)
Stalling speed (attainable only with autopilot disengaged)	25 knots (47 km/h; 29 mph)
Max rate of climb at S/L	209 m (685 ft)/min
Operational ceiling	2,500 m (8,200 ft)
Typical radius of operation	13.5 nm (25 km; 15.5 miles)
Max command operating range	43 nm (80 km; 50 miles)
Max endurance	2 h
g limits	+3/−1

FRL RAVEN 2

The production version of the RAE XRAE-2 (which see) is manufactured by FRL and known as the Raven 2. Three prototypes had been built by early 1987. (See Addenda.)

FRL HORNET and SEAFLY

The Hornet, first flown in October 1986, is a delta-winged general purpose target drone of GRP and plywood construction, powered by a 19.4 kW (26 hp) WAEL 342 engine driving a pusher propeller. Seafly is a sea-skimming variant (first flight January 1987) for use with close-in weapons such as Phalanx, Meroka and Goalkeeper, and can fly as close as 250 m (820 ft) from the ship under 'attack' before breaking away. Either target can be launched pneumatically or by bungee, with skid or parachute recovery. Visual and radar enhancement devices and a miss distance indicator are carried.

Two Hornet and four Seafly targets had been produced by spring 1987.

DIMENSIONS:

Wing span	2.16 m (7 ft 1 in)
Wing area	1.854 m² (19.96 sq ft)
Length overall	2.75 m (9 ft 0.25 in)
Height overall	0.90 m (2 ft 11.5 in)

XRAE-2 prototype for the FRL Raven 2 *(RAE)*

Flight Refuelling Hornet

WEIGHTS:

Max fuel	10 kg (22 lb)
Max payload	10 kg (22 lb)
Max launching weight:	
Hornet	68 kg (150 lb)
Seafly	75 kg (165 lb)

PERFORMANCE (Seafly):

Max level speed	150 knots (278 km/h; 173 mph)
Operating height range	S/L to 2,440 m (8,000 ft)
Max range	16.2 nm (30 km; 18.6 miles)
Max endurance	more than 1 h

GEC AVIONICS LIMITED
Airport Works, Rochester, Kent ME1 2XX

GEC Avionics, and its Elliott/Marconi predecessors, have been involved in remote control technology since the late 1940s, having been responsible for nearly 800 remote control autopilots for the Canberra U. Mk 10, Meteor U. Mks 15/16, and Jindivik Mks 1/2/102B/103A/103B/4A.

Phoenix represents one of several current involvements by GEC Avionics in unmanned aircraft. Others include the development of control systems (e.g. for the FRL Falconet); lightweight surveillance equipment, including TV systems; and associated data link equipment.

GEC AVIONICS MACHAN

Machan, a name derived from the old Hindi word for a treetop surveillance platform, was an unmanned flight research aircraft funded by the Ministry of Defence via the RAE Farnborough, with a substantial private-venture investment by GEC Avionics. Cranfield Institute of Technology was a major subcontractor for the airframe, power plant and digital flight control system.

The main purposes of the programme were to investigate the surveillance role, including target recognition and designation; navigation; and environmental/operational aspects. The aim was to gain a fuller understanding of the operational role of RPVs, and to provide information that would lead to cost-effective procurement and deployment of vehicles with enhanced capability.

With the emphasis on research capability, Machan was designed to simplify changes of onboard avionics and mission

GEC Avionics Machan

equipment. The air vehicle reflected not only the research aspect of this programme but also an inherent flexibility of design. For example, a 2.44 m (8 ft) span wing was designed, without control surfaces, as the basic configuration was intended to provide a highly stable aircraft with low agility. An extended-span wing, with ailerons, was installed to facilitate early testing; the ailerons could be disconnected during flight to permit evaluation of the simpler wing configuration. The diamond-shaped fuselage cross-section presented a low radar signature, and provision existed for glassfibre fuselage and propeller construction to be used. The parachute system, used for test range recovery, was housed in a detachable pod.

The first prototype Machan made its first flight at RAE Bedford on 19 February 1981. Its useful work was completed in 1984.

TYPE: Experimental research RPV.
AIRFRAME: Shoulder-wing monoplane. Wings of composite construction with light alloy spar, urethane foam core and glassfibre skin. Ailerons, installed on first three prototypes, could be disconnected in flight to allow aircraft to be evaluated in its basic form. Diamond cross-section fuselage, of mainly metal construction. Aft-mounted propulsor duct, with foam filled double metal skin, carrying three identical all-flying control surfaces and a GRP tailskid. Single vertical surface (rudder); two horizontal 'tailerons' combined functions of ailerons and elevators, operating differentially for roll control and collectively for pitch control. Alternatively, they could operate collectively only, for pitch control, when using ailerons. Mode of operation was selectable in flight.
POWER PLANT: One 13.4 kW (18 hp) NGL WAM 274-6 flat-twin engine, mounted in rear of fuselage and driving a two-blade wooden pusher fan within a propulsor duct. Four-blade wooden and glassfibre fans also evaluated. Fuel in centre fuselage tank, capacity 14 litres (3 Imp gallons; 3.6 US gallons).
LAUNCH AND RECOVERY: Launched originally by radio controlled, steerable tricycle-type dolly; later by a pneumatic catapult launch system. Normal recovery by Irvin (GB) cruciform parachute stored in detachable dorsal canister. Conventional landing on skids also demonstrated.
SYSTEMS, AVIONICS AND EQUIPMENT: 28V DC electrical system, incorporating engine-driven alternator, with central rectifier and regulator, plus a sealed 28V lead-acid battery. Digital microprocessor-based flight control system with VHF command link. Stability augmentation and attitude reference from three-axis 'strapdown' sensor package. Command and telemetry facilities capable of use in conjunction with ground station computer to investigate outer loop control

without modifying onboard equipment. Aircraft designed to permit carriage of a variety of sensors in nose bay. As first flown, experimental surveillance equipment consisted of a vibration-insulated TV camera with remotely controlled zoom, focus and aperture, but not stabilised or steerable. Gimballed, stabilised and steerable camera installed later, to permit more detailed investigation of surveillance role.

DIMENSIONS (first prototype):
Wing span	3.66 m (12 ft)
Length overall	2.13 m (7 ft)
Height overall	0.55 m (1 ft 9.5 in)

WEIGHTS (first prototype):
Weight empty	64 kg (140 lb)
Mission equipment	15 kg (33.1 lb)
Max T-O weight	82 kg (180 lb)

PERFORMANCE (first prototype, at max T-O weight):
Max level speed at S/L	115 knots (213 km/h; 132 mph)
Cruising speed	64 knots (119 km/h; 74 mph)
Stalling speed	43 knots (80 km/h; 50 mph)
Operational ceiling	305 m (1,000 ft)
Range	130 nm (241 km; 150 miles)
Endurance at cruising speed	2 h

GEC AVIONICS PHOENIX

Phoenix is the British Army's first fully equipped pilotless aircraft system for real-time remote targeting and battlefield surveillance. After entry into service, it is intended to play a part in supporting long-range artillery.

The requirement for Phoenix arose out of an earlier programme known as Supervisor (see Westland Wideye entry), which was cancelled in 1979.

To meet the Army's requirement, Phoenix had to be highly mobile, capable of quick deployment, and flexible in operation, in extreme environments and demanding conditions of electronic warfare. The complete system comprises a small air vehicle, an air-to-ground data link, a mobile ground station, and logistics vehicles for launch and recovery. The parachute-recoverable fixed-wing air vehicle carries advanced avionics and a thermal imager (stabilised infra-red camera) with a germanium zoom telescope. It is designed to have low radar, infra-red and acoustic signatures, to make it hard to detect. Modular construction and small size make it easy for soldiers to assemble, launch and recover.

Thirteen different proposals were considered initially, of which four were selected by the Ministry of Defence (Procurement Executive) for more detailed consideration. Two of them (team entries from GEC Avionics/Flight Refuelling

'A' model prototype of the GEC Avionics Phoenix

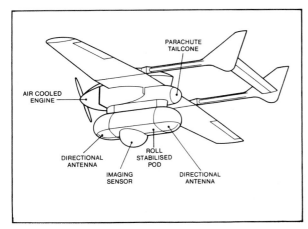

Salient features of the 'A' model Phoenix RPV

and Ferranti/Slingsby Aviation) were chosen to undergo a 15-month competitive engineering design phase, and in February 1985 this resulted in the award of a development and production contract to the GEC Avionics team. GEC Avionics is overall programme manager for the complete system; the air vehicle is manufactured under subcontract by FRL, which is also responsible for the launch and recovery systems.

The 'A' model prototype (first flown 30 May 1986) was not fitted with the thermal imager and was recovered right way up. The pre-production 'B' model, to which the description applies, has aerodynamic differences and is recovered inverted; it made its first flight in spring 1987.

TYPE: Battlefield surveillance and target acquisition RPV.

AIRFRAME: Mid-wing monoplane, with central fuselage nacelle and twin tailbooms; detachable underfuselage pod contains the mission-related avionics, including the imaging sensor and data link. Pod is gimballed to remain horizontal regardless of aircraft attitude, and is roll-stabilised to minimise demands on the sensor and the directional antenna used for the data link. Modular construction, to facilitate assembly/launch/recovery by soldiers in the field. Wing centre section integral with fuselage nacelle; tapered 'plug-in' outer panels, with ailerons. Fuselage tailcone jettisonable for parachute deployment. Crushable recovery module fairing on top of fuselage. Sweptback endplate fins, integral with tailbooms, fitted with rudders and supporting a central tailplane with one-piece elevator. Aircraft components of sandwich composite construction, for low radar signature, are manufactured by F. R. Hitco Ltd.

POWER PLANT: One 18.6 kW (25 hp) NGL WAEL 342 two-stroke flat-twin aircooled piston engine, in hinged module at front of nacelle, driving a two-blade wooden propeller. Electronic ignition and fuel injection. Fuel tank in fuselage.

LAUNCH AND RECOVERY: Hydraulic catapult launch from vehicle mounted ramp. Recovery by parachute stored in fuselage. (RPV is inverted during recovery phase, landing on crushable dorsal fairing to protect mission pod and IR sensor on impact.)

GUIDANCE AND CONTROL: Flight control and navigation systems derived from those used in Machan. They include Ferranti FS 60 vertical and FDG 60 directional gyros, and a Thorn EMI HR3 magnetic sensor for heading reference. Air vehicle commands and surveillance data are transmitted via a jamming-resistant uplink/downlink using advanced component technology. The complex ground control facility interfaces with the Army's Marconi Command and Control Systems Ltd BATES battlefield command and control system and includes a GEC Avionics digital moving map display; software consultancy for GCS by Scicon Ltd. Electronic equipment in GCS housed in Marconi Radar Systems Isolator lightweight shelter. Three-man crew for GCS.

MISSION EQUIPMENT: Ball mounting beneath ventral mission systems pod houses thermal imager, based on the GEC Avionics TICM II (thermal imaging common modules) and fitted with a Pilkington PE lens having zoom capability. Electrical power output 1 kW. Mission pod can be adapted to carry alternative payloads, such as EW, air defence

First pre-production 'B' model Phoenix battlefield reconnaissance UMA

Phoenix launch truck, produced by Flight Refuelling
(Kenneth Munson)

suppression, laser designator, communications relay, decoy, or NBC monitor, if required.

DIMENSION:
Wing span	approx 4.27 m (14 ft)

WEIGHT:
Max launching weight	approx 160 kg (353 lb)

PERFORMANCE:
Launching speed	over 70 knots (130 km/h; 81 mph)
Endurance	more than 4 h

HOER

c/o South Western Water Authority, Peninsula House, Rydon Lane, Exeter, Devonshire

HOER WASP

The Wasp was designed by Mr Jeffrey Hoer, and several examples were built. They have been used by the South Western Water Authority to photograph water movements, using a downward-looking Pentax ME camera mounted in the nose. Configuration is that of a high-wing monoplane, with twin mainwheels and a tailskid, powered by a 1.1 kW (1.5 hp) 10 cc two-stroke engine mounted on an overfuselage pylon; fuel capacity is 0.45 kg (1 lb). Ground control is by a hand-held Futaba FM transmitter, aerodynamic control by conventional three-axis moving surfaces.

Further details were requested, but not received.

DIMENSIONS:
Wing span	2.59 m (8 ft 6 in)
Wing area	0.92 m² (9.9 sq ft)

WEIGHTS:
Weight empty	3.6 kg (8 lb)
Max T-O weight	5 kg (11 lb)

PERFORMANCE:
Max level speed	39 knots (72 km/h; 45 mph)
Stalling speed	18 knots (33 km/h; 20 mph)
T-O run (wind 10 knots; 18 km/h; 11 mph)	25 m (82 ft)
Average sortie time	15 min
Max endurance	30 min

INTERGARD ELECTRONICS LTD

No. 5, 34 Frognal, Hampstead, London NW3

Last news from this company was received in 1981. At that time it had developed the following three types of unmanned aircraft:

INTERGARD IETS 7501 SHRIKE

This in-sight vehicle, for gunnery practice with small arms and anti-aircraft guns, had been ordered by two Middle Eastern countries and the Malaysian Army by 1980. It can be flown in a low-flying attack-mode, to simulate an attack directly upon the operator's gun position; as a target towing system for live weapon practice; and as a target training system for ground-to-air missiles. The complete system includes the air vehicle, self-contained transporter and optional launcher, ground control and support equipment, operator spares pack, drogue assembly, and spare drogue.

Intergard Sky-Eye

TYPE: Miniature aerial gunnery target or target-towing vehicle.

AIRFRAME: Shoulder-wing monoplane, with dihedral wings, built of balsa wood, plywood, expanded plastics foam and glassfibre. Twin-skid metal landing gear.

POWER PLANT: One 32–56 cc spark ignition or glow ignition two-stroke piston engine, driving a small-diameter two-blade propeller. Petrol/oil or methanol/oil mixture fuel, depending upon engine chosen.

LAUNCH AND RECOVERY: Aircraft can be launched from a four-wheeled drop dolly or bungee launcher, or can take off conventionally with skid landing gear. Recovered by conventional landing on skids.

GUIDANCE AND CONTROL: Radio command guidance system, operating on one of 12 spot frequencies in 27 MHz band with a bandwidth of approx 25 kHz. Different frequency required for each system if two or more targets are flown at the same time within radio control range of each other (approx 2.2 nm; 4 km; 2.5 miles). Aerodynamic control by rudder and elevators. Electronic fail-safe device automatically closes engine throttle if aircraft is accidentally flown beyond visual range or suffers a radio link malfunction.

DIMENSIONS:
Wing span	3.05 m (10 ft)
Length overall	2.31 m (7 ft 7 in)

WEIGHT:
Launching weight	14 kg (31 lb)

PERFORMANCE:
Max speed (depending on engine fitted)	80–120 knots (148–222 km/h; 92–138 mph)
Cruising speed	60 knots (111 km/h; 69 mph)
Operating altitude, and range	limited only by operator's visual range
Flight duration	up to 50 min

INTERGARD IETS 7502 PIPIT

Pipit, designed to train radio control operators to use the larger Shrike, is of generally similar configuration, construction and operation to the latter vehicle. Being smaller, it has a less powerful engine (1.1 kW; 1.5 hp 10 cc glow plug ignition type), and has twin landing skids attached directly to the underside of the fuselage.

DIMENSIONS:
Wing span	2.01 m (6 ft 7 in)
Length overall	1.22 m (4 ft)

WEIGHT:
Launching weight	3 kg (6.6 lb)

PERFORMANCE:
Max speed	60 knots (111 km/h; 69 mph)
Cruising speed	25 knots (46 km/h; 29 mph)
Operating altitude, and range	limited only by operator's visual range
Flight duration	up to 30 min

INTERGARD GTS 7901 SKY-EYE

Ordered by RAE Farnborough and customers in two countries in the Middle East, Sky-Eye was developed as a close support information relay vehicle for use by forward and front line troops. It was designed to provide, directly to a command headquarters or forward artillery control centre, information about the deployment and movement of hostile troops or armour. Alternatively, by removing the TV camera and transmitter, a chaff dispenser or radar jammer can be installed for use against enemy ground radar sites; or, for use in conjunction with close-support aircraft, a laser designator can be fitted for accurate target identification.

Other applications include TV surveillance of urban areas, border surveillance, and forest fire location and assessment.

TYPE: Multi-purpose surveillance/ECM mini-RPV.
AIRFRAME: High-wing monoplane, with pod and boom fuselage and sweptback fin and rudder; non-swept dihedral wings and non-swept tailplane. Construction of balsa wood, plywood, expanded plastics foam, glassfibre and aluminiun alloy. Rudder and full-span elevator standard; ailerons optional.
POWER PLANT: As for Shrike, but installed at rear of fuselage pod to drive a pusher propeller.
LAUNCH AND RECOVERY: As for Shrike.
GUIDANCE AND CONTROL: Similar to that for Shrike. For flight programmes in areas of high air turbulence an electrostatic stabilisation system, using a slightly radioactive polonium element at each wingtip, can be installed for improved pitch and roll control. Ailerons are required if this system is fitted, since for it to be effective the RPV must initially be unstable in flight.
MISSION EQUIPMENT: TV camera and transmitter standard; these can be replaced, according to mission, by a multi-frame 35 mm still camera, 8 mm cine camera, chaff dispenser, radar jammer, laser designator or other sensor. Electronic fail-safe throttle closure/engine stop, as in Shrike.

DIMENSIONS:
Wing span	2.44 m (8 ft)
Length overall	2.03 m (6 ft 8 in)

WEIGHT:
Launching weight	12 kg (26.5 lb)

PERFORMANCE:
Max speed (depending on engine fitted)	
	60–80 knots (111–148 km/h; 69–92 mph)
Cruising speed	30 knots (56 km/h; 35 mph)
Operating altitude	
	limited only by operator's visual range
Range	
	limited only by operator's visual range, but guidance system range is up to 5.4 nm (10 km; 6.2 miles) with high-power transmitter
Flight duration	up to 45 min

MILTRAIN LIMITED

West Wing, Building C2, Fairoaks Airport, Chobham, Woking, Surrey GU24 8HX

MILTRAIN FLYRT B

Designed and first flown in 1984, the Flyrt B was put into production in 1985.

Miltrain Flyrt-B targets with ground equipment boxes

TYPE: Recoverable airborne small arms target system.
AIRFRAME: Low-wing monoplane of double-delta planform, with triangular fin; no rudder or horizontal tail surfaces. Constructed from composite materials, laminated wood, polyurethane high density foam and epoxy resins.
POWER PLANT: One 0.63 kW (0.85 hp) single-cylinder piston engine, driving a two-blade composite (nylon/glassfibre) propeller. Integral fuel tank in forward fuselage.
LAUNCH AND RECOVERY: Ramp or hand-launch, at user's option. Recovery by parachute on command of operator; target can also be recovered safely under operator command, on to a suitable site, without deploying parachute system.
GUIDANCE AND CONTROL: Radio command guidance system, with three servos for precise control by operator within 1.1 nm (2 km; 1.2 miles) of control site. Full span elevons for pitch and roll control; automatic yaw compensation and variable power setting.

DIMENSIONS:
Wing span	0.81 m (2 ft 8 in)
Wing area	0.32 m² (3.47 sq ft)
Length overall	1.22 m (4 ft)
Fuselage: Max width	10.8 cm (4.25 in)

WEIGHTS:
Basic operating weight empty	2.4 kg (5.3 lb)
Max fuel	0.34 kg (0.75 lb)
Max launching weight	3 kg (6.6 lb)

PERFORMANCE:
Never-exceed speed	150 knots (278 km/h; 173 mph)
Max level speed at S/L	110 knots (204 km/h; 127 mph)
Min flying speed	25 knots (47 km/h; 29 mph)
Operating height: min	3 m (10 ft)
max	2,000 m (6,560 ft)
Endurance	30 min
g limit	+10

MINISTRY OF DEFENCE (MoD)
Whitehall, London SW1A 2HB

The Royal Navy has a requirement for a sea-skimming aerial target system to be used in conjunction with the Goalkeeper close-in weapon system being fitted in Type 22 Batch 3 frigates now being built. A number of proposals were under consideration during 1986, known cases having the names Sea Falcon (FRL ASAT), Seafly (TTL with FRL), Sea Star (ML Aviation) and Seawitch (British Aerospace). No decision on a selected system had been made up to the spring of 1987. At that time the possibility of a collaborative programme with NATO was being explored.

The MoD is also considering options for a full size aerial target aircraft which could be used in connection with ASRAAM and Rapier missile systems. The need for such a target arose following abandonment of the Sea Vixen drone programme (see FRL entry), and seems most likely to be met either by purchase of QF-100 Super Sabres from the USA (see Flight Systems Inc entry) or by drone conversion of retired RAF Lightning jet fighters.

The Royal Air Force has stated a requirement (Air Staff Target 1232, issued in 1985) for a drone system, for entry into service in the mid-1990s, fitted with an anti-radar seeker to suppress enemy air defence units in a battlefield area. The drones may also be required to serve as decoys. The possibility of combining AST 1232 with the West German DAR programme was being explored in 1986–87.

ML AVIATION COMPANY LTD (Flight Systems Division)

White Waltham Aerodrome, Maidenhead, Berkshire SL6 3JG

Founded in the mid-1930s, ML Aviation has design approval for aeroplanes and rotorcraft up to a design gross weight of 6,000 kg (13,227 lb). Its aerospace activities include the design and manufacture of RPVs, aero-structures, bomb carriers and release units, ground handling equipment, and electronic equipment and test sets.

ML's Flight Systems Division activities include the design and development of RPV systems, and helicopter rotor test equipment.

ML AVIATION SPRITE

The Sprite is a private venture RPH which derives its name from the initial letters of the six principal roles for which it is intended: surveillance, patrol, reconnaissance, intelligence gathering, target designation, and electronic warfare. Basic role envisaged is that of a 'pop-up' battlefield surveillance RPV; other military, naval and civil uses are also foreseen.

Design began in January 1981, and the first untethered flight was made in January 1983. Trials are continuing with the three prototype Sprites. Five others are under construction and were to begin flying in mid-1987.

A large number of military and civilian authorities have expressed interest in the Sprite, and flight demonstrations have been given in the UK, USA and Europe.

TYPE: Multi-role mini-RPH.

AIRFRAME: Two two-blade coaxial counter-rotating rotors, with blades attached to hub by teetering hinges; no rotor brake. Blades are of glassfibre composite construction, with a modified Göttingen aerofoil section. Mechanical transmission via oil lubricated spur gear; rotor/engine rpm ratio 1:5. Symmetrical planform body of glassfibre and carbonfibre, with sandwich construction frames, carefully shaped and constructed to offer minimal radar, thermal, noise and optical signatures. Divided internally into four compartments for power plant, fuel tanks, guidance systems and sensors. Landing gear comprises four radar-transparent non-retractable glassfibre legs.

POWER PLANT: Two 4.5 kW (6 hp) MLH 2/88 two-stroke flat-twin engines. Petrol/oil fuel mixture carried in two

ML Aviation Sprites, with and without rotor head fairing

Sprite with current Land-Rover transport and control vehicle

plastics tanks, combined capacity approx 8 litres (1.75 Imp gallons; 2.1 US gallons). Sprite can be maintained airborne on only one engine, thus providing a full 'one engine out' capability. This is considered essential for civil operations.

LAUNCH AND RECOVERY: Vertical take-off and landing, without additional aids.

GUIDANCE AND CONTROL: Skyleader PCM radio command system permits direct ground control through the fully automatic flight control system. Sprite can be pre-programmed for autonomous flight or automatic recovery to base in the event of loss of control link.

MISSION EQUIPMENT: Two 28V 500W alternators provide power for aircraft functioning and for sensors. The sensor pack is one quadrant of the airframe and can be changed easily as required. Many different sensors can be installed, including stabilised TV or infra-red cameras, low light level TV, laser target designator, chemical sensors, elint and ECM. The experimental aircraft are currently fitted (1987) with a black and white CCD TV camera with 5:1 zoom lens, and a Thorn EMI Electronics laser altimeter.

DIMENSIONS:
Rotor diameter (each)	1.60 m (5 ft 3 in)
Body diameter (max)	0.65 m (2 ft 1.5 in)
Height to top of rotor head	0.90 m (2 ft 11.5 in)

WEIGHTS:
Weight empty	28 kg (61.7 lb)
Max fuel	6 kg (13.2 lb)
Sensor pack (max)	6 kg (13.2 lb)
Max T-O and landing weight	40 kg (88.2 lb)

PERFORMANCE (at max T-O weight):
Max level speed (estimated)	70 knots (130 km/h; 80 mph)
Max cruising and econ cruising speed	60 knots (111 km/h; 69 mph)
Climb rate at optimum speed of 45 knots (83 km/h; 52 mph)	366 m (1,200 ft)/min
Normal operating height range	250–500 m (820–1,640 ft)
Operating ceiling	2,440 m (8,000 ft)
Maintainable height on one engine	2,440 m (8,000 ft)
Typical mission radius	17 nm (32 km; 20 miles)
Endurance (mixed mission)	2 h

RCS GUIDED WEAPONS SYSTEMS

This company, a division of Radio Control Specialists Ltd, manufactured a wide range of small, low-cost radio or optically guided target drones and RPVs in the 1970s, offering payload capabilities up to 13.6 kg (30 lb) and visual control ranges of up to 2.7 nm (5 km; 3.1 miles). Last news of RCS was in early 1979, at which time the following types of UMA were in production:

RCS FALCON

Generally similar to the Merlin (which see) but larger, with a greater payload, longer endurance, and a 7.5 kW (10 hp) engine. Launch, guidance and recovery as for Merlin. Three versions known, as follows:

RCS4012 Target System. For training air defence weapon crews to acquire and track low level high-speed aircraft. Able to carry X- and S-band radar enhancement devices. Facility for trailing a 3.05 m (10 ft) towed target on a 152 m (500 ft) cable. Supplied to Libyan government in 1973–74.

RCS4015 Camera System. For short-range aerial reconnaissance; same equipment as Merlin, including optional processing/printing kit. Target location by photo/map comparison. Supplied to Libyan government 1973–74.

RCS4017 Composite Target/Camera System. Combines facilities of RCS4012 and 4015.

DIMENSIONS:
Wing span	2.13 m (7 ft)
Length overall	1.98 m (6 ft 6 in)

WEIGHTS:
Payload	5.4 kg (12 lb)
Max launching weight	16.3 kg (36 lb)

PERFORMANCE:
Max level speed	110 knots (204 km/h; 127 mph)
Max controllable range (optical)	2.7 nm (5 km; 3.1 miles)
Endurance	45 min

RCS HERON and HERON HS

This high-wing monoplane RPV is powered by a 7.5 kW (10 hp) engine. Fuel capacity is 4.5 litres (1 Imp gallon; 1.2 US gallons). Although designed specifically for target work, payload capacity and 0.03 m³ (1 cu ft) payload bay confer suitability for other applications, and up to 5 kg (11 lb) of total payload can consist of pylon-mounted underwing stores such as flares or small bombs. A good X-band radar signature is provided for tracking; launch, guidance and recovery as for Merlin. Ordered by British Army.

Heron HS is a high-speed version, improved aerodynamically by reducing wing thickness and area, introducing linear taper, and eliminating wing struts and pylons. Wheeled landing gear replaced by sprung metal skid and catapult launching points; alternative launch from take-off dolly, permitting a 25 per cent increase in payload.

Both versions have provisions for a laser gun hit simulation system, in which hits are recorded on an airframe counter and marked with a small flare or flash when a hit is made.

DIMENSIONS:
Wing span:	
Heron	3 m (9 ft 10 in)
Heron HS	2.44 m (8 ft)
Length overall (both)	2.13 m (7 ft)
Fuselage: Max width (both)	25.4 cm (10 in)

WEIGHTS:
Max payload:	
catapult launch:	
Heron	6.8 kg (15 lb)
Heron HS	4.5 kg (10 lb)
ground T-O: Heron	13.6 kg (30 lb)
Max weight:	
catapult launch	15.4 kg (34 lb)
ground T-O	24 kg (53 lb)

RCS Falcon delta winged target

RCS Heron 'model aircraft' target

Max level speed:	
Heron	104 knots (193 km/h; 120 mph)
Heron HS	122 knots (225 km/h; 140 mph)
Max controllable range (optical):	
both	2.7 nm (5 km; 3.1 miles)
Endurance (both)	30 min

RCS MERLIN

The Merlin system consists of a delta-shaped 'flying wing' drone, built of polystyrene foam with a plywood skin, powered by a 10 cc piston engine, and fitted with a tricycle landing gear. A six-function pulse width modulated VHF guidance system with RF output of 5 W is used. Three known versions are:

RCS4018 Target System. For training air defence weapon crews to acquire and track target aircraft. Able to carry X- and S-band radar enhancement devices. A 2.13 m (7 ft) drogue target can be towed on a 152 m (500 ft) cable for live firing work.

RCS4019 Camera System. For short-range aerial reconnaissance with radio triggered Robot f/2.8 35 mm camera at heights up to 915 m (3,000 ft). Optional kit for rapid film processing and printing.

RCS4020 Composite Target/Camera System. Combines facilities of RCS4018 and 4019.

LAUNCH AND RECOVERY: T-O from ground or launch from system launcher. Recovered by orthodox landing.

DIMENSIONS:
Wing span	1.45 m (4 ft 9 in)
Length overall	1.22 m (4 ft)

WEIGHTS:
Payload	1.4 kg (3 lb)
Max T-O/launching weight	4.8 kg (10.5 lb)

PERFORMANCE:
Max level speed	78 knots (145 km/h; 90 mph)
Max controllable range (optical)	1.6 nm (3 km; 1.9 miles)
Endurance	30 min

RCS Merlin target

RCS Mossette and ground control equipment

RCS MOSSETTE

Mossette is a re-usable sweptwing target drone with an in-flight profile similar to that of mid-1970s wire-guided anti-tank missiles, and was developed to train operators of helicopter and vehicle launched missiles of that type. Powered by a 6 cc engine, it was launched from a system catapult and recovered in a retrieval net; guidance system was as for the Merlin.

A smokeless flare was fitted at the base of the underfin to enable the trainee operator to align Mossette with the target, thus realistically simulating the operational missile. Nosecone was expendable, being replaced for each new exercise. System catching net was erected immediately in front of the target.

DIMENSIONS:
Wing span	1.22 m (4 ft)
Length overall	1.07 m (3 ft 6 in)

WEIGHT:
Max launching weight	1.8 kg (4 lb)

PERFORMANCE:
Max level speed	69 knots (128 km/h; 80 mph)
Stalling speed	18 knots (33 km/h; 21 mph)
Max controllable range (optical)	1.6 nm (3 km; 1.9 miles)
Endurance	20 min

RCS ROTARY-WING DRONE

This small rigid-rotor target drone was intended primarily to train operators of radar controlled missiles. It took off and landed like a conventional helicopter, using tricycle landing gear, and was powered by a 0.9 kW (1.2 hp) 10 cc piston engine. Fuel capacity was 0.5 litre (0.10 Imp gallon; 0.12 US gallon).

GUIDANCE AND CONTROL: Six-channel proportional radio control (four for pitch/roll/yaw/throttle and two for camera control).

MISSION EQUIPMENT: Choice of half-frame (f/2.8) or full frame (f/2.5) 35 mm camera with automatic film advance. Heavy duty 12 V electric starter optional.

DIMENSIONS:
Main rotor diameter	1.63 m (5 ft 4 in)
Tail rotor diameter	0.36 m (1 ft 2 in)
Length overall	1.83 m (6 ft)

Small rotary-wing drone built by RCS

WEIGHTS:
Weight empty	5 kg (11 lb)
Payload	0.9 kg (2 lb)

PERFORMANCE:
Max level speed	61 knots (113 km/h; 70 mph)
Range	0.9 nm (1.6 km; 1 mile)
Endurance	20 min

RCS ROTARY-WING RPV

Much larger than the rotary-wing target drone, this surveillance mini-RPV was of entirely different configuration. Two versions were tested: one with twin engines and an 18 kg (40 lb) payload, and a single-engined version with a 7.5 kW (10 hp) two-stroke. Details apply to the latter aircraft.

LAUNCH AND RECOVERY: Conventional helicopter T-O and landing, using wide-track tubular skid landing gear.
MISSION EQUIPMENT: Standard payload of ground surveillance TV system, cameras, sensors and other equipment. Gyro-stabilisation optional.

DIMENSIONS:
Main rotor diameter	2.29 m (7 ft 6 in)
Length overall	1.83 m (6 ft)

WEIGHTS:
Payload	8.5 kg (18.7 lb)
Max T-O weight	20 kg (44 lb)

PERFORMANCE:
Max level speed	32 knots (60 km/h; 37 mph)
Guidance/control radius	2.7 nm (5 km; 3.1 miles)
Endurance	1 h

RCS rotary-wing reconnaissance RPV

RCS SATS

SATS (Small Arms Target System) was controlled with a hand-held transmitter and intended for use as a 'live' target for infantry anti-aircraft firing practice with rifles and sub-machine guns.

DIMENSIONS:
Wing span	2.21 m (7 ft 3 in)
Length	1.98 m (6 ft 6 in)

WEIGHTS:
Payload	0.7 kg (1.5 lb)
Launching weight	4.1 kg (9 lb)

PERFORMANCE:
Max level speed	74 knots (137 km/h; 85 mph)
Endurance	40 min

RCS SWIFT

Swift was a photographic or target drone of sweptwing aircraft configuration, having a glassfibre fuselage and wings of plywood with a styrofoam core. Power plant is not known.

LAUNCH AND RECOVERY: Launched from specially designed toggle action catapult.
GUIDANCE AND CONTROL: Flown along fixed heading at fixed climb angle, using a tripod-mounted high-power radio transmitter (range 5.4 nm; 10 km; 6.2 miles) and optical sight. Also capable of being operated with a six-channel hand-held transmitter.
MISSION EQUIPMENT: 35 mm camera, barometric trip switch and marker flash.

DIMENSIONS:
Wing span	1.83 m (6 ft)
Length overall	0.91 m (3 ft)

WEIGHTS:
Payload	0.9 kg (2 lb)
Max launching weight	4.5 kg (10 lb)

PERFORMANCE:
Max level speed	
	100–120 knots (185–222 km/h; 115–138 mph)
Range	4.3 nm (8 km; 5 miles)
Endurance	30 min

RCS TELEDRONE II

Intended as a real-time TV surveillance drone, the Teledrone had an airframe of glassfibre, plywood, expanded foam and duralumin. It could be powered by a single 4.5 kW (6 hp) or two 1.5 kW (2 hp) piston engines, and was launched either by catapult or from a take-off dolly. Recovery was by parachute or by skid landing.

GUIDANCE AND CONTROL: Eight-channel VHF radio control normally; 20 W power amplifier optional.
MISSION EQUIPMENT: TV camera standard; options included chaff dispenser, ECM, radar augmentation or radar transponders.

DIMENSIONS:
Wing span	2.90 m (9 ft 6 in)
Length overall	1.98 m (6 ft 6 in)

WEIGHTS:
Weight empty	10 kg (22 lb)
Fuel	3.85 kg (8.5 lb)
Normal payload (incl fuel)	9 kg (20 lb)
Max T-O/launching weight	20.5 kg (45 lb)

RCS Teledrone twin-engined UMA

PERFORMANCE:

Max level speed	90 knots (167 km/h; 104 mph)
Cruising speed	65 knots (120 km/h; 75 mph)
Max operating altitude	3.050 m (10,000 ft)
Max range	5.4 nm (10 km; 6.2 miles)
Max endurance	2 h

RCS TRAINING DRONE

Designed to train users of operational drones and RPVs, the RCS4030 was broadly similar to the Heron externally, but slightly smaller.

POWER PLANT: One 10 cc piston engine with two-blade propeller.

LAUNCH AND RECOVERY: As for Merlin.

GUIDANCE AND CONTROL: Six-channel proportional radio control, designed for use with standard RCS ground control system.

DIMENSIONS:

Wing span	2.13 m (7 ft)
Length overall	1.83 m (6 ft)

WEIGHTS:

Weight empty	5 kg (11 lb)
Payload	1.8 kg (4 lb)

PERFORMANCE:

Max level speed	52 knots (97 km/h; 60 mph)
Endurance	35 min

ROYAL AIRCRAFT ESTABLISHMENT (RAE)

Radio and Navigation Department (RN2 Division), Building Q146, Farnborough, Hampshire GU14 6TD

RAE XRAE-1

The XRAE-1 was designed originally for homing head trials in 1981; it has also carried video and still cameras, and electronic warfare payloads. The concept was acquired in 1983 by Flight Refuelling (see Raven 1 entry under FR heading).

TYPE: Experimental mini-RPV.

AIRFRAME: Mid-wing monoplane with pod and boom fuselage and T tail. Tapered wings and non-tapered tailplane are of foam-cored GRP and obeche; fuselage is of GRP or Kevlar over a plywood or Kevlar internal structure. Wings and tailplane attached by bolts; with propeller, they can be detached easily for transportation and storage. Landing skids under fuselage.

POWER PLANT: One 1.9 kW (2.5 hp) 15 cc Webra 91 or OS 90 two-stroke engine, driving a two-blade pusher propeller. Max fuel capacity 1.5 litres (0.3 Imp gallon; 0.4 US gallon).

LAUNCH AND RECOVERY: Either by dedicated trailer-mounted launcher or by stretched elastic cable from suitable sites. Skid landing.

GUIDANCE AND CONTROL: Radio command link via RAE autopilot. Air vehicle is continuously autostabilised, and commands can be input either manually or automatically (pre-programmed) via ground-based microprocessor working co-operatively with Plessey WF3 X-band tracking radar. Automatic mode includes pre-programming of flight path through designated waypoints. Auto mode can be re-programmed during mission or interdicted manually. Three-axis aerodynamic control surfaces.

MISSION EQUIPMENT: Payload bay in nose can contain real-time JVC video camera, filming obliquely through nose transparency, and vertical Cosina Compact 35 mm still camera. Video transmitter (1W) and PCM telemetry operate in D-band. Onboard receiver/decoder, transponder and nickel-cadmium battery.

DIMENSIONS:

Wing span	2.70 m (8 ft 10.25 in)
Length overall	2.10 m (6 ft 10.75 in)
Height overall (over propeller)	0.50 m (1 ft 7.75 in)
Propeller diameter	0.36 m (1 ft 2 in)

WEIGHTS:

Typical payload	2.5 kg (5.5 lb)
Typical launching weight	17.5 kg (38.5 lb)

PERFORMANCE (typical):

Operating speed range	32–65 knots (60–120 km/h; 37–74 mph)
Rate of climb at S/L	152 m (500 ft)/min
Endurance	1 h

RAE XRAE-2

Design of the XRAE-2 began in late 1982, and the first flight was made in October 1984. In general terms, it is a scaled-up development of XRAE-1, and its original purpose was to carry a British Aerospace miniature infra-red linescan (MIRLS) to demonstrate the feasibility of a low-cost system. It can also carry a Barr & Stroud MIRLS, an ECM or ESM payload, or chaff. Payloads under development in 1985 included Marconi Defence Systems passive and active EW systems. Equipped with passive ESM, the RPV can be pre-programmed to carry out surveillance in areas of interest and pass the processed data direct to the ground by data link. Control of the onboard system can also be exercised by the same method. A range of expendable jammers is also being developed by MDS; these, too, are suitable for use in a ground environment.

Thirteen prototypes were ordered, of which 11 had been completed by early 1986. The slightly modified production version is being manufactured by Flight Refuelling with the name Raven 2.

TYPE: Experimental surveillance and electronic warfare RPV.

AIRFRAME: Configuration generally as for XRAE-1. Wings have NACA 4415 or Wortmann FX-63-137 section, 2°30′ incidence and 2° sweepback at quarter-chord, but no dihedral or anhedral, and are of Kevlar and GRP with a foam core. On trailing edge between each wingtip and aileron are sheet metal upper and lower surface airbrakes. Fuselage is a glassfibre or Kevlar monocoque, reinforced with foam or Nomex honeycomb and incorporating an integral fin. Movable surfaces are powered by electric servos; later version will have electrically actuated variable tailplane incidence. Fixed energy absorbing skids under fuselage. Interchangeable nose modules, of basically same shape but differing in size depending upon volume of payload required.

POWER PLANT: One 2.2 kW (3 hp) Quadra 50 cc single-cylinder or 3.7 kW (5 hp) Horner 70 cc two-cylinder two-stroke engine, driving a two-blade pusher propeller. Fuel tank in fuselage beneath wing centre-section, capacity 5.56 litres (1.22 Imp gallons; 1.46 US gallons). External fuel tanks under development.

LAUNCH AND RECOVERY: As for XRAE-1. Alternative recovery can be made by 5.5 m (18 ft) diameter GQ cruciform parachute.

GUIDANCE AND CONTROL: As for XRAE-1.

MISSION EQUIPMENT: Autopilot, telecommand receiver, payload information transmitter and telemetry transmitter. Chaff cartridges can be fitted to fuselage sides underwing. Engine-driven alternator and two 2Ah 28V DC batteries. For other payloads, see opening paragraph.

DIMENSIONS:
Wing span	3.62 m (11 ft 10.5 in)
Wing area	1.659 m² (17.86 sq ft)
Length overall:	
standard	2.58 m (8 ft 5.5 in)
alternative	2.755 m (9 ft .5 in)
	or 2.845 m (9 ft 4 in)
Fuselage: Max width	0.50 m (1 ft 7.75 in)
Height overall	0.70 m (2 ft 3.5 in)
Propeller diameter (either engine)	0.51 m (1 ft 8 in)
Payload compartment volume (standard)	
	0.033 m³ (1.16 cu ft)

WEIGHTS:
Max fuel	5 kg (11 lb)
Max payload	10 kg (22 lb)
Max launching weight	40 kg (88 lb)

PERFORMANCE (estimated):
Never-exceed speed	104 knots (193 km/h; 120 mph)
Max level speed	69 knots (129 km/h; 80 mph)
Max cruising speed	61 knots (113 km/h; 70 mph)
Econ cruising speed	52 knots (96 km/h; 60 mph)
Stalling speed, engine idling	35 knots (65 km/h; 40 mph)
Max rate of climb at S/L	183 m (600 ft)/min
Ceiling	1,525 m (5,000 ft)
Range with max fuel	61 nm (113 km; 70 miles)

SHORT BROTHERS PLC (Missile Systems Division)
Montgomery Road, Belfast BT6 9HN, Northern Ireland

SHORTS SKYSPY

This remotely controlled VTOL aerial reconnaissance vehicle was developed by Shorts as a private venture for use in military battlefield or naval applications. Its small size and low power produced low radar and infra-red signatures, low noise level, low gust response, and a very small visual silhouette. Surveillance could be carried out at all angles of attack between conventional forward flight and hover mode.

A wide variety of applications was envisaged, including army reconnaissance; naval over-the-horizon viewing; weapon control and delivery, including the capability of providing a command link for over-the-horizon weapon control systems; target spotting; coastguard surveillance; border patrol and police duties; fishery protection; search and rescue operations; forest fire spotting; emergency relief and medical support service; electronic countermeasures (ECM); and, mounting an airborne laser, as a guidance facility for missiles.

A development programme involving partially tethered hovering and forward flight trials began in 1975, and by 1978, when the programme ended, more than 100 hours of tethered and free flight trials had been completed.

Shorts Skyspy, with and without fairing over payload module

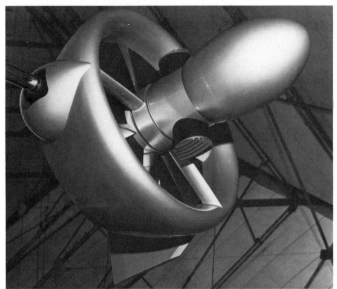

TYPE: Remotely controlled VTOL aerial reconnaissance and surveillance drone.

AIRFRAME: Basic vehicle consisted of a centrebody carrying engine, fuel, and control and stabilisation actuators; a low-pressure fan; and an axially symmetrical duct connected to centrebody by an engine mounting spider and stators. Aerofoil surfaces, for pitch, roll/yaw, and rotational stabilisation and control, were set across duct exit to integrate in part with low aspect ratio wings located on exterior of duct. Centrebody comprised major part of vehicle weight, duct being a simple, light but rigid structure. Equipment/payload pod fairing located on outer surface of duct. Autopilot and power supply equipment at rear, in wall of duct.

POWER PLANT: Lift and propulsive thrust obtained by vectoring gross thrust output of a single-stage multi-blade fixed-pitch low-pressure ducted fan, powered by a two-stroke inline engine of 48.4 kW (65 hp) and augmented by aerodynamic force components generated on the duct surfaces and intake lip.

LAUNCH AND RECOVERY: A launching arm supported vehicle in T-O attitude until it achieved required vertical thrust and lifted free. Although Skyspy could land vertically on level ground, a technique to cater for rough terrain was developed, using a 6.1 × 6.1 m (20 × 20 ft) landing net which could be set up in virtually any type of terrain or on board ship. The vehicle was brought to the hover and then descended smoothly under power into the net, to be retrieved and refuelled for its next mission.

MISSION EQIPMENT: Payload capability for TV camera, sensors, automatic data-gathering and other equipment, installed in pod fairing on outer forward surface of duct. Skyspy was intended to be flown under remote control to chosen surveillance area, where it could hover over a stationary target (or track a moving one) and relay positional details in real time, using secure data links, to a ground or ship based controller.

DIMENSIONS:

Overall diameter	1.08 m (3 ft 6.5 in)
Fan diameter	0.85 m (2 ft 9.5 in)
Height overall	1.37 m (4 ft 6 in)

WEIGHTS:

Weight empty	85 kg (187 lb)
Payload	20 kg (44 lb)
Fuel	25 kg (55 lb)
Max T-O weight	130 kg (286 lb)

PERFORMANCE (typical):

Max level speed	102 knots (190 km/h; 118 mph)
Ceiling	1,825 m (6,000 ft)
Endurance	1 h 30 min

SHORTS MATS-B

First flown in about 1975, MATS-B (Military Aircraft Target System) is a compact, highly manoeuvrable radio-controlled aerial target for use in target tracking, training and practice firings of close-range missiles and guns. Acceptance trials were completed in January 1977, at the Ministry of Defence missile range at Benbecula in the Hebrides, and the target is now in production against a MoD contract.

TYPE: Recoverable aerial target.

AIRFRAME: High-wing monoplane configuration. Fuselage built of metal and GRP. Polyurethane foam filled glassfibre wings, fin and tailplane.

POWER PLANT: One 13.43 kW (18 hp) NGL WAM 274-6 two-cylinder two-stroke engine, driving a two-blade propeller. Fuel tank in centre of fuselage.

LAUNCH AND RECOVERY: Launched pneumatically from simple two-wheel launcher, with compressed air capacity for 20 launches. Visual control sight with binoculars assists controller in flying the drone visually to over 5 km range and to enable repeatable flight paths to be flown. Recovery by parachute or by conventional landing, using fuselage underfairing as a skid. Launching and flight can be carried out into headwinds of up to 25 knots (46 km/h; 29 mph).

GUIDANCE AND CONTROL: Seven-channel (pitch, roll, throttle, trim, height hold, visual enhancement) radio command system (hand-held transmitter), in the 68MHz band. Aerodynamic control by servo-operated ailerons and all-moving tailplane. Roll stabilisation and automatic (barometric) height control optional.

MISSION EQUIPMENT: Underwing equipment pods for visual enhancement flashing strobe light or smoke flares. Reflector in fuselage for radar signature enhancement. Stabilisation sensors in each wing, near tip. Parachute in forward fuselage, deployed either by pilot demand or automatically in event of engine, power supply or radio control failure.

DIMENSIONS:

Wing span	3.35 m (11 ft)
Length overall	2.44 m (8 ft)

WEIGHTS:

Payload	6.8 kg (15 lb)
Max launching weight	48.5 kg (107 lb)

PERFORMANCE:

Max level speed	110 knots (203 km/h; 126 mph)
Range	over 2.7 nm (5 km; 3.1 miles)
Min endurance	45 min

Shorts MATS-B being recovered by parachute

SHORTS SKEET Mk 1

The Skeet, now in service with the British Army and some overseas operators, provides a realistic, quick-reaction and cost-effective aerial target for use in both target tracking and practice firings of guns and close range weapon systems such as Blowpipe. It combines simplicity with high manoeuvrability and ease of operation, but offers the additional advantages of higher speed, greater range and better payload, and has a maximum endurance nearly twice that of the earlier MATS-B. The Skeet completed acceptance trials in September 1979, and was in production until 1986 for the British Army and for export.

TYPE: Aerial target system for use with close range weapons.

AIRFRAME: Modular construction high-wing monoplane. Fuselage of metal and GRP. Polyurethane foam filled glassfibre wings, fin and tailplane.

POWER PLANT: One 13.4 kW (18 hp) NGL WAM 274-6 274 cc two-cylinder two-stroke engine.

LAUNCH AND RECOVERY: Launched pneumatically from self-contained two-wheel trailer, having a capacity of eight launches from one charging, or from launch rail mounted on a four-wheel truck. Recovery by Irvin (GB) cruciform parachute (in forward fuselage), or by conventional landing using fuselage underfairing as a skid. Parachute can be deployed either by pilot demand, or automatically following failure of engine, power supply or radio link. Launches can be carried out in crosswinds of up to 25 knots (46 km/h; 29 mph), and aircraft can be operated from land or on board ship.

GUIDANCE AND CONTROL: Eight-channel (pitch, roll, throttle, smoke generator firing, height hold, and three spare) radio command system (hand held transmitter and 10 W rf amplifier), in the 68 MHz band. Height hold uses a simple barometric device to maintain aircraft at desired altitude. Visual control sight with binoculars to assist pilot in flying the aircraft visually to over 2.7 nm (5 km; 3.1 miles) range and to enable repeatable tracks to be flown.

MISSION EQUIPMENT: X-band radar reflector in rear fuselage. Sixteen 40 s smoke generators fitted in landing skid. Two wing-mounted pods can carry, for example, Simflak for training, and the fuselage can accept either a miss distance indicator or a transponder. An autopilot, complete with heading device, is under development for out-of-sight operation. An automatic parachute release can be provided. Skeet can accept mission equipment loads of up to 18 kg (40 lb) of a non-target nature (e.g. for surveillance and tactical aggression).

Shorts Skeet Mk 2 on its rail launcher

DIMENSIONS:
Wing span	3.35 m (11 ft)
Wing area	1.53 m² (16.5 sq ft)
Length overall, incl MDI aerial	2.72 m (8 ft 11 in)
Height overall	0.45 m (1 ft 5.75 in)

WEIGHTS:
Basic aircraft, empty	42 kg (92.5 lb)
Parachute pack	4.1 kg (9 lb)
Fuel	9.1 kg (20 lb)
Mission equipment (normal)	8 kg (17.5 lb)
Max launching weight	68 kg (150 lb)

PERFORMANCE:
Max level speed	130 knots (241 km/h; 150 mph)
Stalling speed	50 knots (93 km/h; 58 mph)
Max in-sight range	2.7 nm (5 km; 3.1 miles)
Max range under control	more than 5.4 nm (10 km; 6.2 miles)
Endurance at max speed	1 h 15 min

SHORTS SKEET Mk 2

Proposals from various British manufacturers for a Skeet replacement were considered by the Army in mid-1986, resulting in the selection of the Skeet Mk 2 to meet this requirement. The Mk 2 can be recognised by its more bulky 18.6 kW (25 hp) NGL WAEL 342 engine, and by the addition of a horizontal surface on top of the fin to give improved directional control. Some weights have been increased, and the Mk 2 is also slightly faster. An initial production contract was announced in June 1987.

DIMENSIONS:
As for Mk 1

WEIGHTS:
Basic aircraft, empty	50 kg (110 lb)
Parachute pack	4.1 kg (9 lb)
Fuel	9.1 kg (20 lb)
Mission equipment (normal)	9.1 kg (20 lb)
Max launching weight	72.6 kg (160 lb)

PERFORMANCE: As for Mk 1 except:
Max level speed	140 knots (259 km/h; 161 mph)

SKYLEADER RADIO CONTROL LIMITED
Airport House, Purley Way, Croydon CR0 0XZ

Skyleader was formed in 1965 to manufacture remote control equipment, and today is one of the leading suppliers of telecommand, remote control and associated electronic systems for incorporation in all kinds of unmanned aircraft. It also designed, and continues to produce, the MATS-A aerial target system in use by the British Army.

SKYLEADER MATS-A

MATS-A has been in use for many years by the British Army, and production was continuing in 1987.

TYPE: Aerial target system.

AIRFRAME: High-wing monoplane configuration. Fuselage built of glassfibre reinforced resin material with additional strengthening. Wings have polystyrene foam core with veneer covering. Tail surfaces are of balsa. All flying surfaces further covered with tough vinyl.

POWER PLANT: One 10 cc single-cylinder piston engine, driving a two-blade propeller. Methanol/castor oil fuel mixture.

LAUNCH AND RECOVERY: Hand-launched. Normal recovery by belly landing on fuselage undersurface; parachute recovery system optional.

GUIDANCE AND CONTROL: Line-of-sight radio command system, using hand-held transmitter. Conventional moving surfaces for aerodynamic control.

MISSION EQUIPMENT: Four-channel superhet receiver, operating on 27 MHz bandwidth, within which 12 spot frequencies are available. Rechargeable nickel-cadmium battery pack and three or four proportional feedback servos provide outputs to control surfaces. Transmitter power (1W) is adequate for operating distance of up to 1.1 nm (2 km; 1.25 miles). Other frequencies available up to 72 MHz.

DIMENSIONS:

Wing span	1.73 m (5 ft 8 in)
Length overall	1.22 m (4 ft)

WEIGHT:

Max launching weight	3.85 kg (8.5 lb)

PERFORMANCE:

Max level speed	78 knots (145 km/h; 90 mph)
Operating range	approx 1.7 nm (3.2 km; 2 miles)
Endurance	15–20 min

Hand launch of a Target Technology BTT-1 Imp

TARGET TECHNOLOGY LTD (TTL)

Unit 3, Brunswick Industrial Centre, Ashford, Kent
TN24 9QP

In addition to its own range of RPVs and targets described in this entry, TTL manufactures a range of launchers, engines, propellers and ground support equipment for a variety of unmanned aircraft. Customers for these items have included AEL, BAe, Flight Refuelling, ML Aviation, Racal and the RAE in the UK, and others in the Middle East, Africa, the USA and Canada.

TTL BTT-1 IMP

The Imp is a hand-launched target for use both on land and at sea. By early 1987 more than 350 had been produced for the British Army, Navy and Air Force, the Royal Guard Brigade of the Sultanate of Oman, and the armed forces of Egypt, Indonesia, Qatar, Saudi Arabia and Turkey. They are operated as targets for a variety of light air defence weapons, including 0.50-in general purpose machine-guns, and a range of towed and self-propelled 20 mm cannon systems.

TYPE: Training and all-arms air defence target.

AIRFRAME: Mid-wing monoplane of 'cropped delta' planform, with sweptback vertical tail. No horizontal tail surfaces. Fuselage is of glassfibre reinforced resin, with additional strengthening; wings are of plywood over a polystyrene foam core. All flying surfaces are further covered with a tough vinyl material, and primary components are interchangeable to simplify replacement.

POWER PLANT: One 15 cc glow-plug engine, driving a two-blade propeller.

LAUNCH AND RECOVERY: Hand launch. Recovery by conventional skid landing or, optionally, by parachute. Latter can be commanded manually, or automatically in the event of target damage or failure of command link.

GUIDANCE AND CONTROL: Radio command system (hand-held transmitter), developed from a Skyleader four-channel digital system giving independent proportional control of elevons, engine and (optionally) recovery parachute. Variety of frequencies available.

DIMENSIONS:

Wing span	1.83 m (6 ft)
Length overall	1.09 m (3 ft 7 in)
Height overall	0.43 m (1 ft 5 in)
Propeller diameter	0.33 m (1 ft 1 in)

WEIGHTS:

Weight empty	4.5 kg (10 lb)
Fuel	0.45 kg (1 lb)
Max launching weight	5.9 kg (13 lb)

PERFORMANCE:

Max level speed	82 knots (153 km/h; 95 mph)
Stalling speed	13 knots (24 km/h; 15 mph)
Endurance	30 min

TTL BTT-2 DEMON

The Demon has a configuration generally similar to that of the AEL Snipe Mark II. Twelve Demons had been built and were in service by mid-February 1986, at which time a further ten were on order for a Middle East customer. Production ended later that year.

TYPE: Basic training target.

AIRFRAME: High-wing monoplane, built of GRP composite materials.

POWER PLANT: One 6.7 kW (9 hp) Piper P.100 single-cylinder two-stroke engine driving a two-blade propeller. Fuel capacity 5 litres (1.1 Imp gallons; 1.3 US gallons).

LAUNCH AND RECOVERY: Similar to those described for Banshee.

GUIDANCE AND CONTROL: By VHF PCM equipment similar to, and compatible with, that used for Banshee.

MISSION EQUIPMENT: Payloads can include a 9-shot smoke flare pod, laser reflectors, infra-red flares, and a miss distance indicator with telemetry downlink.

DIMENSIONS:

Wing span	2.59 m (8 ft 6 in)
Length overall	2.13 m (7 ft)
Height overall	0.63 m (2 ft 1 in)
Propeller diameter	0.51 m (1 ft 8 in)

WEIGHTS:

Weight empty	20.4 kg (45 lb)
Max payload	5.9 kg (13 lb)
Max launching weight	34 kg (75 lb)

PERFORMANCE:

Launching speed	45 knots (84 km/h; 52 mph)
Max level speed	130 knots (241 km/h; 150 mph)
Stalling speed	35 knots (65 km/h; 40 mph)
Visual range with optical tracking system	3.2 nm (6 km; 3.7 miles)
Endurance	1 h 10 min

TTL BTT-3 BANSHEE

The Banshee is a low-cost target system designed primarily to simulate the threat of missiles (including sea-skimming weapons) and aircraft for missile and cannon air defence systems. The first of six prototypes made its initial flight in January 1983, and the Banshee is currently in service with the British Army and with the armed forces of Abu Dhabi, Canada, Egypt, Indonesia, Oman, Qatar, Saudi Arabia and Turkey. It has also been in operational service in Italy and the USA, and was operated as the target in both the 1985 and 1986 Gulf Co-operation Council naval exercises. Banshee was selected by the UK MoD as an interim target for Blowpipe and Javelin surface-to-air missile systems, and entered service with the

British Army in July 1986. It is also operated for British Aerospace, Contraves and Electronique Serge Dassault, under contracts for the provision of targets and services for weapon systems trials and development.

Recently, the Banshee has been modified to be able to tow a target banner or target sleeve. Under the name **Vindicator**, Banshee is marketed in North America by Boeing of Canada (which see). TTL produces a payload carrying RPV version of the Banshee, known as **Spectre**, and a reconnaissance version known as **Hawkeye**; these are described separately.

By mid-February 1987, Banshee production had exceeded 500, with a further 150 then on order. Output at that time was at the rate of 30 per month.

TYPE: Remotely controlled aerial target.

AIRFRAME: Low-wing monoplane with clipped delta wings and sweptback fin. No horizontal tail surfaces. Wings have 50° sweepback and approx 3° dihedral. Entire airframe of GRP composite material; elevons are of injection moulded epoxy composite. Payload bays situated in detachable nosecone, centre and rear fuselage. All aircraft subsystems are watertight for recovery from sea.

POWER PLANT: One 19.4 kW (26 hp) NGL WAEL 342 two-cylinder two-stroke or 26.1 kW (35 hp) Norton single-rotor rotating-piston engine, driving a two-blade laminated fixed-pitch pusher propeller with spinner. Fuel in integral fuselage tank with capacity of up to 15 litres (3.3 Imp gallons; 4 US gallons). Engine can be fitted with a Thorn EMI/TTL 300W alternator.

LAUNCH AND RECOVERY: Launch is achieved with an elastic power band catapult launcher which is normally mounted on ground support trailer, but can be removed and used separately (e.g., on board ship). Recovery is by belly landing on land or water, or by deployment of cruciform parachute. Underfuselage flare pod acts as landing skid and mission payload bay. Parachute mode can be commanded manually or automatically by a fail-safe system in the event of in-flight damage or failure of radio command link. Maximum

Omani TTL Banshees (note different noses) during 1986 Gulf exercises

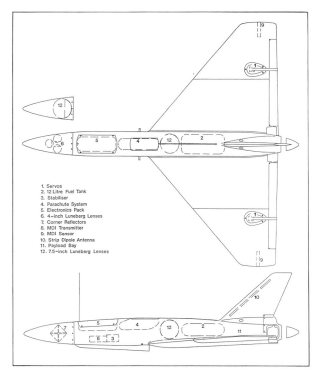

Main internal features of the TTL-3 Banshee

1. Servos
2. 12 Litre Fuel Tank
3. Stabiliser
4. Parachute System
5. Electronics Pack
6. 4-inch Luneberg Lenses
7. Corner Reflectors
8. MDI Transmitter
9. MDI Sensor
10. Strip Dipole Antenna
11. Payload Bay
12. 7.5-inch Luneberg Lenses

turnaround time on land or at sea is 30 min after return to launch site.

GUIDANCE AND CONTROL: High power (PCM) radio command guidance system, utilising VHF radio and line-of-sight optical tracking system incorporating gyrostabilised optics, for ranges of up to 5.4 nm (10 km; 6.2 miles). Two-axis aerodynamic control is achieved with elevon control surfaces. Autostabilisation with height lock is available as an option, incorporating rate gyros controlling yaw, pitch and roll which can be switched on and off during flight. Radio tracking system is available for target control over ranges of up to 10.8 nm (20 km; 12.5 miles). Banshee can also be operated with Vega tracking system for control at ranges of up to 24.3 nm (45 km; 28 miles). Onboard power supplied by rechargeable battery packs.

MISSION EQUIPMENT: Alternative mission loads include flare pod able to contain up to 24 smoke and/or infra-red flares, or a chaff dispenser. Corner array sets can be carried, consisting of an optimised triple array of reflective corners giving a spherical cardioid polar diagram with phase-interacted global fine structure and echo peaks tuned to customer requirement. Up to three Luneberg lenses can be carried, providing radar enhancement in a range of bandwidths and attitudes. Acoustic and Racal Doppler radar miss distance indicating (MDI) systems can be carried. Banshee can also tow target banner or target sleeve which can be fitted with MDI system: banner and sleeve are towed from rear of strengthened ventral fin.

DIMENSIONS:
Wing span	2.49 m (8 ft 2 in)
Wing area	2.14 m² (23 sq ft)
Length overall	2.84 m (9 ft 4 in)
Height overall	0.86 m (2 ft 10 in)
Body diameter (max)	0.305 m (1 ft)
Propeller diameter	0.61 m (2 ft)

WEIGHTS:
Weight empty	38.5 kg (85 lb)
Max payload	22.7 kg (50 lb)
Max launching weight	72.6 kg (160 lb)

PERFORMANCE:
Launching speed	52 knots (97 km/h; 60 mph)
Max level speed	174 knots (322 km/h; 200 mph)
Stalling speed	39 knots (73 km/h; 45 mph)
Max range:	
optical tracking system	5.4 nm (10 km; 6.2 miles)
radio tracking system	10.8 nm (20 km; 12.5 miles)
Vega tracking system	24.3 nm (45 km; 28 miles)
Endurance at max speed	1 h 15 min

TTL ASR-4 SPECTRE and HAWKEYE

The ASR-4 Spectre is the payload carrying RPV version of the Banshee, able to carry various opto-electronic packages including a downlink, and is operated primarily as an airborne payload test vehicle. Hawkeye is the reconnaissance derivative of Spectre, and can be fitted with a high power surveillance system comprising a solid state TV camera, 35 mm film camera and wide-range zoom lens with sightline stabilised by a gyro-controlled mirror. Five Hawkeye systems have been purchased by a Canadian consortium for civilian use.

Control information, vehicle weights and ranges are as quoted for the Banshee, but dimensions and other data differ as follows:

TYPE: Remotely controlled payload carrying RPV.

POWER PLANT: One 26.1 kW (35 hp) Norton single-rotor rotating-piston engine, driving a two-blade laminated fixed-pitch pusher propeller.

DIMENSIONS:
Wing span: min	2.13 m (7 ft)
max	2.90 m (9 ft 6 in)

ASR-4 Spectre RPV version of the Banshee

TTL Hawkeye supplied to Canada for evaluation

Length overall	2.74 m (9 ft)
Height overall	0.71 m (2 ft 4 in)
Propeller diameter	0.66 m (2 ft 2 in)

WEIGHT:

Max payload	27.2 kg (60 lb)

PERFORMANCE:

Launching speed	49 knots (90 km/h; 56 mph)
Max level speed	148 knots (273 km/h; 170 mph)
Loiter endurance	up to 4 h

TTL JTT-5 VOODOO

Voodoo is a new high-speed, turbojet powered aerial target, first shown publicly at the 1986 Farnborough air show. It will be operated as a remotely controlled target to simulate the threat of aircraft and missiles, including sea-skimming weapons, for low to medium range missile and cannon air defence systems based both on land and at sea. It is particularly suitable as an aerial target for the new generation of line-of-sight forward (LOS-F), line-of-sight rear (LOS-R) and low-level air defence (LLAD) weapon systems currently being deployed. The Voodoo is designed to achieve significantly higher speed and improved performance over existing basic training targets, and to provide a low-cost alternative to the current generation of sophisticated jet powered targets. As with the Banshee series of target/RPVs, Voodoo embodies modular construction to maximise versatility, and range data and payload configurations are as given for the BTT-3.

The flight development programme was expected to begin in May 1987, with production scheduled to start in early 1988.

TYPE: Remotely controlled high-speed aerial target.

AIRFRAME: Low-wing monoplane, with clipped delta wings (similar to those of Banshee) and sweptback fin; no horizontal tail surfaces. Engine air intake above fuselage, forward of fin. Detachable nose cowling payload bay. Elevons of injection moulded epoxy composite; remainder of airframe of GRP composite, with aluminium spar strengthening for engine mounting. No landing gear.

POWER PLANT: One NGL WAEL 600N turbojet, rated initially at 0.525 kN (118 lb st).

DIMENSIONS:

Wing span	2.56 m (8 ft 5 in)
Length overall	2.84 m (9 ft 4 in)
Height overall	0.86 m (2 ft 10 in)

WEIGHTS:

Weight empty	50 kg (110 lb)
Max launching weight	81.5 kg (180 lb)

TTL-5 jet powered Voodoo subsonic target

PERFORMANCE (estimated):

Max level speed at S/L	more than 261 knots (483 km/h; 300 mph)
Stalling speed	52 knots (97 km/h; 60 mph)

TASUMA (UK) LTD

Unit A1, Forelle Centre, Ebblake Industrial Estate, Verwood, Dorset

Tasuma (Target And Surveillance UnManned Aircraft) was formed originally to manufacture model aircraft for the hobby trade, but development into higher technology structures led to requests to produce airframe components for major RPV manufacturers. This resulted in disposal of the hobby business to concentrate entirely on RPV work, which has included components and subassemblies for Flight Refuelling, Shorts, RAE Farnborough, ARE Portsdown and Plessey Aerospace.

Such work is still the company's mainstay, but private ventures also led Tasuma to develop designs of its own. These include both surveillance RPVs, for which composite construction methods make possible a high ratio of payload to take-off weight, and high performance target drones. These are available either for direct sale or as an airframe hire service to avionics companies needing air vehicles for flight testing and proofing experiments.

TASUMA T1 WASP

Tasuma's first own-design RPV, the Wasp was produced for the central electricity generating board and the Cranfield Institute of Technology, a total of ten being manufactured between 1979 and 1982. It was used by the CEGB for altitude air sampling over power stations.

TYPE: Recoverable airborne surveillance mini-RPV.

AIRFRAME: Conventional high-wing monoplane configuration, with tricycle landing gear. Constructed of GRP (fuselage) and epoxy laminated foam (wings).

POWER PLANT: One 1.9 kW (2.5 hp) reciprocating engine, driving a two-blade propeller.

LAUNCH AND RECOVERY: Conventional T-O and landing from smooth terrain.

GUIDANCE AND CONTROL: Manual line-of-sight, using digital proportional radio on 35 or 68 MHz.

DIMENSIONS:

Wing span	3.20 m (10 ft 6 in)
Length overall	1.90 m (6 ft 2.75 in)

WEIGHTS:

Max payload	10 kg (22 lb)
Max T-O weight	18 kg (40 lb)

PERFORMANCE:

Cruising speed	51 knots (95 km/h; 59 mph)
Endurance	40 min

Tasuma T1 Wasp

Tasuma mini-target

TASUMA MINI-TARGET VEHICLE

This aircraft was designed, developed and prototyped in the early 1980s for submission to the UK Ministry of Defence to meet a requirement of the Admiralty Surface Weapons Establishment. Development has ended.

TYPE: High-speed aerial target.

AIRFRAME: Delta wing mid-wing monoplane, without horizontal tail surfaces but with optional canards. Constructed from GRP and Kevlar composites.

POWER PLANT: Single engine (type and power not known), driving a two-blade pusher propeller.

LAUNCH AND RECOVERY: Launched by Tasuma bungee catapult system. Recovered by ventral skid landing on level terrain, or by shipboard retrieval net.

GUIDANCE AND CONTROL: As for T1 Wasp.

DIMENSIONS:

Wing span	1.05 m (3 ft 5.33 in)
Length overall	1.40 m (4 ft 7 in)

WEIGHTS:

Max payload	3 kg (6.6 lb)
Max launching weight	10 kg (22 lb)

PERFORMANCE:

Max level speed	135 knots (250 km/h; 155 mph)
Endurance	30 min

TASUMA T4

TYPE: Recoverable (surveillance) or expendable (hazard threat) mini-RPV.

AIRFRAME: High-wing monoplane with dihedralled outer wings, nacelle-type fuselage, twin-boom/twin-fin and rudder

Tasuma T4 twin-boom target/RPV

tail assembly, and tricycle landing gear. Airframe is of GRP and Kevlar composite construction, and can be quickly assembled and ready to fly in 1 min after unpacking from compact carrying crate.

POWER PLANT: One 2.2 kW (3 hp) engine, mounted in rear of fuselage driving a two-blade pusher propeller.

LAUNCH AND RECOVERY: Can take off conventionally from smooth ground; alternatively, can be given assisted launch by bungee catapult, or by rocket boost from rails on carrying crate. Recovery, when required, by ventral skid landing on smooth ground or by retrieval net.

GUIDANCE AND CONTROL: By simple telemetry control using radar map positioning for location. Aircraft is self-stable in flight and carries height hold facility.

DIMENSIONS:

Wing span	2.80 m (9 ft 2.25 in)
Length overall	2.40 m (7 ft 10.5 in)

WEIGHTS:

Max payload	10 kg (22 lb)
Max T-O/launching weight	18 kg (40 lb)

PERFORMANCE:

Cruising speed	59 knots (110 km/h; 68 mph)
Endurance	2 h

TASUMA T5

TYPE: Recoverable multi-role surveillance mini-RPV.

AIRFRAME: High-wing pod and boom monoplane with T-tail, of Kevlar composite construction.

POWER PLANT: One 3 kW (4 hp) engine, mounted in fuselage pod aft of wing and driving a two-blade pusher propeller.

LAUNCH AND RECOVERY: Three alternative launch systems: (a) from jettisonable T-O dolly on smooth terrain, (b) by bungee-assisted take-off from grass field, or (c) by proprietary bungee or compressed air launcher. Recovery by ventral skid landing (smooth terrain) or optional catchnet system.

GUIDANCE AND CONTROL: To customer's requirements.

DIMENSIONS:

Wing span	3.30 m (10 ft 10 in)
Length overall	2.30 m (7 ft 6.5 in)

WEIGHTS:

Max payload	12 kg (26.5 lb)
Max T-O/launching weight	22 kg (48.5 lb)

PERFORMANCE:

Cruising speed	65 knots (120 km/h; 75 mph)
Endurance	2 h

Tasuma T5 surveillance mini

Tasuma T7 surveillance RPV

Tasuma T10/T11 Gyr

TASUMA T7

TYPE: Prototype development surveillance RPV with multi-role capability.

AIRFRAME: Twin-boom 'pusher' monoplane of Kevlar composite construction. Optional payload pods according to mission requirements.

POWER PLANT: One 7.5 kW (10 hp) Quadra 100 cc engine driving a two-blade pusher propeller.

LAUNCH AND RECOVERY: Proprietary bungee or pneumatic launcher. Skid landing or optional catchnet system.

GUIDANCE AND CONTROL: To customer's requirements.

DIMENSIONS:
Wing span	3.60 m (11 ft 9.75 in)
Length overall	3.20 m (10 ft 6 in)

WEIGHTS:
Max payload	22 kg (48.5 lb)
Max launching weight	42 kg (93 lb)

PERFORMANCE:
Cruising speed	67 knots (125 km/h; 78 mph)
Endurance (depending on payload)	2–5 h

TASUMA T10 and T11 GYR

Tasuma's latest target aircraft, the Gyr was designed in 1986. Three examples were completed of the **T10 Gyr I**, each powered by a 7.5 kW (10 hp) Quadra 100 two-stroke engine. Development was continuing in 1987 on the **T11 Gyr II**, which has the same configuration but is a larger vehicle and is powered by a 25.4 kW (34 hp) Norton-Wankel rotating-piston engine. Ground support for the Gyr comprises a trailer unit plus launcher assembly, capable of transporting six complete aircraft and the necessary operating equipment.

The following description applies to both Gyr models, except where a specific version is indicated:

TYPE: Recoverable target aircraft.

AIRFRAME: High-wing monoplane, with fuselage of vinyl resin bonded Kevlar and glassfibre. Wings, tailplane, elevators, fin and rudder have a foam core with epoxy vacuum bonded skins. Constant chord wings have an Eppler 374 aerofoil section (thickness/chord ratio 11%) and 2° incidence; no anhedral or dihedral.

POWER PLANT: One piston engine (details in opening paragraph), driving a two-blade fixed-pitch wooden propeller.

LAUNCH AND RECOVERY: Bungee-operated launch from zero-length trailer-mounted rail. Recovered by landing on underfuselage skids.

GUIDANCE AND CONTROL: Radio command link (10W PCM type transmitter), with full fail-safe mode and incorporating sequencing system for firing flares. Ailerons, elevators and rudder for conventional aerodynamic control. Optical sighting enhancement assembly for ground operator.

MISSION EQUIPMENT: 45 s coloured smoke canisters (up to eight on Gyr I and 16 on Gyr II), or infra-red emitters (two on Gyr I, four on Gyr II). Proprietary MDI and radar enhancement devices.

DIMENSIONS:
Wing span:	
Gyr I	2.75 m (9 ft 0.25 in)
Gyr II	3.40 m (11 ft 1.75 in)
Length overall:	
Gyr I	2.20 m (7 ft 2.5 in)
Gyr II	2.80 m (9 ft 2.25 in)
Height overall:	
Gyr I	0.43 m (1 ft 5 in)
Gyr II	0.50 m (1 ft 7.75 in)

WEIGHTS:
Weight empty:	
Gyr I	16 kg (35.3 lb)
Gyr II	26 kg (57.3 lb)
Max launching weight:	
Gyr I	25 kg (55.1 lb)
Gyr II	42 kg (92.6 lb)

PERFORMANCE:
Max level speed:	
Gyr I	135 knots (250 km/h; 155 mph)
Gyr II	159 knots (295 km/h; 183 mph)
Stalling speed:	
Gyr I	38 knots (70 km/h; 44 mph)
Gyr II	41 knots (75 km/h; 47 mph)
Range with optics:	
Gyr I	3.2 nm (6 km; 3.7 miles)
Gyr II	3.8 nm (7 km; 4.3 miles)
Endurance at full throttle:	
Gyr I and II	1 h

THORN EMI ELECTRONICS LTD (Defence Systems Division)
Victoria Road, Feltham, Middlesex TW13 7DZ

The Defence Systems Division of Thorn EMI Electronics has built two types of experimental UMA, known as Argus, and completed a design study for a third, entirely different type, known as Himet. All three projects were undertaken on behalf of the UK Ministry of Defence, and are not production vehicles.

THORN EMI ARGUS 1

The Argus 1 was developed as a private venture for applications in which rapid or remote deployment is required, or in which very low thermal and acoustic signatures are necessary. An electric propulsion system was chosen, to offer minimal power plant induced vibration and independence from atmospheric oxygen.

A technology demonstrator prototype flew for the first time in 1979, and a batch of Argus 1s was subsequently built under contract to the UK Ministry of Defence and operated by the Royal Aircraft Establishment. Further improvements are planned.

TYPE: Experimental electrically powered unmanned aircraft.
AIRFRAME: Conventional high-wing monoplane of stressed skin lightweight construction. Tricycle landing gear.
POWER PLANT: Thorn EMI purpose-designed DC electric motor, with power range of 300–900W, controlled by a pulse-width modulated throttle and driving a two-blade propeller. Energy source is a battery pack, which can be rechargeable or of the primary lithium anode type.
LAUNCH AND RECOVERY: Aircraft can be launched from a tricycle undercarriage or by winch, bungee or vehicle-mounted launcher. Recovery can be achieved by skid landing on grass, or wheels on a prepared surface.
GUIDANCE AND CONTROL: Range of options available, from manually controlled radio link to full autopilot systems.
MISSION EQUIPMENT: Various payloads can be accommodated, depending upon particular mission.
DIMENSIONS:

Wing span	3 m (9 ft 10 in)
Wing area	1 m² (10.76 sq ft)

WEIGHTS:

Basic weight empty	8 kg (17.6 lb)
Fuel	2 kg (4.4 lb)
Max payload	5 kg (11 lb)
Max T-O/launching weight	15 kg (33 lb)

PERFORMANCE:

Max level speed	43 knots (80 km/h; 50 mph)
Max range	26.5 nm (49 km; 30.5 miles)
Max endurance	1 h 3 min
g limits	±5

Thorn EMI Argus 1 electrically powered UMA

Argus 2, based on experience gained from Argus 1

THORN EMI ARGUS 2

Argus 2 was designed to exploit the technology demonstrated by Argus 1, and flew for the first time in January 1984. It demonstrated improved performance, and has a large bay in the nose which can accommodate a significantly greater payload. Prototype testing has been completed.

TYPE: Experimental electrically powered unmanned aircraft.
AIRFRAME: Square-section fuselage, tail unit and landing gear generally similar to Argus 1, with new high-mounted gull wings of increased span and area. Wings have an Eppler 387 aerofoil section, with constant chord inboard and tapered outer panels, and attach to fuselage by a single plug and socket and six screws.
POWER PLANT: Two DC electric motors of the type that power Argus 1, thus giving a total power which can be varied from 600–1,800W. These drive pusher propellers at the rear end of small trailing edge pods at the 'knuckles' of the gull wing. Control and energy source as described for Argus 1.
LAUNCH, RECOVERY, GUIDANCE, CONTROL AND MISSION EQUIPMENT: As described for Argus 1.
DIMENSIONS:

Wing span	5 m (16 ft 4.75 in)
Wing area	2 m² (21.53 sq ft)

WEIGHTS:

Basic weight empty	16 kg (35.3 lb)
Fuel	4 kg (8.8 lb)
Max payload	10 kg (22 lb)
Max T-O/launching weight	30 kg (66.1 lb)

PERFORMANCE:

*Max level speed	43 knots (80 km/h; 50 mph)
Max range	54 nm (100 km; 62 miles)
*Max endurance	1 h 42 min
g limits	±5

*with 6 kg (13.2 lb) payload

THORN EMI HIMET

Himet was a design study, on behalf of the Ministry of Defence, for a high-altitude, long-endurance unmanned aircraft for meteorological research, though it was also potentially suitable for many other applications. Thorn EMI was responsible for the airframe and propulsion system study, which was based on the use of a proprietary 15 metre sailplane and a small turbojet engine. Collaborative avionics, navigation and ground equipment studies were carried out by Theta Analysis and Systems Ltd.

TYPE: High-altitude, long-endurance unmanned aircraft.
AIRFRAME: Existing mid-wing 15 metre Class sailplane, with T-tail unit and monowheel landing gear.
POWER PLANT: One 1.33 kN (300 lb st) Noel Penny Turbines NPT 301 turbojet engine, mounted in dorsal pod above wing centre section.
LAUNCH AND RECOVERY: Launch under own power from any area suitable for glider or light aircraft operations. Recovery by conventional landing at any similar site.
GUIDANCE AND CONTROL: Can be fitted with any one of a number of alternative systems, depending on mission.
MISSION EQUIPMENT: Up to 35 kg (77 lb) of avionics equipment permissible in addition to fuel and mission payload.

DIMENSIONS:

Wing span	15 m (49 ft 2.5 in)
Wing area	10 m² (107.64 sq ft)

WEIGHTS (estimated):

Basic weight empty	310 kg (683.5 lb)
Payload (incl fuel)	198 kg (436.5 lb)
Max T-O weight	508 kg (1,120 lb)

PERFORMANCE (estimated):

Max level speed: at S/L	120 knots (222 km/h; 138 mph)
at 15,240 m (50,000 ft)	225 knots (417 km/h; 259 mph)
Ceiling	17,375 m (57,000 ft)
T-O to 10.7 m (35 ft)	300 m (985 ft)
*Range at 15,240 m (50,000 ft)	over 1,080 nm (2,000 km; 1,243 miles)
*Endurance at 15,240 m (50,000 ft)	8 h

*with 15 kg (33 lb) payload

W. VINTEN LTD

Western Way, Bury St Edmunds, Suffolk IP33 3TB

In March 1981 Vinten concluded an agreement with autogyro designer Wing Commander K. H. Wallis, permitting it to manufacture Wallis designs for various military and commercial purposes.

Original plans included trials with an unmanned autogyro capable of carrying 160 kg (353 lb) of mission equipment, compared with 75 kg (165 lb) in the manned version, and able to mount any combination of current production Vinten cameras or other payloads. The autogyro's capability as an RPV was demonstrated successfully, and the programme was inactive in 1986. Vinten retains the capability to resume RPV trials if a suitable requirement should occur.

VINTEN VINDICATOR

The initial stage of Vinten's programme to develop an autogyro RPV was to convert a Wallis aircraft for remote control and downlink telemetry. This was flight tested using a piloted WA-116/W (G-SCAN), powered by a 61.1 kW (82 hp) Weslake engine, and met all its programme objectives. The PCM telecommand system controlled five functions in the air (ignition, throttle, rudder, pitch and roll), and nosewheel/rudder steering on the ground. Real-time video downlink was provided by an onboard TV camera filming the instrument panel; the ground station comprised a portable generator and video receiver mounted in a Ford Escort van.

Subsequent work was directed chiefly to defining payloads for specific applications; navigation and guidance systems for tactical use; reduction of the logistic problems of handling,

Vinten Vindicator unmanned demonstration version of the Wallis WA-116 autogyro

launching and retrieving an RPV of this size; and reducing noise levels of the engine, rotor and propeller.

Vinten also used a lower-powered, unpiloted WA-116/Mc as part of its RPV development programme, and the following description applies to this aircraft:

TYPE: Experimental remotely piloted autogyro.
AIRFRAME: Two-blade teetering rotor, with blades of laminated birch ply. Rotor head incorporates reduction gear for pre-take-off spin-up drive. Head is gimbal-mounted to allow movement in pitch and roll. Basic airframe comprises a keel and rotor pylon manufactured from light alloy. These two main members support the engine, fuel tank, landing gear, rotor, tail unit, payload mountings, instrumentation and all other components. Tail unit consists of a spruce framed fin and rudder, covered with birch ply, and a small, strut braced tailplane. Fin offset from centreline to counteract propeller torque; rudder is horn and mass balanced. Landing gear comprises two mainwheels, a steerable nosewheel (connected to rudder control) and small solid tailwheel, with brakes on all wheels. Low-pressure tyres, size 260 × 85 mm, on nosewheel and mainwheels.
POWER PLANT: One 52 kW (70 hp) modified McCulloch 4318A flat-four two-stroke engine, mounted on rotor pylon. Rearward extension of crankshaft drives both the two-blade fixed-pitch wooden pusher propeller and a power take-off drum for rotor spin-up drive. Fuel in 36.4 litre (8 Imp gallon; 9.6 US gallon) tank mounted beneath engine.

DIMENSIONS:

Rotor diameter	6.15 m (20 ft 2 in)
Length overall, excl rotor	3.38 m (11 ft 1 in)
Height to top of rotor head	1.85 m (6 ft 1 in)
Propeller diameter	1.14 m (3 ft 9 in)

WEIGHT:

Payload capability	80 kg (176 lb)

PERFORMANCE:

Max cruising speed	80 knots (148 km/h; 92 mph)
Loiter speed	30 knots (55 km/h; 34 mph)
Max endurance	5 h

WESTLAND HELICOPTERS LTD

Yeovil, Somerset BA20 2YB

Westland Helicopters began the study of remotely controlled unmanned rotorcraft, initially in a search for a low-vulnerability successor to the British Army Gazelle helicopter in the surveillance/reconnaissance role, in early 1968. In mid-1971, responding to an MoD General Staff Target for a medium-range unmanned aerial surveillance system, it put forward a proposal based on the use of a fairly sophisticated 'plan symmetrical' RPH (i.e., symmetrical about the rotor shaft axis) as the airborne element. A feasibility study contract, awarded in March 1972, permitted the start of wind tunnel model tests. Design was also initiated of a flight demonstration vehicle known as Pupil, to be preceded by a more primitive private venture testbed (Mote) which would be used to gain control experience.

WESTLAND MOTE

Designed and built in eight months using many off-the-shelf aeromodelling components, including the engines and coaxial rotors, Mote carried no payload or telemetry equipment, being intended purely to prove the 'plan-symmetric' concept of an air vehicle with no preferred aerodynamic heading. Powered by two 1.1 kW (1.5 hp) model aircraft engines, it flew for the first time on 13 July 1975. It carried batteries for electrical power, and with pitch and roll (vertical gyro) stabilisation it flew quite well at an all-up weight of approx 11.3 kg (25 lb). Adding a

Westland's first mini-RPH, the Mote

heading gyro increased this to 13.6 kg (30 lb), at which weight it could just become airborne, but despite only marginal performance it provided much instructive data. It was operated by two 'pilots', one flying the horizontal control (cyclic pitch) and one the yaw control, vertical control and throttle. Pitch/roll/yaw stabilisation and autopilot channels were added as flight testing progressed, eventually transforming the Mote into a readily handleable aircraft.

WESTLAND WISP

Wisp was funded by MoD(PE) in October 1975, after the early flight trials of Mote, as a short-range daylight-only complete military surveillance system. Design parameters included simplicity, safety, reliability, mobility (operable from a single Land-Rover by a two-man crew), and the ability to be brought to mission readiness within 30 minutes of arrival on site. The air vehicle had a GRP body shell; aerials were to be housed within the landing gear legs, control rods and linkage within the GRP rotor hub cowl.

Prototype Westland Wisp

Three Wisps were built for trials, the first free flight being made on 2 December 1976; the second and third aircraft flew in May and August 1977. They were evaluated by the British Army before work was halted by Westland at the end of that year. Plans for a production system known as **Vista** (visual intelligence, surveillance and target acquisition) did not materialise.

TYPE: Experimental surveillance mini-RPH.

AIRFRAME: Small glassfibre body, shaped like a flattened sphere, containing the power plant and payload. Modular construction, comprising four basic modules. Mechanical module comprised rotor systems, their drive, main power actuators and mechanical controls, reduction gearbox, and gearbox and electrical power generation. Payload module included stabilised camera system or other payload, on anti-vibration mounts, and automatic flight control system. Gyro module contained three gyros and power amplifiers. Airframe module consisted of basic structure plus landing gear, fuel tanks, communications equipment and cable looms, with space provision for height sensing system (barometric altimeter and laser rangefinder). Two coaxial two-blade counter-rotating rotors, each with teetering flap hinge. Fixed, four-legged landing gear on underside of body.

POWER PLANT: Two 3 kW (4 hp) Kolbo D238 two-stroke engines, each with independent ignition and fuel supply.

LAUNCH AND RECOVERY: Conventional helicopter take-off and landing.

GUIDANCE AND CONTROL: Radio command guidance system, operated by crew of two. Operators protected against inadvertent rotor spin-up during start-up by two rotor tip gags, either of which prevented rotors turning and stalling the engines. Rotor system of relatively low energy, so that in event of rotor hitting an obstacle on landing, blades would shatter and be contained within short distance of aircraft. Ignition cut-off to permit aborting mission if control lost completely. Inadvertent loss of radio link resulted in control system bringing aircraft to hover and into slow vertical descent, followed by ignition cut-off after pre-set delay. Provision also for fuel cut-off. Rotor speed governed electrically; directional control by differential change of collective pitch angle.

MISSION EQUIPMENT: Unstabilised Philips LDH 830 black and white TV camera with 28° fixed field of view, trainable in elevation from 15° above to 105° below horizontal. Azimuth orientation by aircraft rotation in yaw. Omnidirectional video signal transmission. Electrical power supply backed up by emergency battery.

DIMENSIONS:

Rotor diameter (each)	1.52 m (5 ft)
Rotor blade chord (each)	0.055 m (2.16 in)
Rotor disc area (each)	1.82 m² (19.63 sq ft)
Body: Max diameter	0.61 m (2 ft)
Max depth	0.41 m (1 ft 4 in)
Height overall	0.86 m (2 ft 10 in)

WEIGHTS:

Payload	1.5 kg (3.3 lb)
Typical fuel	2 kg (4.4 lb)
Typical T-O weight	32 kg (70.5 lb)

PERFORMANCE (S/L, ISA):

Cruising speed	55 knots (102 km/h; 63 mph)
Typical endurance	30 min

WESTLAND PUPIL

Designed in 1975, Pupil was intended to have a gross weight of 45.5 kg (100 lb) and a power plant of one 8.9 kW (12 hp) four-cylinder model aircraft engine. Equipment was to include elementary test and telemetry equipment, plus a Marconi-Elliott (now GEC Avionics) stabilised platform capable of carrying a black and white TV camera. Work on Pupil included engine testing, but was suspended in 1977 (much of its work having been done by Wisp) in favour of the similar but larger Wideye.

Drawing of the proposed Westland Pupil

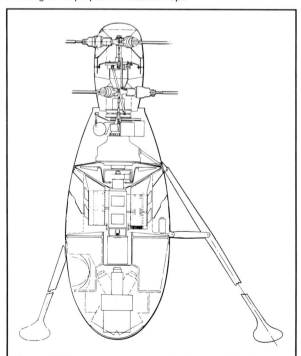

WESTLAND WIDEYE

Developed originally for an MoD programme called **MRUASTAS** (Medium Range Unmanned Aircraft Surveillance and Target Acquisition System), Wideye was intended to be driven by a small turboshaft engine, but in the event was powereed by a pair of NGL (Weslake) two-stroke engines. Essentially an enlarged development of Pupil, it was intended for the battlefield reconnaissance/surveillance role, and was a shared programme, with Marconi (now GEC) Avionics providing the payload, sensors and radio control system. In British Army service, Wideye was meant to perform at distances of up to 27 nm (50 km; 31 miles) beyond the FEBA, but only one prototype was built, this making its first flight on 24 August 1978. It was evaluated to define a fully operational system, but proved to be oversized and overweight after only a few unsuccessful hops. The MRUASTAS programme, later renamed **Supervisor**, as a result became something of a political 'football', was cancelled in December 1979, and was eventually superseded by the Phoenix programme now in the hands of GEC Avionics. Further British endeavours with 'plan-symmetric' RPHs are now exemplified by the ML Aviation Sprite (which see).

TYPE: Experimental battlefield surveillance RPH.

AIRFRAME: Barrel-shaped glassfibre body containing power plant, fuel and payload. Retractable four-legged splayed landing gear on underside. Two coaxial two-blade contra-rotating rotors. Directional control by differential changes in collective pitch angle of rotors. Low radar, infra-red and noise signatures.

POWER PLANT: Two 13.5 kW (18 hp) NGL WAM 274-3 two-cylinder two-stroke engines.

LAUNCH AND RECOVERY: Conventional helicopter take-off and landing.

Wideye RPH, based on Pupil and developed for the Supervisor battlefield surveillance programme

GUIDANCE AND CONTROL: Two-way radio link to convey command data from ground to Wideye and video data from RPH to ground control vehicle.

MISSION EQUIPMENT: Small Marconi (GEC) Avionics stabilised TV camera.

DIMENSIONS:
Rotor diameter (each)	2.13 m (7 ft)
Rotor disc area (each)	3.58 m² (38.48 sq ft)
Body diameter (max)	0.74 m (2 ft 5 in)
Height overall:	
landing gear extended	1.83 m (6 ft)
landing gear retracted	1.52 m (5 ft)

WEIGHT:
Max T-O weight	125 kg (275 lb)

PERFORMANCE:
No details known

WESTLAND WITE

This name was given in 1977 to a design project for a more advanced RPH than Wideye, tailored specifically to naval applications. It did not reach the hardware stage.

United States of America

AAI CORPORATION (Missiles and Robotics Division)

PO Box 6767, Baltimore, Maryland 21204

AAI is developing a non-ballistic high-speed, high-altitude reconnaissance mini-RPV with VTOL capability, including hovering. For this mission it can be equipped with a miniature TV camera. Its rate of climb is quoted as 'about six times that of conventional mini-RPVs', and it is reported to be capable also of acting as an anti-tank and anti-helicopter missile. Another current in-house programme in 1986 was for a rocket launched drone utilising a lightweight zero-length launcher.

AAI is teamed with Mazlat of Israel (which see) in producing the latter's Pioneer RPV for the US Navy.

AEROBOTICS INC (Subsidiary of Moller International Inc)

1222 Research Park Drive, Davis, California 95616

Aerobotics Inc was formed in 1985 as a subsidiary of Moller International to concentrate the parent company's accumulated knowledge of small VTOL 'flying saucer' aircraft into a specific product line of unmanned models, known collectively as Aerobots.

AEROBOTS

In early 1985 a 0.81 m (2 ft 8 in) diameter electrically powered Aerobot, with a 4.5 kg (10 lb) payload, was constructed as a demonstrator under contract to the US Naval Ocean Systems Command, flying with an onboard video camera for remote viewing. Subsequently, the company developed a range of Aerobots designed to carry payloads of up to 181 kg (400 lb) over distances of up to 373 nm (692 km; 430 miles) and at speeds of up to 217 knots (402 km/h; 250 mph). Several electric powered Aerobots were in production in 1987 under a DARPA funded contract.

The Aerobots combine VTOL capability with the extensive use of plastics to minimise radar cross-section, and their power

The Moller developed 0.76 m (2 ft 6 in) diameter Aerobot R124M

plant systems have a low noise signature. A complex thrust vectoring system within the ducts is used to accomplish stability and control; all models also carry onboard flight stabilisation equipment and various radio or 'wire guidance' control links, depending upon the range and operating altitude required. Surveillance payload packages can include TV cameras and laser equipment, and the Aerobots can transition from vertical to horizontal flight to reach a region of interest, hover or loiter for a period, then return to their launch point.

The announced product range in 1987 comprised four models, identified as follows:

E410M. Powered by 1.5 kW (2 hp) electric motor; four fan ducts, each with two-blade fan.

P115M. Powered by 3.7 kW (5 hp) two-cylinder piston engine, driving a two-blade fan in a single duct.

R124M. Powered by 37.3 kW (50 hp) rotary engine, driving a seven-blade fan in a single duct.

200-XR. Powered by 298 kW (400 hp) rotary engine; eight fan ducts, each with a seven-blade fan.

DIMENSIONS:
  Diameter overall:

E410M	0.86 m (2 ft 10 in)
P115M	0.51 m (1 ft 8 in)
R124M	0.76 m (2 ft 6 in)
200-XR	2.84 m (9 ft 4 in)

  Diameter of duct(s):

E410M	0.25 m (10 in)
P115M	0.38 m (1 ft 3 in)
R124M	0.61 m (2 ft)
200-XR	0.51 m (1 ft 8 in)

  Height overall:

E410M	0.25 m (10 in)
P115M	0.46 m (1 ft 6 in)
R124M	0.71 m (2 ft 4 in)
200-XR	0.91 m (3 ft)

WEIGHTS:
  Max payload:

E410M, P115M	4.5 kg (10 lb)
R124M	20.4 kg (45 lb)
200-XR	181 kg (400 lb)

  Max T-O weight:

E410M	10.4 kg (23 lb)
P115M	13.6 kg (30 lb)
R124M	91 kg (200 lb)
200-XR	544 kg (1,200 lb)

PERFORMANCE (estimated):
  Max level speed:

P115M	56 knots (105 km/h; 65 mph)
R124M	152 knots (282 km/h; 175 mph)
200-XR	78 knots (145 km/h; 90 mph)

  *Service ceiling:

E410M**	over 61 m (200 ft)
all other models	4,575 m (15,000 ft)

  Typical mission range:

P115M	30.4 nm (56 km; 35 miles)
R124M	278 nm (515 km; 320 miles)
200-XR	104 nm (193 km; 120 miles)

  Max hover time:

E410M	indefinite
P115M	30 min
R124M	1 h 45 min
200-XR	1 h 15 min

  *Requires trade-off against payload
  **According to power/control cable: this model designed for local surveillance above ground station

AERODYNE SYSTEMS ENGINEERING LTD

1140 19th Street NW, Suite 600, Washington, DC 20036

AERODYNE CH-84 PEGASUS

Aerodyne Systems Engineering has re-engineered the Gyrodyne QH-50 DASH (drone anti-submarine helicopter, which see) of the 1960s by replacing the original 224 kW (300 shp) Boeing T50 turboshaft with a lighter and more powerful Allison 250-C20 and fitting a new electronic control system. Renamed CH-84 Pegasus, it is now configured as a recoverable airborne surveillance RPH. Design modification began in 1981, and construction of a prototype started in 1983. This made its first flight in 1984, in which year Aerodyne

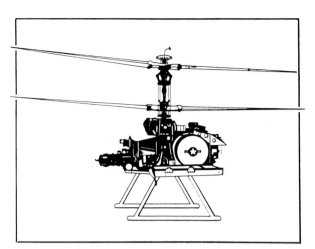

Aerodyne CH-84 Pegasus, based on the Gyrodyne QH-50

Systems also completed one pre-production and one production standard example.

The Pegasus was expected to be submitted in response to RFPs (requests for proposals) from the US Army and US Navy. The former requirement is for an off-the-shelf elint/EW RPV, the latter for a medium-range reconnaissance vehicle.

TYPE: Recoverable airborne surveillance RPH.

ROTOR SYSTEM: Two two-blade semi-rigid counter-rotating coaxial rotors, with glassfibre blades, incorporating linear taper (in planform and thickness) and negative twist. Rotor controls operated by automatic stabilisation and remote control equipment: pitch and roll via cyclic control of swashplates, collective pitch control by collective movement of swashplates. Control in yaw exercised by movable tip brakes connected to both upper and lower blade tips, which create unequal torque distribution. Lower tip brakes are deflected to turn left, upper tip brakes to turn right.

ROTOR DRIVE: Transmission system consists of two-stage gear reduction, two coaxial rotor driveshafts, integral lubricating system, generator drive and rotary actuator drive. Engine power transmitted to rotors via two-stage reduction, second stage of which divides torque to the two rotor shafts. Generator and rotary actuator driven by accessory drives, in mesh with a single drivegear mounted on lower rotor shaft.

POWER PLANT: One 313 kW (420 shp) Allison 250-C20F turboshaft engine. Single cylindrical fuel tank, capacity 197 litres (43.3 Imp gallons; 52 US gallons). Provision for 303 litre (66.6 Imp gallon; 80 US gallon) auxiliary tank.

LAUNCH AND RECOVERY: Conventional helicopter take-off and landing.

GUIDANCE AND CONTROL: Remote control consists of an airborne four-axis stabilisation system and a receiver/decoder, interfaced with a Vega 6104 ground-based target tracking control system. Aircraft is stabilised in pitch, roll, yaw and altitude, with rotor rpm maintained at constant speed by engine governor. Vertical gyro for pitch and roll reference, directional gyro for yaw and barometric altimeter for altitude reference. Lear Siegler autopilot. The CH-84 is equipped with a loss of carrier and/or destruct system. In former case, aircraft will enter a hover mode within 30 s; destruct is a command function shutting off engine fuel supply.

MISSION EQUIPMENT: 'Mini-view' concept of OTH (over the horizon) surveillance utilises a tethered aerostat as a repeater for simultaneous control of two CH-84 drone helicopters. Each drone sends back a TV signal through the aerostat repeater together with telemetry of its 'housekeeping' functions. In addition, two separate command channels, operating at UHF to the drone, are afforded via the aerostat. Using the aerostat as a repeater allows the CH-84s to operate within line of sight up to 130 nm (241 km; 150 miles) from the aerostat tether point. Aerostat-to-ground uplinks/ downlinks can be in 2, 4, 6 or 8GHz region, at customer's choice.

DIMENSIONS:

Rotor diameter (each)	6.10 m (20 ft)
Rotor disc area (each)	29.19 m² (314.2 sq ft)
Fuselage: Length (basic)	2.04 m (6 ft 8.25 in)
Max width	1.60 m (5 ft 3 in)
Height to top of rotor head	2.79 m (9 ft 2 in)
Skid track	1.52 m (5 ft)

WEIGHTS:

Basic weight empty	338 kg (745.5 lb)
Payload:	
normal	661.7 kg (1,459 lb)
military	463 kg (1,020 lb)
Max fuel weight (standard tank)	170 kg (375 lb)
Max T-O weight	1,179 kg (2,600 lb)

PERFORMANCE (at max T-O weight):

Max level speed at S/L	115 knots (213 km/h; 132 mph)
Typical cruising speed at S/L	80 knots (148 km/h; 92 mph)
Econ cruising speed at S/L	55 knots (102 km/h; 63 mph)
Forward rate of climb at 1,525 m (5,000 ft)	570 m (1,870 ft)/min
Service ceiling	4,875 m (16,000 ft)
Hovering ceiling:	
IGE	4,575 m (15,000 ft)
OGE	3,355 m (11,000 ft)
Endurance at 55 knots (102 km/h; 63 mph) at S/L:	
standard fuel	1 h 45 min
with auxiliary fuel	5 h 30 min

AERO-MARINE RESEARCH (AMR)

This company, founded by Cdr W. Benson in 1953, designed and flight tested a number of experimental mini-RPVs in the early and mid-1970s, some of them under subcontract to major UMA manufacturers. AMR ceased operating in about 1976–77.

AMR RPV-004

Dating from the late 1960s, the RPV-004 was used as a systems testbed in several programmes, including feasibility studies for the Teledyne Ryan Model 272 mini-RPV, and in presentations to the US Army and US Navy. Of cropped delta planform, with twin overwing fins and aileron/elevon surfaces on the wing trailing edge, it was powered by a small nose-mounted model aircraft engine.

DIMENSIONS AND WEIGHTS:
    Not known
PERFORMANCE:

Max level speed	113 knots (209 km/h; 130 mph)
Max rate of climb at S/L	366 m (1,200 ft)/min

AMR/RYAN RPV-007

Designed, built and flown for Teledyne Ryan as a half-scale testbed for that company's Model 272, the RPV-007 was powered initially by a small K & B engine mounted dorsally and driving a four-blade Benson Rotorduct ducted propeller; a more powerful (1.6 kW; 2.2 hp) K & B was fitted later. The overwing fins were relocated further rearward, and differential ailerons were employed instead of the aileron/elevon system of the RPV-004.

DIMENSION:

Wing span	1.52 m (5 ft)

WEIGHT:

Max T-O weight	5.4 kg (12 lb)

AMR XD 110

First flown in 1969, the initial **XD 110A** was powered by a 3 kW (4 hp) Ross engine, driving a rear-mounted Benson Rotorduct via an extension shaft. The wings, of double delta planform,

Aeromarine Research RPV-004 (left) and RPV-007

AMR's delta winged XD 110A

Aeromet AURA unmanned version of the Rutan Long-EZ

were claimed to be non-stalling. Successful test flights were made in very hot and very cold temperatures, and the XD 110A was employed as a payload testbed for autopilot, laser sensor and TV navigation system payloads on behalf of other manufacturers. The slightly larger **XD 110B**, first flown in early 1976, featured twin Rotorducts buried in the rear fuselage and was capable of net recovery instead of the more normal wheeled landing.

DIMENSIONS:
  Wing span:
    110A   1.98 m (6 ft 6 in)
    110B   2.13 m (7 ft)
  Wing chord at centreline:
    110A   2.82 m (9 ft 3 in)
    110B   3.05 m (10 ft)
WEIGHTS:
  Max payload:
    110A   22.7 kg (50 lb)
    110B   36.3 kg (80 lb)
PERFORMANCE:
  Max flying speed:
    110A   228.2 knots (422.9 km/h; 262.8 mph)
    110B   260 knots (483 km/h; 300 mph)
  Min flying speed:
    110A   11 knots (20.4 km/h; 12.7 mph)
    110B   9 knots (16.7 km/h; 10.4 mph)

AEROMET INC

PO Box 701767, Jones Airport, Tulsa, Oklahoma 74170-1767

AEROMET AURA

Remotely piloted versions of the Rutan Long-EZ lightplane are being used by some US armed services. These are known by the acronym AURA (Aeromet Unmanned Reconnaissance Aircraft).

Aeromet developed the AURA for use on national test ranges, for applications where a manned aircraft is unsuitable for reasons of personnel safety, mission duration or operating costs. The AURA still offers the capability of being flown manned; this feature permits operation in populated areas,

flight tests for equipment performance evaluation, and use as a surrogate unmanned aircraft. Essentially an IR&D development by Aeromet, the AURA has had some contract support from the US Army Strategic Defense Command and the US Navy Pacific Missile Test Center. In 1986 the USAF Ballistic Missile Office was sponsoring development of meteorological instrumentation to be installed in the AURA for missile re-entry tests at Kwajalein Missile Range.

The AURA programme was begun in late 1983, underwent evaluation at the Pacific Missile Range in early 1985, and remotely controlled take-off and landing were demonstrated in August 1985.

TYPE: Recoverable airborne reconnaissance system.
AIRFRAME: Modified Rutan Long-EZ, of all-composite glass-fibre construction with rigid foam core. Canard foreplane, highly swept wings with winglets, and tricycle landing gear.
POWER PLANT: Engine used in standard AURA is an 85.75 kW (115 hp) Avco Lycoming O-235 flat-four with fixed-pitch wooden pusher propeller. Fuel capacity 197 litres (43.3 Imp gallons: 52 US gallons).
LAUNCH AND RECOVERY: Conventional take-off and landing, controlled by ground pilot through autopilot system.
GUIDANCE AND CONTROL: Independent primary and manual control systems. Primary system controls aircraft in all regimes except take-off and landing, which are performed through the manual system. Manual system also provides backup to primary control. Aircraft controlled at all times through a rate-based autopilot, mated to a Litton LTN-3000 VLF/Omega navigation system. Vertical flight modes commanded through digital interface control. Navigation waypoints programmed before flight, and can be re-programmed during flight. Aircraft position and situation data downlinked, with mission data, to ground station, which has telemetered displays of flight and performance parameters, aircraft position and mission data. In manual mode, ground pilot controls aircraft through autopilot. Ground pilot can direct changes in aircraft attitude and heading, and operate aircraft controls such as brakes, throttle, carburettor heat and other functions. System has built-in limits on bank angle and rate of ascent. In the event of primary control system failure, ground pilot can assume control through manual system and return aircraft for landing.

MISSION EQUIPMENT: AURA payload compartment can accommodate a variety of sensors and other equipment for missions such as reconnaissance, meteorological data gathering and communications relay. Depending on fuel load, equipment weight can be up to 181 kg (400 lb), including the Aeromet distributed data acquisition system of microprocessors and centralised computer. A fast-scan video system is provided for visual surveillance.

DIMENSIONS:

Wing span	7.96 m (26 ft 1.75 in)
Wing area	7.62 m² (81.99 sq ft)
Foreplane span	3.59 m (11 ft 9.5 in)
Foreplane area	1.19 m² (12.8 sq ft)
Length overall	5.12 m (16 ft 9.5 in)
Height overall	2.40 m (7 ft 10.5 in)

WEIGHTS:

Basic operating weight empty	362 kg (800 lb)
Max mission load	181 kg (400 lb)
Max T-O weight	725 kg (1,600 lb)

PERFORMANCE:

Never-exceed speed, and max level speed at S/L	190 knots (352 km/h; 218 mph)
Normal cruising speed	167 knots (309 km/h; 192 mph)
Econ cruising speed	110 knots (204 km/h; 127 mph)
Min flying speed	65 knots (121 km/h; 75 mph)
Max ceiling	6,100 m (20,000 ft)
Range with max fuel	2,000 nm (3,706 km; 2,303 miles)
Max endurance	12 h
g limits	+5/−2

AEROTRONICS INC

21000 NE 28th Avenue, Suite 109, Miami, Florida 33180

This company has produced and flight demonstrated two small remotely piloted helicopters known as Dragonfly, designed by Mr Michael J. Mas.

AEROTRONICS DRAGONFLY

The Dragonfly was developed as a private venture to demonstrate the feasibility of a lightweight, simple RPH with fundamental reliability and low cost. A helicopter configuration was chosen to eliminate the need for separate launch and recovery systems. The first prototype, designed **RPH-1**, was flown for the first time in 1984 and proved stable, responsive

Aerotronics RPH-1 Dragonfly mini-drone helicopter

and dependable. A second, identical example confirmed performance repeatability, and was subsequently modified and upgraded to **RPH-2** standard to increase its payload capability to a more useful level. In this latter form it has a slightly enlarged and strengthened airframe and increased engine power.

A wide variety of civil and military applications is foreseen, and the Dragonfly has demonstrated the carriage of such payloads as a TV camera, and radar and infra-red augmentation devices. It was used by Martin Marietta for an eight-month programme measuring guidance-beam cross-sections, and to measure miss distances during test firings of the latter's air defence anti-tank system (ADATS). Presentations have been made to the US Army, Air Force, Navy, Marine Corps and Coast Guard, as well as to the CIA, DIA and FBI.

TYPE: Remotely piloted mini-helicopter.
AIRFRAME: Simple minimum airframe of weldless aluminium tube, with lightening holes. Two-blade main and tail rotors, former having blades mainly of wood with metal and glassfibre reinforcement at hub end. Stabilised hub of proprietary design. Main landing skids are aluminium; shock mounted tailskid.
POWER PLANT: One single-cylinder two-stroke marine piston engine, mounted at nose; of increased power on RPH-2.
LAUNCH AND RECOVERY: Conventional helicopter take-off and landing.
GUIDANCE AND CONTROL: By HF proportional radio remote control system.
MISSION EQUIPMENT: Demonstrated payloads have included video cameras, transmitters, instrumentation, and heat and radar augmentation panels. Other potential payloads can include closed circuit TV, ciné and/or still cameras; autopilot; com/nav, infra-red or ECM equipment; laser rangefinder/designator; or military weapons and explosives.

DIMENSIONS (A: RPH-1, B: RPH-2):

Main rotor diameter:	
A	3.05 m (10 ft)
B	3.66 m (12 ft)
Tail rotor diameter: A, B	0.99 m (3 ft 3 in)
Length overall:	
A	2.44 m (8 ft)
B	2.74 m (9 ft)

WEIGHTS:

Weight empty:	
A	31.75 kg (70 lb)
B	36.3 kg (80 lb)
Useful load (payload + fuel):	
A	13.6 kg (30 lb)
B	31.75 kg (70 lb)

PERFORMANCE:

Max level speed: A, B	109 knots (201 km/h; 125 mph)
Max operating altitude: A, B	3,050 m (10,000 ft)

AMERICAN AIRCRAFT INC

4310 Rankin Lane NE, Albuquerque, New Mexico 87107

AMERICAN AIRCRAFT FALCON

A remotely controlled version of the Falcon microlight sport aircraft was developed by American Aircraft Inc, originally to test the aircraft's recovery parachute system. Since then, considerable interest has reportedly been shown in a pilotless version for various applications, and at least three have been sold: two to the US Army as low-level battlefield communications platforms (with radio equipment by Cincinnati Electronics), and one to the Los Alamos Laboratory in New Mexico for atmospheric and environmental tests.

APPLIED PHYSICS LABORATORY (APL)

The Johns Hopkins University, Aeronautics Division, Johns Hopkins Road, Laurel, Maryland 20707

APL RPD-1 SYMDEL

APL's first drone, the RPD-1 was a very small delta-winged aircraft, powered by a 'pusher' engine and launched from a dolly that was accelerated to flight speed in about 21.3 m (70 ft) by bungee. Launch, and parachute/airbag recovery, were similar to those of the later RPD-2, and wing span was 2.29 m (7 ft 6 in). No other details are known.

APL RPD-2 PARADEL

The RPD-2, which first flew on 13 June 1975 at the US Naval Surface Weapons Center, was developed from the earlier US Army RPD-1 as a delta-winged miniature target for evaluating improved shipboard fire control systems, including gun ranging radar. Four RPD-2s were built, their test programme ending in about 1979–80.

POWER PLANT: One 7.5 kW (10 hp) McCulloch MC-101A single-cylinder piston engine, driving a two-blade pusher propeller.
LAUNCH AND RECOVERY: Launch by catapult system. Parachute recovery, with airbag impact absorbers stowed in each wing. Fin tip jettisoned on parachute release.
GUIDANCE AND CONTROL: System included autopilot which used Earth's electrostatic field for pitch and roll stabilisation.
MISSION EQUIPMENT: Included passive radar augmentation device in nose and Luneberg lens in fairing on fin trailing edge. Pitch sensor above nose; roll sensors at wingtips.
DIMENSIONS:

Wing span	2.03 m (6 ft 8 in)
Wing area	1.74 m² (18.75 sq ft)
Length overall	2.057 m (6 ft 9 in)
Height overall	0.72 m (2 ft 4.25 in)
Propeller diameter	0.51 m (1 ft 8 in)

Applied Physics Laboratory RPD-2 Paradel drone

WEIGHTS:

Weight empty	23 kg (50.5 lb)
Payload	12 kg (26.4 lb)
Max launching weight	46 kg (101 lb)

PERFORMANCE:

Max level speed	150 knots (278 km/h; 173 mph)
Cruising speed	65 knots (120 km/h; 75 mph)
Service ceiling	5,500 m (18,000 ft)
Endurance	2 h 30 min

APL MAP/UV 8001

Design of the MAP/UV (Maneuverable Atmospheric Probe/ Unmanned Vehicle) 8001 began in August 1978, and prototype construction started in June of the following year. By early 1981 four prototypes had been completed, the first of which made its initial flight in August 1979.

The RPV was designed to be low in cost, operable in hazardous regions, and capable of slow flight and tight manoeuvres, to provide a means of gathering data in more confined locations than would be possible with a manned aircraft. It was used in the early 1980s to investigate meteorological and electrical characteristics of the lower atmosphere near a laser test facility at the White Sands Missile Range, in co-operation with the US Army Atmospheric Sciences Laboratory, the Army Research Office, and the University of Texas at El Paso (UTEP).

The main programme objective was to measure atmospheric processes and characteristics that might affect the performance of electro-optical devices in battlefield environments, such as obscuration by smoke, dust and aerosol particles; and diffraction caused by turbulence or other forms of temperature and density gradients. Another objective was to investigate meteorological factors affecting the electrical field (which does not remain vertical in the presence of some forms of adverse weather), and to define types of weather or other phenomena that might impair or prevent the operation of vehicles stabilised by the type of lightweight vertical reference system fitted to the MAP/UV vehicle.

Typical early tests included attempts to define the rate of dispersal of dust clouds formed above exploding projectiles, at altitudes as low as 9 m (30 ft). In July 1980 the RPV was flown close to the face of a cliff and at 2,440 m (8,000 ft) near the peak of a mountain, controlled during take-off and landing by a 'valley' pilot in the foothills and in mid-flight by a 'mountain' pilot at the mountain peak. The latter was able to operate the RPV safely to within 91–182 m (300–600 ft) of the cliff face, using visual inputs to control the flight path. The test programme had ended by early 1983.

TYPE: Meteorological research mini-RPV.
AIRFRAME: High-wing monoplane, with 4° dihedral from roots. Wing and tail surfaces of composite construction, consisting of a glassfibre/epoxy skin laid over polystyrene expanded foam. Fuselage made up of moulded glassfibre/epoxy shells. Non-retractable tricycle landing gear. Underwing or wingtip sensor pods.
POWER PLANT: One 8.2 kW (11 hp) Herbrandson Dyad 180 two-cylinder two-stroke engine, driving a two-blade APL propeller. Single fuselage fuel tank, capacity 5.7 litres (1.25 Imp gallons; 1.5 US gallons).
LAUNCH AND RECOVERY: Conventional runway T-O and landing.
GUIDANCE AND CONTROL: Radio command guidance and telemetry system. Two independently operable vertical

APL's MAP/UV 8001 atmospheric research RPV

stabilisation systems, both developed by APL and used in several of its earlier delta-planform mini-RPVs. One of these systems, based on fluidic angular rate sensors, provided wing levelling and pitch stabilisation in all weather. The other was an advanced version of an electrostatic autopilot, previously invented at APL, which sensed the attitude of the aircraft in relation to an electrical field in the atmosphere. In fair weather, and in certain types of bad weather, the electrical field is usually vertical, but in some adverse conditions (eg, thunderstorms) the device is not adequate to derive a vertical reference. One of the goals of the MAP/UV programme was to investigate meteorological conditions that disturb the atmospheric electrical field, and to measure and record atmospheric characteristics influencing laser propagation in the lower atmosphere. Aerodynamic control of the RPV was exercised by conventional ailerons, wing flaps, rudder and elevators.

MISSION EQUIPMENT: Sensors developed at APL included airspeed, engine tachometer, heading, altitude, three components of the electrical field, and yaw and pitch gust probes. The telemetry system, and sensors for temperature, humidity, ozone concentration, and high frequency turbulence, were developed at UTEP. Devices for gathering aerosol samples and dust particles were carried in pods slung underneath the wing (or, optionally, located at the wingtips). A radar transponder assisted in accurate tracking of the flight path.

DIMENSIONS:
Wing span	3.05 m (10 ft)
Span over wingtip pods	3.35 m (11 ft)
Wing area	1.44 m² (15.48 sq ft)
Length overall	2.41 m (7 ft 11 in)
Fuselage: Max diameter	0.23 m (9 in)
Height overall	0.81 m (2 ft 8 in)
Propeller diameter	0.56 m (1 ft 10 in)
Sensor pod diameter	0.15 m (6 in)

WEIGHTS:
Weight empty, equipped	21.8 kg (48 lb)
Sensors	11.3 kg (25 lb)
Fuel	4.8 kg (10.5 lb)

T-O weight:
at 1,770 m (5,800 ft)	37.9 kg (83.5 lb)
at S/L	43.5 kg (96 lb)

PERFORMANCE (at T-O weight of 37.9 kg; 83.5 lb):
Max level speed at S/L	91 knots (169 km/h; 105 mph)
Econ cruising speed at S/L	54 knots (100 km/h; 62 mph)
Stalling speed, flaps down	27 knots (50 km/h; 31 mph)
Max rate of climb at S/L	579 m (1,900 ft)/min
Service ceiling (calculated)	7,620 m (25,000 ft)
T-O run	46 m (150 ft)

APL AIR-EXJAM

Smaller than the RPD-1/-2 deltas, the Air-Exjam mini-drone was developed in co-operation with the US Naval Surface Weapons Center and flew for the first time in the spring of 1982. Flying autonomous (pre-programmed) missions, it was intended to demonstrate the feasibility of a low-cost expendable mini-drone able to carry a jammer or other EW payload in a loiter pattern for 24 hours after navigating to a preselected target area up to 27 nm (50 km; 31 miles) from the launch site.

Seven examples were built, and had made more than 60 flights by the end of 1983. Some were fitted with larger wings (2.54 m; 8 ft 4 in span) in order to carry heavier payloads; the following description applies to the standard-span version:

AIRFRAME: Low-wing 'cropped delta' monoplane, with upward reflexed trailing edges. Clark Y aerofoil section; 37° 30′ sweepback on leading edges; anhedral on tip sections. Wings made from a hot-wire-cut core of polystyrene foam, with balsa leading- and trailing edges and overall covering of glasscloth; ailerons and elevators for roll and pitch control. Wings could be detached for transportation and storage, being refitted by sliding on to transversely mounted 3 in diameter aluminium tube which served also as fuel tank. Hatches in fuselage upper surface for access to equipment and engine bays. Sweptback fin and rudder; no horizontal tail surfaces. Tricycle landing gear.

POWER PLANT: One 2.2 kW (3 hp) two-cylinder two-stroke chain-saw engine, driving a two-bladé propeller.

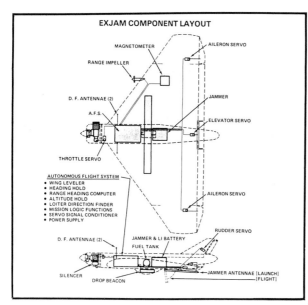

Main features of the APL Air-Exjam jamming drone

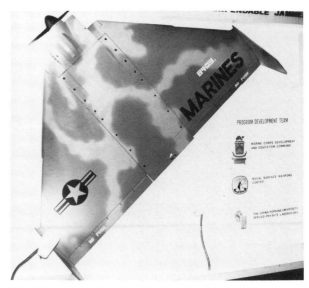

The delta-winged Air-Exjam developed for the USMC by APL
(Terry J. Gander)

LAUNCH AND RECOVERY: Conventional wheeled take-off and landing in suitable conditions; parachute/airbag recovery optional for rough-field operation.

GUIDANCE AND CONTROL: Radio command control system. Navigation by dead reckoning for direct flight to preselected target area; range to target area determined by air-driven impeller, dead reckoning cruise mode being terminated after pre-set number of impeller revolutions. Drone then dropped small R/F transmitter to ground, switching to loiter mode by engaging altitude hold loop and transferring heading loop from magnetometer to modified L-Tronics onboard R/F direction finder. Single- or two-axis magnetic heading sensors. Rate gyro to enable autopilot, via onboard microprocessor, to adjust wing-levelling function.

DIMENSIONS:

Wing span	2.03 m (6 ft 8 in)
Wing area	1.50 m² (16.11 sq ft)

WEIGHTS:

Payload	4.5 kg (10 lb)
Max launching weight	approx 18.1 kg (40 lb)

PERFORMANCE:

Max level speed	95 knots (177 km/h; 110 mph)
Optimum cruising speed	48 knots (88 km/h; 55 mph)
Max endurance	3 h

APL SYMDEL 3

Symdel 3 (symmetrical delta 3) was a proposed USN supersonic drone programme. It did not reach maturity, and was cancelled in the early 1980s. No details are known.

APL (USMC) EXDRONE

This small tail-less delta-winged drone has been developed for the US Marine Corps as a very low cost (less than $5,000) expendable mini for communications jamming. Of virtually all-plastics construction, it has a nose-mounted Sachs-Daimler piston engine and sweptback fin and rudder. First flight was made in 1986; production was anticipated in 1987.

DIMENSIONS:

Wing span	2.44 m (8 ft)
Length overall	1.29 m (4 ft 3 in)

WEIGHTS:

Weight empty	11.8 kg (26 lb)
Max launching weight	19 kg (42 lb)

PERFORMANCE:

Max level speed	87 knots (161 km/h; 100 mph)
Loiter speed	48 knots (88 km/h; 55 mph)
Endurance (standard fuel)	2 h 30 min

ATLANTIC RESEARCH CORPORATION (ARC)

5390 Cherokee Avenue, Alexandria, Virginia 22312

ARC 003

The ARC 003 was designed and built, with company funds, as a rotating-wing research aircraft able to carry a 4.5 kg (10 lb) payload, remain aloft for 1 hour, and operate reliably within operator line of sight. The first of three prototypes was flown in the autumn of 1973, and the basic objectives were substantially achieved. The 003 was last heard of in 1977, when development was continuing, mainly to optimise the aircraft, assess training requirements, and evaluate various payloads.

Dimensions, weights and performance data are approximate only, owing to frequent changes during the flight test programme.

TYPE: Experimental mini-RPH.

AIRFRAME: Two-blade rigid main rotor, with balance arms, and two-blade tail rotor, of wooden construction. Fuselage of aluminium tube, with flat sheet panels over avionics installations. Underfin suspended from tailboom. Non-retractable four-legged landing gear (base 0.56 × 0.56 m; 1 ft 10 in × 1 ft 10 in), with aluminium tube legs and flat circular pad feet.

Atlantic Research Corporation ARC 003 mini-RPH

Beechcraft MQM-61A being launched by rocket booster

POWER PLANT: One 1.5 kW (2 hp) piston engine (type not known). Fuel capacity (petrol/oil mixture) 2.4 litres (0.52 Imp gallon; 0.63 US gallon).
LAUNCH AND RECOVERY: Conventional helicopter T-O and landing. Aircraft stable in hover.
GUIDANCE AND CONTROL: Radio command control system, with gyro-stabilised yaw axis.
MISSION EQUIPMENT: Payloads flown by 1977, in weight range 2.7–3.6 kg (6–8 lb), included one comprising a TV camera, video transmitter and battery; another using same TV camera but with video signal returned to ground via lightweight expendable fibre optic cable; and one consisting of a standard cine camera.

DIMENSIONS:
Main rotor diameter	1.63 m (5 ft 4 in)
Tail rotor diameter	0.43 m (1 ft 5 in)
Length of fuselage, tail rotor turning	
	1.37 m (4 ft 6 in)
Height to top of rotor head	0.56 m (1 ft 10 in)

WEIGHTS (approx):
Weight empty	8.2 kg (18 lb)
Max payload	4.5 kg (10 lb)
Max T-O and landing weight	15.9 kg (35 lb)

PERFORMANCE:
Max level speed	approx 52 knots (96 km/h; 60 mph)
Endurance	1 h

BEECH AIRCRAFT CORPORATION
PO Box 85, Wichita, Kansas 67201-0085

In addition to manufacturing piloted aircraft, Beech has been designing and producing pilotless target drones since 1955. By June 1987 it had built more than 7,000 target drones, including more than 2,200 MQM-39As and MQM-61As, more than 4,000 AQM-37s, and more than 800 MQM-107s.

BEECHCRAFT MODELS 1001 and 1025

US Navy designation: MQM-39A (formerly KDB-1)
US Army designation: MQM-61A Cardinal
The Model 1001 pilotless remotely-controlled target drone won a US Navy design competition in 1955 and was the first design

by Beech's missile engineering division. As the XKDB-1, it flew for the first time in the spring of 1957. Production began in 1959 and well over 900 **MQM-39A**s were built by 1971. They entered service as 'out-of-sight' targets for surface-to-air and air-to-air missiles, rockets and predicted-fire weapons. Equipment could be carried by the Model 1001 to give a radar image equivalent to that produced by high-performance aircraft of very much larger size.

The generally similar **MQM-61A Cardinal** (Model 1025) was used to train US Army crews of Hawk, Redeye, Chaparral and other missiles, and supported training exercises in Canada, Alaska, Okinawa, Taiwan, Korea, Germany, Panama and Hawaii.

Production of the Model 1025 ended in spring 1972 after completion of 20 for the Spanish Army. Production for the US Army exceeded 1,360.

The Cardinal was used to tow targets and banners and, on its own, to evaluate the accuracy of anti-aircraft missiles and gunfire by means of miss distance and scoring devices. The Beech-built tow targets had tubular glassfibre bodies, with cruciform tail-fins, and were equipped with molten infra-red sources when heat-seeking missiles were to be tested. Two targets could be carried under each wing of the Cardinal.

TYPE: Pilotless target.
AIRFRAME: Cantilever high-wing monoplane. No dihedral. Incidence 3° at root, −30' at tip. Conventional ailerons. Cylindrical fuselage. Cantilever 'butterfly' tail unit with included angle of 90°.
POWER PLANT: One 93 kW (125 hp) McCulloch TC6150-J-2 flat-six turbocharged engine, driving a two-blade constant-speed propeller.
LAUNCH AND RECOVERY: One JATO bottle attached under rear fuselage for zero-length launches, accelerating drone to more than 180 knots (333 km/h; 207 mph) in under 2 s. Recovery by drogue parachute stowed in rear of fuselage.
GUIDANCE AND CONTROL: Radio command guidance system. Aerodynamic control by ailerons and 'ruddervators'.
DIMENSIONS:
Wing span (over wingtip containers)	
	3.95 m (12 ft 11.5 in)
Wing area	2.27 m² (24.4 sq ft)
Length overall	4.60 m (15 ft 1 in)
Body diameter (max)	0.45 m (1 ft 5.75 in)
Height overall (excl JATO bottle)	1.02 m (3 ft 4 in)

Propeller diameter	1.32 m (4 ft 4 in)
Wingtip containers:	
Length	1.24 m (4 ft 1 in)
Diameter	0.25 m (10 in)

WEIGHTS:
Max launching weight (incl JATO)	301 kg (664 lb)
Flight weight	254 kg (560 lb)

PERFORMANCE:
Max level speed	
	more than 303 knots (560 km/h; 350 mph)
Min operating speed	80 knots (148 km/h; 92 mph)
Service ceiling	over 13,100 m (43,000 ft)
Endurance at 7,620 m (25,000 ft)	more than 1 h

BEECHCRAFT AQM-37 (US VERSIONS)

Winner of a 1959 joint USN/USAF design competition, the AQM-37 (then designated XKD2B-1) is a supersonic, air-launched expendable target drone, powered by a liquid propellant rocket motor. First flown on 31 May 1961, it entered US Navy service two years later and has been in continuous production and development ever since, with more than 4,200 examples manufactured by mid-1987, most of them for the USN. Current US Navy launch aircraft are the A-4 Skyhawk, A-6 Intruder and F-4 Phantom. Variants produced for the US services are as follows:

US NAVY

AQM-37A. Original basic USN target version (Beech **Model 1019**). Became operational in September 1963; total of approx 3,700 delivered by 1985. Twenty **Model 1019A**s delivered in 1975–76 in Sea Skipper configuration, capable of flying at heights between 10 and 300 m (33–985 ft) for weapon system evaluation; these had an autopilot incorporating a homing device for longitudinal guidance, and a radar altimeter for height control. Ten other AQM-37As modified in about 1981, under name **Challenger**, to operate at 24,385 m (80,000 ft) at Mach 3. These had enlarged and high temperature resistant tail surfaces, and a refined (high-*g*) autopilot to cater for higher speeds and altitudes; they exceeded the quoted altitude and speed, and also demonstrated end-of-flight dives simulating attack by air-to-surface missiles. Final Navy AQM-37A version was Beech **Model 1107**.

    AQM-37C. New (and current) basic USN target version (Beech **Model 1104**), following evaluation of ten specially modified aircraft in 1980–81 for speeds up to Mach 3 and altitudes up to 27,430 m (90,000 ft). Digital autopilot with

The Beechcraft AQM-37A, a standard US Navy target for many years

improved flight control features, radar augmentation in four frequency bands, and provision for on-command controlled dive angle and ground command of cruise heading control. Total of 351 ordered by mid-1987; deliveries began in 1986.

    AQM-37C Variant. Eight ordered, as Beech **Model 1105**, for 1984 evaluation, resulting in funding of kits to modify standard AQM-37Cs to Variant configuration. Designed for missions at Mach 3.5 and 27,430 m (90,000 ft), but successfully flown on test at Mach 4.7 and 34,140 m (112,000 ft) after launch from a Navy F-4. Thermal protection for wing and fin leading edges and nosecone.

US ARMY

AQM-37A. First Army evaluation was of three modified Model 1019s in 1968–69. No immediate orders, but in 1976 Army received a further 20 modified, government-furnished AQM-37As. These were followed in 1976–77 by 28 **Model 1100s** and **1101s**, which were first (and so far only) recoverable versions of this target. Model 1100 was low altitude version, with radar altimeter, flyable down to within 55 m (180 ft) of ground; Model 1101, equipped with barometric sensor, for high altitude operation up to 21,335 m (70,000 ft) and speeds up to 1,182 knots (2,188 km/h; 1,360 mph). Both versions equipped with two-stage parachute recovery system, and with radio controlled guidance system permitting both longitudinal and vertical positioning. Major Army orders were for 415 non-recoverable **Model 1102s**, with solid state autopilot, improved design wings, and other changes providing enhanced performance. These were delivered during 1977–80.

US AIR FORCE

AQM-37A. Air Force received ten modified Model 1019s in 1968–69, following earlier use of modified AQM-37As to flight test hybrid propulsion and command manoeuvring systems for proposed **Sandpiper** rocket-powered target. Sandpiper was abandoned in 1971 in favour of HAST programme, in which Beech bid unsuccessfully against Teledyne Ryan Firebolt (which see).

    The following description applies to the basic AQM-37A/Model 1019 and AQM-37C/Model 1104, except for the variations noted:

TYPE: Air-launched expendable target.

AIRFRAME: Mid-wing monoplane, of canard configuration, with slim delta main wings at rear. Of double-wedge section and bonded aluminium honeycomb construction, these have 76° sweepback on leading edges, 0° dihedral, 0° incidence, and full-span ailerons. Movable foreplanes, of modified double-wedge section. Fixed endplate fin (of 40 per cent greater area on AQM-37C) at tip of each main wing. Cylindrical centre fuselage, with ogival nose section (lengthened on AQM-37C) and detachable tapering rear section over rocket chambers. Underbelly tunnel for rocket engine cartridge-operated start valves, plumbing, infra-red flare and miss distance scoring system antenna.

POWER PLANT: One Rocketdyne/AMF LR64 P-4 two-chamber variable thrust liquid propellant rocket motor. Four preset thrust levels, ranging from 0.31 kN (70 lb) to 3.78 kN (850 lb), are available from booster thrust chamber. Three stainless steel propellant tanks, for nitrogen pressurant, mixed amine fuel (MAF-4) and IRFNA oxidiser, form integral part of centre-fuselage.

LAUNCH AND RECOVERY: Air-launched from launcher adapted to A-4, A-6, F-4 and other aircraft. Non-recoverable (except Models 1100/1101).

GUIDANCE AND CONTROL: Pre-programmed (A and C) or (AQM-37C only) command control guidance system. Flight normally terminated by automatic destruct system, which also operates in event of a major failure. Command standby destruct system for added range safety. Compared with AQM-37A, the AQM-37C has a digital autopilot with improved flight control features; greater range and endurance, achieved by an optimum energy management programme; and command control capability which permits dual launch and in-flight heading control. Dives of $15°–65°$, and pullout from dives, can be initiated upon command from ground. Radar augmentation is also improved, covering several frequency bands.

MISSION EQUIPMENT: Approx 0.033 m³ (1.16 cu ft) of space in nose section for optional scoring and augmentation systems. Target is compatible with most non-co-operative scoring systems.

DIMENSIONS:

Wing span (over fins)	1.00 m (3 ft 3.5 in)
Wing area (exposed)	0.87 m² (9.35 sq ft)
Foreplane span	0.65 m (2 ft 1.5 in)
Length overall:	
AQM-37A	3.83 m (12 ft 6.75 in)
AQM-37C	4.27 m (14 ft 0 in)
Height overall:	
AQM-37A	0.59 m (1 ft 11.33 in)
AQM-37C	0.66 m (2 ft 2 in)
Body diameter (max)	0.33 m (1 ft 1 in)

WEIGHTS:

Weight empty: AQM-37C	123.5 kg (272 lb)
Max payload: AQM-37C	14.5 kg (32 lb)
Max launching weight:	
AQM-37A	256 kg (565 lb)
AQM-37C	272 kg (600 lb)

PERFORMANCE (AQM-37C) :

Cruising height and speed:	
from Mach 0.87 (573 knots; 1,062 km/h; 660 mph) at	
	305 m (1,000 ft)
to Mach 3.0 (1,719 knots; 3,186 km/h; 1,980 mph) at	
	24,385 m. (80,000 ft)
Range (incl glide to impact)	
	more than 174 nm (322 km; 200 miles)
Endurance (powered)	5 min

BEECHCRAFT AQM-37 (EXPORT VERSIONS)

Six variants of the AQM-37, known by Beech Model numbers, have been sold to other countries:

Model 1072. Version of Model 1019 for UK, mainly for use at Llanbedr range; air-launched from Canberra PR. Mk 3. First launch 1 August 1968; successive orders totalled 190 by early 1980s. Fitted by Beech with single-chamber rocket motor; modified for RAF use by Shorts as **SD.2 Stiletto**, incorporating EMI T44/1 telemetry system; additional 15V flight breakup system (WREBUS); radioactive miss distance indicator (RAMDI) with associated radio link; Plessey IR 112A/IR 310 telecommand system and heading and turns command circuitry; modification to propulsion system to give Mach 2 performance at 18,300 m (60,000 ft); changes in radar augmentation system; and various optional mission kits.

Model 1088. Version of Model 1019 for Italian Air Force, for air launch from F-104S. Total of 11 ordered in mid-1970s. Pre-programmed dive manoeuvre to give supersonic presen-

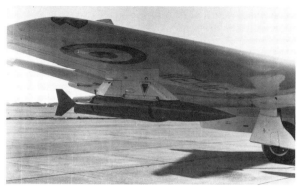
Shorts Stiletto (Beech AQM-37) on a Canberra launch aircraft

tation at medium altitudes. Radio controlled lateral manoeuvring capability to position target accurately.

Model 1094. French Air Force version (50 delivered in 1974–76). Modified by Matra, as **Vanneau** (Lapwing), primarily for evaluating air-to-air weapons. Primary missions performed at Mach 1.6 at 16,750 m (55,000 ft) or Mach 2 at 21,335 m (70,000 ft). Modifications include addition of scoring, radar augmentation, telemetry and tracking beacon systems.

Model 1095. Second version for UK, with different modifications (by Shorts) for use at Hebrides range. Total of 40 ordered.

Model 1098. Version for Israeli Air Force (20 ordered).

Model 1108. Training version of Model 1095, for UK (60 delivered by 1987). Single-chamber engine and modified performance.

BEECHCRAFT MODELS 999 and 1089

US military designation: MQM-107 Streaker
Swedish Air Force designation: RB06 and RB06B Girun

Following a March 1972 development contract, Beech's Model 1089 was declared winner of the US Army's VSTT (variable speed training target) competition with the award in April 1975 of the first instalment of a three-year production contract. Manufacture, under the designation MQM-107A, began in December 1975, and deliveries started in the following April. Contracts included design, development and delivery of the air vehicles, ground support equipment, spares and ancillaries, as well as operation and maintenance of the system by the company's subsidiary, Beech Aerospace Services Inc.

The principal function of the MQM-107 is to provide a variety of threat simulations for training with missiles and automatic weapons. It is the primary subsonic missile training target for the US Army, and is also used in R & D testing of weapon systems. It was designed to operate originally at altitudes from sea level up to 12,200 m (40,000 ft) and at speeds of up to 516 knots (956 km/h; 594 mph), depending upon version.

The following versions have been announced:

MQM-107A. Initial production version, with 2.85 kN (640 lb st) Teledyne CAE J402-CA-700 turbojet and 5.13 m (16 ft 10 in) long fuselage as standard. Deliveries to US Army, completed in early 1979, totalled 385. Supplied also to Abu Dhabi (**Model 999E** with TRI 60-2 engine), Iran, Jordan, Republic of Korea (as **Model 999D**), Sweden (**999A**) and Taiwan (**999F**).

The US Army's variable speed training target, the Beechcraft MQM-107A Streaker

MQM-107B. Introduced in 1982, primary reason for redesignation being the installation of a 3.70 kN (831 lb st) Microturbo North America TRI 60-2 Model 074 engine, permitting an increase in max operating speed. Other changes include a longer fuselage (5.51 m; 18 ft 1 in) with more volume available for payload, and systems improvement arising from experience with MQM-107A. Deliveries to US Army (139) and US Air Force (70) began in 1984 and were completed in 1986. Export customers include Egypt (Models **999H** and **999L**), Sweden (**999B**) and Taiwan.

MQM-107C. Similar to MQM-107B, with long fuselage, but powered by 2.85 kN (640 lb st) Teledyne CAE J402-CA-700 turbojet. Total of 69 delivered to US Army in 1985. (Non-standard model, created to use up existing J402-700 engines.)

MQM-107D. As for MQM-107C, but with 4.27 kN (960 lb st) Teledyne CAE 373-8 engine. Initial US Army contract (for 90) awarded 24 October 1985, with deliveries to begin in January 1987; follow-on contracts in March (for 108) and September 1986 (for 107, bringing total to 305) extend deliveries into 1989. Of this total, 75 are for US Air Force.

MQM-107E. Improved variant of MQM-107B. New wings of 1.84 m² (19.85 sq ft) area, with high-speed aerofoil section and composites construction, resulting in a faster and more manoeuvrable target. Capable of using Teledyne CAE 373-8 or Microturbo North American TRI 60-3 Model 097 turbojet. Fuselage lengthened to 5.71 m (18 ft 9 in), enabling payload compartment to be extended by 20.3 cm (8 in). Max payload increased to 68 kg (150 lb) internal or 136 kg (300 lb) external; max level speed increased to 580 knots (1,075 km/h; 668 mph) and ceiling to 13,410 m (44,000 ft); endurance shortened to 1 h 50 min.

Raider. Tactical RPV version; described separately.

Total deliveries of the MQM-107 (all versions) had exceeded 800 by the beginning of 1987.

TYPE: Re-usable variable speed target.

AIRFRAME: Low-wing monoplane, with sweptback wings, fin, tailplane and elevators; no rudder. Engine suspended on pylon beneath centre of mainly cylindrical fuselage. Modular design throughout, with flat section wing and tail surfaces of bonded honeycomb (fixed surfaces) or foam filled aluminium (ailerons and elevators). Ogival nose and tail cones. Improved waterproofing on MQM-107B and later models.

POWER PLANT: Single turbojet, pylon-mounted in an under-fuselage pod. Standard fuel capacity in MQM-107A is 246 litres (54 Imp gallons; 65 US gallons); provision in longer fuselage versions to increase this to about 284 litres (62.5 Imp gallons; 75 US gallons). Wing insert fuel tanks, available as a kit, can add a further 113 litres (25 Imp gallons; 30 US gallons).

LAUNCH AND RECOVERY: Normally surface-launched, using RATO booster, from lightweight zero-length launcher/checkout system which can be transported in two suitcase-size containers. Booster jettisoned approx 2 s after ignition, after accelerating target to approx 220 knots (408 km/h; 253 mph). Improved and more powerful booster, to permit launch with heavier payloads, under development by Thiokol. Command recovery system, using 1.65 m (5.4 ft) diameter drogue and 15.24 m (50 ft) main parachutes stowed in rear of fuselage. Recovery cycle can be initiated by remote command, by 6 s loss of command carrier, or by electrical power loss.

GUIDANCE AND CONTROL: Guidance and control systems, either analog or digital, provide for both ground control and pre-programmed flight, with trajectory pre-programmed for first 20 s after RATO ignition. Flight controller provided with all pertinent flight information by radio link from sensors located in air vehicle, and can command vehicle manoeuvres and recovery. In flight, the guidance and control system stabilises automatically around the roll, yaw and pitch attitudes and provides altitude and velocity hold modes. Flight control developments include a terrain following guidance capability which has demonstrated extremely low altitude flight profiles. MQM-107B, in addition, has provisions for a high-g autopilot, to extend the manoeuvring and high-g envelope of the vehicle. Flight controller can select either constant airspeed or constant altitude high-g manoeuvres, and $6g$ manoeuvres can be maintained during use with air-to-air or surface-to-air weapons systems. Extended payload section available on long-fuselage versions also provides easier access to payload and vehicle electronics, and has specialised waterproofing provisions for sea water recoveries.

MISSION EQUIPMENT: Total of 0.092 m³ (3.26 cu ft) available in short fuselage version (0.136 m³; 4.79 cu ft in B, C and D models) for mission equipment and core avionics. Principal function is to tow a variety of targets for missile training and evaluation. Two TRX radar, TIX infra-red or TVX radar/visual augmentation targets, or 2.23 m² (24 sq ft) gunnery banners with a corner reflector, can be carried on each mission and towed separately up to 2,440 m (8,000 ft) behind the MQM-107. With wingtip augmentation and scoring devices, Streaker itself serves also as aerial target for such air defence systems as Chaparral, Redeye, Hawk, Improved Hawk, Patriot and Stinger, and the Vulcan rapid-fire gun system. A 15 litre (3.3 Imp gallon; 4 US gallon) smoke/oil tank (26.5 litres; 7 US gallons; 5.8 Imp gallons in MQM-107B and subsequent models) is carried for visual augmentation. Typical external payloads can include pyrotechnic optical plume simulators (POPS), Gem 6221 flare dispenser pods, AN/DSQ scorer pods, FC-7B-23 foam cone radar reflectors, 4190 IR augmentor boom assembly, AN/ALE-28 flare/chaff dispenser, AN/DSQ bullet scorer/tow banners, bi-static radar reflector pods, and AZC-4 infra-red wingtip pods.

DIMENSIONS:

Wing span	3.0 m (9 ft 10 in)
Wing area (total projected)	2.52 m² (27.16 sq ft)
Length overall:	
MQM-107A	5.13 m (16 ft 10 in)
MQM-107B/C/D	5.51 m (18 ft 1 in)
Body diameter (max)	0.38 m (1 ft 3 in)
Height overall	1.47 m (4 ft 10 in)
Tailplane span	1.58 m (5 ft 2.25 in)

WEIGHTS (A: MQM-107A; B: MQM-107B):

Weight empty:	
A	218 kg (480 lb)
B	261 kg (575 lb)
Usable fuel:	
A	173 kg (381 lb)
B	176 kg (388 lb)
Mission equipment: A	43 kg (95 lb) internal
	or 113 kg (250 lb) external
Mission equipment: B	45 kg (99 lb) internal
	or 160 kg (353 lb) external
Max launching weight:	
A (incl booster)	460 kg (1,014) lb)
B (excl booster)	664 kg (1,464 lb)

PERFORMANCE:

Operating speed range:	
A	247–500 knots (459–925 km/h; 285–575 mph)
B	200–516 knots (370–956 km/h; 230–594 mph)
Operating height range: A, B	
	S/L to 12,200 m (40,000 ft)
Endurance: A	more than 3 h
B	2 h 18 min

BEECHCRAFT RAIDER

The Raider, which made its public debut at the 1985 Paris Air Show, was a proposed tactical RPV making use of the airframe and power plant of the MQM-107B. Ground-launched, it had both pre-programmed and ground-controlled capabilities, and was recoverable.

Special mission payloads, housed in detachable pods, could include passive and active ECM such as radar jammers, flares, chaff and radar enhancement devices for penetration aid decoy missions. Additional applications could include weapon

Raider tactical drone version of the Beech MQM-107

systems evaluation in the ECM environment, reconnaissance, and intelligence gathering, but the Raider programme was no longer active in 1987.

DIMENSIONS: As for MQM-107B

WEIGHTS:

Max payload	45.5 kg (100 lb) internal
	or 159 kg (350 lb) external

PERFORMANCE:

Max level speed	516 knots (956 km/h; 594 mph)
Operating height range ('clean')	
	S/L to 12,200 m (40,000 ft)
Endurance (depending on speed):	
standard fuel	1 h 12 min
with auxiliary fuel tanks	2 h 36 min

BEECHCRAFT MODEL 997

US Navy designation: BQM-126A

The Beechcraft Model 997 was selected by the US Navy in its competition for a cost-effective recoverable target replacement for the subsonic BQM-34 Firebee I. It flew for the first time in March 1984. The programme resulting from this selection includes full scale development, to be followed by initial production of 700 air vehicles. Procurement requirements have been forecast at 200 vehicles per year for 20 years.

An important feature is the ability to perform precise controlled high-*g* manoeuvres. A load factor of 5*g* can be sustained through 720° of orbit, and 7*g* capability through 180°. Operation of the BQM-126A provides target missions for support of test and evaluation, and fleet readiness assessments of anti-air weapons systems. When equipped with particular sets of the various payloads of radar and IR augmentation, ECM or IRCM, and scoring, the BQM-126A will support the requirements of air-to-air missiles, surface-to-air missiles, anti-ship missile defence and surface-to-air gunnery missions.

The airframe makes extensive use of composite materials, and is launchable from land, ship's deck or an underwing aircraft pylon; parachute recovery can be made from land or water. It incorporates both a digital autopilot and remote control command capabilities, and has provisions for both pre-programmed missions and Tacan guidance. There is 0.17 m³ (6 cu ft) available for internal payload, and an RPV version (**Model 995**) with Martin Marietta surveillance payload has been projected.

The power plant is a 4 kN (899 lb st) Microturbo J403-MT-400 (TRI 60-2 Model 097) turbojet.

DIMENSIONS:

Wing span	3.05 m (10 ft)
Length overall	5.64 m (18 ft 6 in)
Body diameter (max)	0.38 m (1 ft 3 in)

WEIGHTS:

Weight empty	304 kg (670 lb)
Usable fuel	192 kg (424 lb)
Max payload	45.5 kg (100 lb) internal
	or 100 kg (220 lb) external
Launching weight (incl booster)	634 kg (1,398 lb)

PERFORMANCE:

Max level speed	580 knots (1,075 km/h; 668 mph)
Operating height range	S/L to 12,200 m (40,000 ft)
Range (RPV)	750 nm (1,390 km; 864 miles)
Typical endurance	1 h 36 min

Beechcraft BQM-126A missile target for the US Navy

BELL HELICOPTER TEXTRON INC

PO Box 482, Fort Worth, Texas 76101

BELL/BOEING D-340 POINTER

Due to fly in late 1987, the D-340 Pointer has been designed to meet a US Navy follow-on programme for a short-range shipboard surveillance RPV, and utilises the tilt-rotor technology developed by Bell and Boeing for the V-22 Osprey programme. It is intended to be compatible with the Elta GCS-2000 ground control system used for the Mazlat/AAI Pioneer now in US Navy service (see Israeli section); Bell is responsible for the tilt-rotor system, and Boeing for the all-composites main airframe. General appearance of the Pointer is shown in the accompanying photograph.

To meet the US Navy's medium-range surveillance RPV requirement, the Bell/Boeing team has also completed a design study for a larger version, which would include 376 kg (830 lb) of fuel and a 136 kg (300 lb) payload within a take-off gross weight of 952 kg (2,100 lb). Advantages claimed for the tilt-rotor concept in shipboard RPV operations include independence from separate launch and recovery systems

and equipment, since the aircraft is self-launching and self-recoverable.

The following details apply to the first prototype D-340 Pointer:

POWER PLANT: One 70.8 kW (95 shp) Williams International turboshaft engine, installed in centre fuselage with shaft drive to a pod-mounted rotor at each wingtip.

DIMENSIONS:
Width overall, rotors turning	5.61 m (18 ft 5 in)
Rotor diameter (each)	2.36 m (7 ft 9 in)
Distance between rotor centres	3.15 m (10 ft 4 in)
Length overall	4.06 m (13 ft 4 in)

WEIGHTS:
Weight empty, equipped	179 kg (395 lb)
Fuel	73 kg (160 lb)
Payload	34 kg (75 lb)
Max T-O weight	286 kg (630 lb)

PERFORMANCE (estimated):
Max cruising speed	160 knots (296 km/h; 184 mph)
Loiter speed	70 knots (130 km/h; 81 mph)
Service ceiling	7,620 m (25,000 ft)
Hovering ceiling OGE	2,285 m (7,500 ft)
Mission radius (guidance limit)	100 nm (185 km; 115 miles)

Endurance at 50 nm (93 km; 57 miles) from launch site:
loiter at 70 knots	4 h 30 min
hover	2 h

Half-scale mockup of the Bell/Boeing Pointer, the world's first tilt-rotor UMA

BOEING AEROSPACE COMPANY

PO Box 3999, Seattle, Washington 98124

BOEING YQM-94A B-GULL

Under the **Compass Cope** programme sponsored by the USAF (Aeronautical Systems Division) and the National Security Agency, Teledyne Ryan (which see) and Boeing Aerospace were each contracted to build prototype RPVs for competitive evaluation. Performance goals set for the flight demonstration programme included altitude of more than 16,765 m (55,000 ft), endurance of more than 20 hours, and payloads of 317.5–680 kg (700–1,500 lb). These parameters were to allow an eventual operational version to perform

Boeing YQM-94 B-Gull, winner of the Compass Cope HALE RPV demonstration programme

battlefield reconnaissance, sigint, communications relay, photo reconnaissance, ocean surveillance and atmospheric sampling duties, in all weathers, by day or night.

Boeing design studies for such a HALE (high altitude, long endurance) UMA began in September 1970, and on 15 July 1971 the USAF ordered two YQM-94A Compass Cope prototypes. The first of these made a successful first flight on 28 July 1973, but crashed while on final approach at the end of its second flight on 4 August 1973. The second YQM-94A made its first flight on 2 November 1974, and a second, of more than 17 hours, on 23/24 November, which marked successful completion of the flight demonstration programme. More than 16 hours of the latter flight were spent at altitudes above 16,765 m (55,000 ft), during which time the aircraft undertook manoeuvres in temperatures down to − 70.6°C. Fuel for some 3 hours' flying remained at the end of the flight.

On 27 August 1976 the USAF announced selection of Boeing Aerospace as single contractor for pre-production development of the Compass Cope aircraft, the contract being for three test aircraft with, it is believed, an option for 20 operational examples. The pre-production aircraft was to weigh some 7,811 kg (17,220 lb) at take-off, be 15.24 m (50 ft) long, carry a 544 kg (1,200 lb) payload to the prescribed altitude, and remain there for up to 24 hours. It was to be powered by a General Electric TF34-GE-100 turbofan, derated to approx 26.7 kN (6,000 lb st), with a 2.67 kN (600 lb st) secondary EPU mounted within the engine pylon to power the electrical systems, restart the main engine, or extend the airborne range of the aircraft by 174 nm (322 km; 200 miles). Payloads would be carried in interchangeable nosecones, and the production aircraft would have had automatic take-off, landing and mission control – omitted on cost grounds from the prototypes, which were flown under continuous manual control from the ground.

The USAF terminated the pre-production contract, and further YQM-94A development, in July 1977, the stated reason being that the potential payloads then envisaged might not mature in the form or at the time then required. The following description applies to the prototypes, except where indicated:

TYPE: Prototype high-altitude long-endurance RPV.
AIRFRAME: Cantilever shoulder-wing monoplane. Constant chord centre section, slight sweepback on outer wing leading edges. Aluminium skin, with bonded glassfibre honeycomb core. Airbrakes and ailerons on each trailing edge; no trailing edge flaps or leading edge lift devices. Semi-monocoque fuselage of basically circular section, tapering towards rear. Aluminium longerons, glassfibre bulkheads and glassfibre honeycomb skin. Cantilever tail unit, of similar construction to wings. Tailplane indexed in line with wings. Twin endplate fins and rudders, the former having small fore-and-aft pointed fairings at the base. Full-span elevator, with tabs. Retractable tricycle landing gear, with single wheel on each unit. Main units from Aero Commander 400, nose unit from a Learjet 25. All units retract rearward, the main units into fairings projecting aft of the wing trailing edges.

POWER PLANT: One 23.4 kN (5,270 lb st) General Electric J97-GE-100 non-afterburning turbofan engine, installed in pylon-mounted pod above fuselage, in line with wings. Fuel in integral tanks occupying full span of wings. Provision for restarting engine in flight.

GUIDANCE AND CONTROL: Avionics module, located in fuselage forward of wings, removable as a complete unit. Onboard instrumentation, developed by Sperry Flight Systems, included an integrated flight control system with internally generated ILS; a redundant stabilisation system; and an APW-26 airborne transceiver and other data link equipment. TV camera mounted in undernose fairing; heater in second prototype to prevent frosting of camera lens. Antenna bay in rear lower portion of fuselage. Ground control via command module embodying standard cockpit instrumentation, TV screen and navigation display; a video downlink; and a TPW-2A X-band radar van.

MISSION EQUIPMENT: Apart from the nose-mounted TV camera, details of other operational equipment were classified. All sensors and antennae housed in lower half of fuselage, payload being installed in interchangeable nose modules. Nose compartment capacity 3.26 m³ (115 cu ft); rear fuselage avionics compartment capacity 0.99 m³ (35 cu ft).

DIMENSIONS:
Wing span	27.43 m (90 ft)
Wing area (approx)	45.06 m² (485 sq ft)
Length overall (excl nose probe)	12.19 m (40 ft)
Height overall	3.86 m (12 ft 8 in)
Wheel track	6.40 m (21 ft 4 in)
Wheelbase	3.76 m (12 ft 4 in)

WEIGHTS:
Weight empty	2,494 kg (5,500 lb)
Payload for 24 h mission	317.5 kg (700 lb)
Max T-O weight	6,531 kg (14,400 lb)

PERFORMANCE (operational vehicle, estimated, at 7,559 kg; 16,665 lb AUW):
Landing speed	76 knots (141 km/h; 87.5 mph)
Operating altitude	above 18,285 m (60,000 ft)
T-O run	786 m (2,580 ft)
Landing run	905 m (2,970 ft)
Max range	8,600 nm (15,937 km; 9,903 miles)
Endurance	up to 27 h

BOEING ELECTRONICS COMPANY

625 Andover Park West (Building 5), Corporate Square, Seattle, Washington 98188

BOEING EXPERIMENTAL UMA

Boeing has built at Seattle two prototypes of a very large experimental unmanned aircraft, the first of which was rolled

Prototype 1986 US Navy HALE RPV by Boeing Electronics

out in late March 1986 at Moses Lake, Washington.

The programme is highly classified, although Boeing officials have been quoted as saying that the aircraft is potentially suitable for a number of missions including reconnaissance/surveillance, communications relay and border patrol. Clearly, the main clues to its capabilities are internal, the airframe being very unsophisticated in shape and the power plant modest. It almost certainly makes extensive use of composite materials. The fuselage is of unrelieved box section throughout most of its approximately 18.3 m (60 ft) length, having a blunt ogival nosecone and tapering at the extreme rear into a smaller tailcone. Wings are of commensurately high span and aspect ratio, with considerable anhedral outboard of the engine nacelles. The latter are very large, the twin Teledyne Continental liquid-cooled piston engines being mounted overwing but with considerable extension of their nacelles behind and below the wing trailing edges. Each drives a large-diameter three-blade propeller with a blunt conical spinner. Height over the fin and rudder is about 5.5 m (18 ft).

The aircraft appears to have a short-wheelbase zero-track landing gear, apparently non-retractable, with a single wheel forward and twin wheels aft, plus a small outrigged balancer wheel inboard of each wingtip. In October 1986, following collapse of the starboard outrigger, the port wing of one prototype reportedly became detached from the fuselage. Apart from a long nose boom and wingtip pitot, no external antennae are visible on the only photograph seen at the time of going to press. The overall configuration is suggestive of the ability to fly long-endurance, high-altitude missions with a low engine noise signature. The US Navy is reportedly the procurement authority for this RPV, although the USAF is also known to have had a recent active requirement for a high-altitude, subsonic standoff sensor platform for elint and other missions. It has been said (though not by Boeing) that an RPV to meet the US Navy's long-range surveillance and tracking requirements would need a span of over 61 m (200 ft), empty and payload weights of 3,400 kg (7,500 lb) and 680 kg (1,500 lb), and an endurance of 120 hours, cruising at 116–161 knots (215–298 km/h; 133–185 mph) at altitudes of up to 21,335 m (70,000 ft).

BOEING HELICOPTER COMPANY

PO Box 16858, Philadelphia, Pennsylvania 19142

See entry for Bell/Boeing D-340 Pointer.

BOEING MILITARY AIRPLANE COMPANY

3801 South Oliver (PO Box 7730), Wichita, Kansas 67277-7730

BOEING YCGM-121A

Company funded research into mini-drones was started by BMAC in mid-1979, with the basic goal of developing a simple, reliable and flexible 'fire and forget' weapon system, and a number of private venture prototypes were test-flown during 1980–82. This led, in early 1983, to a USAF development contract as part of the latter's **Pave Tiger** programme for a quick-reaction, near-term expendable drone intended to destroy or suppress enemy air defence systems. The initial contract, for 14 air vehicles (12 for testing and two spares), was intended to lead to procurement of about 1,000 production drones, but was terminated by USAF in late 1984. In mid-1987, however, the DoD directed USAF to reinstate the generally similar **Seek Spinner** programme. Meanwhile, flight testing began of Pave Tiger vehicles fitted with a version of the Hercules AN/ALQ-176 radar jamming system, in a separate programme called **Pave Cricket**.

Designated YCGM-121A, the Pave Tiger vehicle is ground (container)-launched, flying a pre-programmed mission using an onboard microprocessor navigation/guidance system, with the ability to carry warhead, ECM or other sensor payloads in interchangeable nosecones. Prototype flight testing was first scheduled to begin in mid-1983, but was considerably delayed, due primarily to problems in integrating the airframe and the E-Systems (Melpar Division) payload.

Boeing is currently marketing a vehicle generally similar to the YCGM-121A, under the name Brave 200 (see next entry).

Early prototype Boeing mini-drone, a predecessor of Pave Tiger and Brave 200

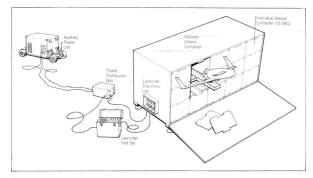

Container stored Pave Tiger/Brave 200 can be operated using only a two-person ground crew

Boeing Brave 200 multi-purpose mini-drone

DIMENSIONS: Generally as for Brave 200
WEIGHTS:

Basic operating weight empty	113 kg (250 lb)
Max payload	27.2 kg (60 lb)
Max launching weight (excl booster)	127 kg (280 lb)

PERFORMANCE (estimated):

Cruising speed	100 knots (185 km/h; 115 mph)
Typical endurance	8 h

BOEING BRAVE 200

Brave 200 (Boeing Robotic Air Vehicle) is the designation of a series of low-cost multi-purpose drones, of which the YCGM-121A Pave Tiger was one variant. Built of moulded plastics, it can be configured for such missions as ECM, defence suppression and reconnaissance.

The central electronics unit, just forward of the fuel tank, interfaces with the payload, located in the nose of the vehicle. The Brave 200 can be surface-launched from train, truck or ship, and has 1.1 kW of regulated power available for payload use. Zero-length rocket assisted launch was chosen for simplicity, reliability and rapid fire rate.

While a dead reckoning navigation system is an integral part of the Brave 200, alternative navigation systems can also be integrated into the vehicle, if necessary. On a typical mission, Brave 200 would climb to an altitude of 2,500–3,500 m (8,200–11,500 ft) and proceed to the target area. The vehicle can loiter in the target area for the duration of its flight, or move to another area and re-initiate its assigned mission.

The Brave 200 vehicles are designed for long-term storage, and are serviced, programmed and launched on their 'fire and forget' mission by a two-man ground crew.

In 1986, at the request of the West German Ministry of Defence, BMAC submitted a **Brave 210 Hornisse** (Hornet) proposal to fulfil Germany's DAR anti-radar drone requirement. If successful, Bodenseewerk would select and integrate German subsystems in the air vehicle, of which up to 3,000 could be required.

TYPE: Tactical mini-drone.
AIRFRAME: Sweptwing monoplane, with wings upswept at tips to form fins and rudders; non-swept canard surfaces, with elevators. Construction mainly of injection moulded composite materials including glassfibre, resin and polyurethane. No anhedral or dihedral. Wings have glassfibre spars and skin with moulded foam core, and fold forward when in launch container, deploying on exit. No flaps or ailerons; roll control spoilers of composite construction above wings. Canard surfaces have same construction as wings and are fitted with elevators. Short, pod shaped monocoque fuselage. No landing gear.

POWER PLANT: One 21 kW (28 hp) 438 cc Cuyuna two-cylinder two-stroke engine, mounted at rear of fuselage and driving a Boeing fixed-pitch pusher propeller with four blades made of injection moulded thermoplastics. Fuel tank in centre of fuselage. Underfuselage UPC rocket motor boosts aircraft to approx 70 knots (130 km/h; 81 mph) and 61 m (200 ft), when piston engine takes over.

LAUNCH AND RECOVERY: Air vehicles can be surface-launched from train, truck or ship, with rocket boost. Alternatively, they can be stored in a GPU-powered 2.44 × 2.44 × 6.1 m (8 × 8 × 20 ft) standard international container, in which 15 drones can be stored, if necessary, for 5 to 10 years without maintenance. Each of the 15 compartments contains a drone, launch rail and electric starter motor. To launch a drone, the compartment door is jettisoned and the drone emerges on its zero-length launch rail. The wings are then unfolded, the drone elevated to its launch angle, fuelled, electrical power connected, the drone checked out by launcher test equipment, and the mission programme fed in. The rocket booster is then fired electronically to launch the drone. Entire system can be handled by a two-man launch crew. Alternatively, drones can be packaged in groups of 2, 4, 6, 9 or 12; or the equipment can be connected to four containers, enabling 60 drones to be programmed and launched sequentially. By reducing range and/or payload weight, a parachute or other recovery system can be installed if required.

GUIDANCE AND CONTROL: Normally pre-programmed, controlled by a Boeing autopilot, but can be re-programmed in the field by tactical commanders. Onboard sensors and microprocessor guide drone along flight path to its destination. Engine-driven alternators; passive homing system for some missions. BMAC three-axis control system integrates a yaw-to-turn capability into the digital autopilot, simplifying tracking and target alignment.

MISSION EQUIPMENT: Payload bay in nose, nearly half of overall fuselage volume. Payloads can include non-nuclear warhead or modular ECM or sensor packages. Regulated electrical power of 1.1 kW available for payload use.

DIMENSIONS:

Wing span	2.57 m (8 ft 5 in)
Foreplane span	1.12 m (3 ft 8 in)
Wing area	0.93 m² (10 sq ft)
Length overall	2.12 m (6 ft 11.42 in)

Height overall	0.61 m (2 ft)
Fuselage: Max depth	0.51 m (1 ft 8.3 in)
WEIGHTS:	
Weight empty	70 kg (154 lb)
Fuel	22.7 kg (50 lb)
Max payload	approx 27 kg (60 lb)
Max launching weight	120 kg (265 lb)
PERFORMANCE:	
Cruising speed	121 knots (225 km/h; 140 mph)
Loiter speed	78 knots (145 km/h; 90 mph)
Max rate of climb at S/L	488 m (1,600 ft)/min
Ceiling	over 3,960 m (13,000 ft)
Range (depending upon payload/fuel ratio)	
	more than 434 nm (805 km; 500 miles)

BOEING BRAVE 3000

BMAC announced this second member of its Brave family in July 1986. It is a jet-powered, container-launched expendable drone for battlefield use, designed for easy and rapid deployment coupled with low cost and low maintenance requirements. Construction makes extensive use of composite materials and aluminium, and the 0.76 kN (170 lb st) NPT 171 turbojet engine is a development by Noel Penny Turbines of the UK. After leaving its container, boosted to flight speed by a solid propellant rocket bottle, the Brave 3000 transitions to flight by deploying its engine air inlet, wing and fins and starting the turbojet engine.

The drone is equipped with a three-axis digital autopilot and central electronics unit which is the heart of the vehicle control system. All mission data are pre-programmed prior to launch, and once in the air the drone is totally autonomous, completing its assigned mission without any further commands or directions. Navigation system employs a Doppler radar velocity sensor, two-axis vertical gyro and three-axis strapdown magnetometer; a deployable side-force ventral fin aids accuracy of the terminal dive.

Development of the Brave 3000 began in 1981, and first flight was made in May 1983. Concept and validation testing have been completed, and flight tests have verified aerodynamic properties, flight and propulsion controls, engine air start operation, climb-out and cruise performance, and Doppler aided navigation. The launch concept has been demonstrated from an enclosed container mounted on a mobile trailer, including ripple firing at 5-10 second intervals. Brave 3000 is compatible with the 12-round launcher of the Multiple Launch Rocket System.

Boeing's 'fire and forget' Brave 3000, launch-compatible with MLRS

DIMENSIONS:	
Wing span	2.26 m (7 ft 5 in)
Wing area	0.56 m² (6 sq ft)
Length overall (excl booster)	3.44 m (11 ft 3.5 in)
Fuselage: Max width	0.295 m (11.6 in)
Max depth	0.30 m (11.8 in)
WEIGHTS:	
Fuel: min	15.9 kg (35 lb)
max	56.7 kg (125 lb)
Payload: min	74.8 kg (165 lb)
max	102 kg (225 lb)
Max launching weight:	
incl booster	285 kg (629 lb)
excl booster	238 kg (525 lb)
PERFORMANCE:	
Max cruising speed	380 knots (704 km/h; 437 mph)
Loiter speed	245 knots (454 km/h; 282 mph)
Max rate of climb at S/L	1,006 m (3,300 ft)/min
Ceiling	7,620 m (25,000 ft)
Range with 83.9 kg (185 lb) payload and 47.6 kg (105 lb) of	
fuel	224 nm (415 km; 258 miles)

BRANDEBURY AEROSTRUCTURES INC

15734 Crabbs Branch Way, Rockville, Maryland 20855

This company manufactures RPV airframe components for various US government agencies, output being at the rate of six to eight airframes per month in the spring of 1986. Details of these airframes are classified, but Brandebury has also developed a mini-RPV of its own, known as the Microdrone.

BRANDEBURY MICRODRONE

The Microdrone embodies an airframe structure of the type developed by Brandebury for all its RPV manufacturing programmes, which consists of a combination of open-cell plastics foam, epoxy impregnated at hardpoints and covered with a glassfibre composite skin. Wing spars are reinforced with carbonfibre.

The Microdrone prototype is of shoulder-wing configuration, with a nose-mounted 35 cc two-stroke engine, wide-span tailplane with twin endplate fins and rudders, and a tailwheel type landing gear. As demonstrated to the US Coast Guard in the autumn of 1985, including launch and recovery from both land and shipboard helicopter platforms, it was equipped with a ParaPlane Corporation ram air inflated rectangular parachute which could be used either to recover the air vehicle or to enable it to loiter on station at low speeds. Payloads included a pod-mounted video or low light level camera, with an onboard transponder to facilitate radar tracking. Guidance and control were by VFR equipment which included airspeed, altitude and magnetic heading telemetry and control centre based display for imagery from the onboard sensor.

It was planned to test, in 1986, a larger version of the Microdrone, powered by a 100 cc engine.

DIMENSIONS (A: 35 cc, B: 100 cc):	
Wing span:	
A	2.74 m (9 ft)
B	not stated
Wing area:	
A	0.93 m² (10 sq ft)
B	1.11 m² (12 sq ft)

WEIGHTS:
  Payload:
    A   not stated
    B   7.25 kg (16 lb)
  Max launching weight:
    A   13.6 kg (30 lb)
    B   not stated
PERFORMANCE:
  Cruising speed (B):
    with parafoil   9–26 knots (16–48 km/h; 10–30 mph)
    without parafoil
          26–78 knots (48–145 km/h; 30–90 mph)

BRANDEBURY VTX-1 MICRODRONE

This Microdrone was proposed in 1986 for a US Army requirement known as BOSS (Battalion Operated Surveillance System). Having a max payload capacity of 36.3 kg (80 lb) for a real-time imagery sensor, it has a high-wing configuration, cylindrical section fuselage with spinnered propeller, anhedral tailplane and single fin and rudder.

No other details of the VTX-1 were received.

BRANDEBURY SKYBALL

Displayed at an AUVS exhibition in July 1986, the Skyball was at that time being proposed to the US Army as a contender in the BOSS (Battalion Operated Surveillance System) competition. Of extremely small and simple configuration, it consists of a slim tubular 'fuselage', to which is fitted a rudimentary tricycle landing gear and a rear-mounted engine driving a shrouded propeller. Attached to this structure is a small ParaPlane Corporation parafoil wing, to provide lift during flight and controlled descent/recovery in the event of an engine failure. The power plant, a 2.24 kW (3 hp) Rossi engine, runs on a fuel mixture of alcohol and oil, and the nose-mounted payload consists of a miniature CCD (charge coupled device) TV camera with a two-way data link. Despite its strange appearance, the Skyball is said to be inherently stable; it has rudder and elevator surfaces in the form of trailing edges to the propeller shroud support struts, and altitude is governed by engine throttle control. The aircraft navigates by TV guided dead reckoning, and carries no autopilot. An area 7.62 m (25 ft) square is adequate for launch and recovery operations.

The parafoil-recoverable Brandebury Skyball *(Jane's/Mike Keep)*

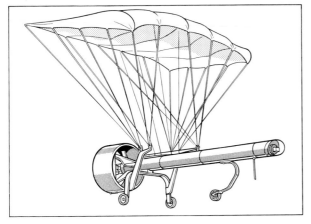

DIMENSIONS:
  No details known
WEIGHT:
  Launching weight   6.4 kg (14 lb)
PERFORMANCE:
  Max endurance   1 h

BRUNSWICK CORPORATION (Defense Division)

3333 Harbor Boulevard, CS 2009, Costa Mesa, California 92626-1009

BRUNSWICK AIR LAUNCHED DECOYS

Brunswick's Defense Division, then known as Celesco Industries, entered the air-launched UMA arena in 1968 with an internally funded R & D programme. Response to a USAF Avionics Laboratory requirement for a high-subsonic electronic warfare glide vehicle yielded the **Model 150 Maxi Decoy** which could be carried, wings folded, on the external stores racks of a strike aircraft and launched to decoy radar-directed weapons away from its manned 'parent'. During flight tests conducted by USAF in April 1973, using an F-4 Phantom launch aircraft, all performance objectives were met on the first two test flights, obviating the need for the remainder of the scheduled trials programme. Three Maxis could be accommodated in each of the F-4's four underfuselage Sparrow missile recesses, plus two more on each 340 kg (750 lb) underwing bomb station, making a possible total of 20 decoys.

The **Model 290P Propelled Decoy**, successfully flight tested by USAF in July 1974, was designed for high speed cruise as well as gliding flight modes, using a rocket propulsion unit. Larger than the Maxi (four instead of eight under the wings of an F-4), with a circular (instead of square) section fuselage, it provided extended range delivery of medium-sized payloads. Technology developed during these programmes was applied in the design of a modified (cylindrical fuselage), unpowered decoy known as **Samson 1**, produced under licence by Israel Military Industries and deployed by IDF manned strike aircraft attacking SAM sites in the Bekaa Valley, Lebanon, in 1982–83.

The US Navy acquired 100 Samsons in 1985, employing some for operational evaluation before assigning the remainder to selected carrier units. The service plans eventually to equip all its carrier air wings with similar type decoys. In 1987 it was to begin receiving the first of a major order for 1,000, and had requested bids for up to 1,500 of a more advanced version known as **TALD** (tactical air launched decoy). Reverting to a square section fuselage, TALD is larger than Samson, enabling it to carry more payload and dispense it over a wider range of speeds and altitudes. A powered version of TALD, for possible use as an expendable 'kamikaze', anti-radiation seeker or reconnaissance RPV, is under study. Any of the decoy models mentioned can also be adapted for use as an expendable training target, with or without threat simulation devices and/or a propulsion unit.

TYPE: Air-launched expendable decoy.
AIRFRAME: High-wing monoplane, of modular construction, with extensive use of composites materials. Flip-out wings, with 30° sweepback when fully deployed. Square cross-section fuselage on Maxi Decoy and TALD, circular

Brunswick Samson decoy drone

The US Navy's tactical air launched decoy (TALD), an advanced version of Samson

section on Propelled Decoy and Samson. Cruciform sweptback tail surfaces on all except TALD, which has no horizontal surfaces.

POWER PLANT: Propelled Decoy powered by Atlantic Research Corporation solid propellant rocket motor with nominal burn time of 5 minutes. Powered (RPV) version of TALD under study.

LAUNCH: Air-launched by pilot command from carrying aircraft. Wings, folded back and faired with fuselage to minimise size and drag prior to separation from launch aircraft, are extended automatically after launch.

GUIDANCE AND CONTROL: By autopilot which is pre-programmed on flight line before mission with variables that include launch altitude, flight profile, attack speed and manoeuvrability. Single-axis (roll/heading) autopilot in Model 150, two-axis (roll/heading and altitude) in Model 290P.

MISSION EQUIPMENT: Can include active or passive ECM, warhead, or special mission packages. Emitters or warhead in nose bay; chaff dispenser in ventral bay. More precise details are generally classified, and vary according to customer requirements, but typical emitters tested on original Model 150 reportedly included a C-band jammer, and a G-band jammer with active radar signature augmentation, provided by RCA (Automated Systems Division).

DIMENSIONS:
Wing span:
150   0.76 m (2 ft 6 in)
290P   1.40 m (4 ft 7 in)
Length overall:
150   1.14 m (3 ft 9 in)
290P   2.24 m (7 ft 4 in)
Body size:
150 (width)   0.13 m (5 in)
150 (depth)   0.13 m (5 in)
290P (diameter)   0.26 m (10.1 in)
Payload volume:
150   0.008 m³ (0.29 cu ft)
290P   0.03 m³ (1.04 cu ft)

WEIGHTS:
Max launching weight:
150   59 kg (130 lb)
290P   136 kg (300 lb)
PERFORMANCE:
Max level speed: 150, 290P   Mach 0.8 to 0.9

JOHN E. BURKAM

c/o Rensselaer Polytechnic Institute, Troy, New York 12180-3590

BURKAM BIG BIRD

This small RPH was designed by Mr Burkam and two asssociates in the mid-1970s, responding to interest expressed by the US Army in a rotating-wing mini-RPV. It was built and flown to acquire experience and flight performance data for the aircraft, its autopilot, the telemetry system, and a semi-automatic landing system. First flight, which was tethered, was made on 30 April 1977. The helicopter was later donated to the Rensselaer Polytechnic Institute, where subsequent airframe changes have included installation of a graphite/epoxy stiffened tailboom. Experiments and developmental research, including tests of a vibration isolation mounting for the engine, were continuing in 1986 as part of the RPI's Center of Excellence in Rotorcraft Technology, sponsored by the US Army Research Office.

TYPE: Experimental RPH.

AIRFRAME: Minimum framework helicopter, with two-blade Hiller type teetering main rotor (with servo-rotor), two-blade tail rotor, glassfibre/epoxy tailboom and metal skid landing gear. Main and tail rotor collective pitch coupled electronically. Non-linear collective pitch control for minimum sensitivity in mid-range.

POWER PLANT: One 8.9 kW (12 hp) McCulloch two-stroke go-cart engine, with rpm governed electronically.

LAUNCH AND RECOVERY: Conventional helicopter T-O and landing.

GUIDANCE AND CONTROL: Seven-channel modified Kraft radio control system (transmitter and receiver). Servos modified to augment torque for control of throttle, collective pitch, yaw, pitch and roll.

Burkam Big Bird in 1986 configuration

EQUIPMENT: Three-phase brushless alternator. Miniature rate gyro for yaw stabilisation.

DIMENSIONS:

Main rotor diameter	3.35 m (11 ft)
Main rotor disc area	8.83 m² (95.03 sq ft)
Tail rotor diameter	0.61 m (2 ft)
Tail rotor disc area	0.29 m² (3.14 sq ft)
Length overall, rotors turning	4.57 m (15 ft)

WEIGHTS:

Weight empty	32.7 kg (72 lb)
Max payload	22.7 kg (50 lb)
Max T-O weight	56.7 kg (125 lb)

DESIGN PERFORMANCE:
Endurance of 1 h 12 min at 50 knots (92 km/h; 57 mph) at 2,745 m (9,000 ft), carrying 10.4 kg (23 lb) payload

CALIFORNIA MICROWAVE INC
(Government Electronics Division)
6022 Variel Avenue, Woodland Hills, California 91365

CALIFORNIA MICROWAVE CM-30 and CM-44

The CM-30, first flown in October 1984, is a direct modification of the Rutan Long-EZ homebuilt aircraft, but the CM-44 is somewhat scaled-up in size and has a number of modifications to improve its 'low observable' signatures. Changes include overwing flush intakes for the rear-mounted engine, underfuselage flaps, and use of composite materials for the three-blade pusher propeller.

Equipped with appropriate nose-mounted sensors, the CM-44 is designed to carry out pre-programmed battlefield reconnaissance, elint, electronic warfare or communications RPV missions. The tandem cockpits are retained, however, to permit occupation by an onboard pilot during development and training flights.

Flight demonstration of the CM-30 took place in April 1987 as one of three contending UMAs in the US Army's IEW-UAV competition. In this entry California Microwave, as prime contractor, was teamed with Lockheed-Austin, Beech Aircraft Corporation, and SAIC.

Further details of both aircraft can be found in the Addenda.

CONTINENTAL RPVs
34924 Victor Street, Barstow, California 92311

CONTINENTAL MiG-27 'FLOGGER-D' TARGETS

Continental RPVs became contractor in 1983 for the US National Training Center at Fort Irwin, California, to supply RCMAT close air support system (CASS) aerial targets based on a scale representation of the Soviet MiG-27 'Flogger-D' combat aircraft. The targets can reach an altitude of more than 3,660 m (12,000 ft), and can be equipped with an IR source, and MILES or AGES equipment for a 'shoot-back' capability.

The 'Flogger-D' targets are manufactured in four sizes, ranging from the one-ninth scale **C19M** through the **C17M** and **C17MG** (both one-seventh) to the **C125M** (one-fifth). The C19M runs on nitro-methanol fuel, the others on a petrol/oil mixture. Manoeuvrability is effected by elevator control, and onboard payloads can include a gas or smoke grenade,

Continental's 'Hind-D' lookalike target *(Erik Simonsen)*

Continental RPVs MiG-27 target

pyrotechnics, infra-red source, cine camera, smoke hit indicator, or near-miss indicator. The aircraft have glassfibre fuselages and tail units with plywood wings. A modified version of the C125M is being produced by Boeing of Canada (which see).

The targets are hand or rail launched, returning to a belly landing, and are used in training crews of air defence artillery and small arms air defence, including such weapons systems as Redeye, Stinger, Vulcan and Chaparral.

DIMENSIONS:

Wing span: C19M	1.52 m (5 ft)
C17M	2.29 m (7 ft 6 in)
C17MG	2.54 m (8 ft 4 in)
C125M	2.84 m (9 ft 4 in)

WEIGHTS:

Weight empty: C19M	3.2 kg (7 lb)
C17M	7.7 kg (17 lb)
C17MG	13.2 kg (29 lb)
C125M	12.7 kg (28 lb)
Payload: C19M	2.3 kg (5 lb)
C17M	2.7 kg (6 lb)
C17MG	8.2 kg (18 lb)
C125M	13.6 kg (30 lb)
Fuel (standard): C19M	0.45 kg (1 lb)
C17M, C17MG, C125M	0.91 kg (2 lb)

PERFORMANCE:
Speed range:

C19M	16–82 knots (29–151 km/h; 18–94 mph)
C17M	17–80 knots (32–148 km/h; 20–92 mph)
C17MG	35–104 knots (64–193 km/h; 40–120 mph)
C125M	26–104 knots (48–193 km/h; 30–120 mph)

Endurance at max speed, standard fuel:

C19M	16 min
C17M	45 min
C17MG, C125M	32 min

Control range (each controller):

C19M	1.08 nm (2 km; 1.24 miles)
C17M, C17MG	1.62 nm (3 km; 1.86 miles)
C125M	2.16 nm (4 km; 2.49 miles)

CONTINENTAL ONE-FIFTH SCALE TARGETS

Continental also produces target or recognition training representations of the Sukhoi Su-7 and Su-25, Mi-24 'Hind-D' helicopter, Fairchild A-10 and General Dynamics F-16, all to within ±10 per cent of one-fifth scale. Details are generally similar to those of the C125M MiG-27.

CONTINENTAL SURVEILLANCE RPV

This short-range RPV (8–9 nm; 15–35 km 9.3–21.75 miles), under development in 1987, has an endurance of approx 2 h and carries a day/night imagery payload.

DEFENSE ADVANCED RESEARCH PROJECTS AGENCY (DARPA)

1400 Wilson Boulevard, Arlington, Virginia 22209

DARPA AMBER

Amber is the project name for a 1986 research study by DARPA for a long-endurance RPV, able to carry a FLIR, communications relay or ESM/elint payload and remain airborne for several days or even weeks. Responsibility was expected to be transferred to the US Army and/or US Navy during 1987.

DEPARTMENT OF THE AIR FORCE

The Pentagon, Washington, DC 20330

XBQM-106 TELEPLANE

This designation covers a series of experimental mini-RPVs designed and built by USAF's Flight Dynamics Laboratory; first flight was made in 1975. By 1982, 23 vehicles had been completed and 13 variants flown, incorporating various alternative wing, nose, tail and engine configurations and with payloads ranging from 11.3 to 59 kg (25–130 lb). Successive flight test programmes have demonstrated, inter alia, use of a fluidic autopilot (1979); several seeker/warhead combinations for a variety of expendable strike missions; use of lightweight composites and 'stealth' technology; and a low-cost autopilot (1983–84) incorporating microprocessor capability. Development effort had ended by early 1986.

The following description is of a typical XBQM-106 vehicle *circa* 1980:

TYPE: Experimental mini-RPV.

AIRFRAME: High-wing monoplane, wings being slightly swept back and having glassfibre skins with a foam plastics core. Pod and boom fuselage of glassfibre cloth and resin, with moulded polyurethane foam bulkheads; Kevlar and graphite in highly stressed areas. Sweptback single fin, integral with rear fuselage; rudder and all-moving tailplane have glassfibre or balsa skin with foam core. Side-force panels

USAF XBQM-106A (c/n 7) with side-force panels and MC-101A engine

above and below wings. Twin dependent endplate fins and rudders on some examples.

POWER PLANT: One 13.5 kW (18 hp) Herbrandson Dyad 220 two-cylinder two-stroke engine, mounted above wing centre section and driving a two-blade fixed-pitch wooden pusher propeller. Single fuel tank in fuselage, capacity 11.5 litres (2.5 Imp gallons; 3 US gallons).

LAUNCH AND RECOVERY: Launched pneumatically by catapult. Normal recovery by landing on ventral skid. Recovery by powered ram air canopy also demonstrated.

GUIDANCE AND CONTROL: Radio and radar command guidance system standard. Real-time ground-based control system; USAF-developed autopilot or manual control optional. Air-to-ground uplink/downlink telemetry; tracking sensors; downlinked video from nose-mounted camera standard. Ailerons, rudder and all-moving tailplane for aerodynamic control. Wings-level steering available via wing mounted side-force control surfaces for accurate target strike experiments. Bosch 28V 17A engine driven alternator for electrical power.

MISSION EQUIPMENT: Various military payloads, installed in interchangeable nose sections of standard or modified shape.

DIMENSIONS:

Wing span	3.63 m (11 ft 11 in)
Wing area	1.80 m² (19.4 sq ft)
Length overall	3.07 m (10 ft 1 in)
Height overall	0.84 m (2 ft 9 in)
Propeller diameter	0.71 m (2 ft 4 in)

WEIGHTS:

Weight empty	47.6 kg (105 lb)
Max fuel	8.2 kg (18 lb)
Max payload	50.8 kg (112 lb)
Max launching weight	106.6 kg (235 lb)

PERFORMANCE (at max launching weight):

Max level speed at S/L	100 knots (185 km/h; 115 mph)
Max cruising speed at S/L	90 knots (167 km/h; 104 mph)
Stalling speed, power on	55 knots (102 km/h; 64 mph)
Max rate of climb at S/L	305 m (1,000 ft)/min
Ceiling	3,050 m (10,000 ft)
Range:	
with max payload	112 nm (207 km; 129 miles)
with max fuel	675 nm (1,250 km; 777 miles)
Max endurance	5 h

DEPARTMENT OF THE ARMY

The Pentagon, Washington, DC 20310

Selection to fill the US Army's **IEW-UAV** (intelligence and electronic warfare unmanned air vehicle) requirement was expected in 1987 following flight demonstrations in the spring by the California Airmotive CM-30, Developmental Sciences R4E-50 SkyEye and Pacific Aerosystem Heron 26 (which see).

At that time the service was also evaluating a concept for a forward area anti-helicopter expendable drone, under a programme known as **Metal Eagle**; and was co-operating with the US Marine Corps in development of the latter's **ExDrone** (see APL entry), a small, inexpensive expendable for high frequency communications jamming, also in forward battle areas.

DEPARTMENT OF THE NAVY

The Pentagon, Washington, DC 20361

XBQM-108A

The XBQM-108A was a Navy in-house design for an experimental test vehicle to demonstrate VATOL (vertical attitude take-off and landing) aboard non-aviation ships. Essentially, it comprised a delta wing and small foreplane married to the fuselage and vertical tail of a Northrop MQM-74A target drone and the midcourse guidance system of an AGM-84A Harpoon missile. Tethered hovering tests were demonstrated successfully on 29 September 1976, but the programme was then terminated without conducting the planned free-flight hover and other tests that were to have followed. The programme was conducted by the David W. Taylor Naval Ship Research and Development Center.

US Navy's XBQM-108A experimental VATOL aircraft

POWER PLANT: One 2.94 kN (660 lb st) Teledyne CAE YJ402-CA-400 turbojet, mounted in rear fuselage and fitted with vane-type thrust vector control system. Ventral air intake in S-shaped glassfibre duct. Fuel capacity 45.4 litres (10 Imp gallons; 12 US gallons).

LAUNCH AND RECOVERY: Vertical attitude ('tail-sitting') take-off and landing, but retaining capability for conventional (horizontal) attitude take-off and landing. Parachute recovery system of MQM-74A retained in case of emergency.

GUIDANCE AND CONTROL: MQM-74A command and control receiver/decoder; IBM/Lear Siegler midcourse guidance unit from AGM-84A Harpoon missile, providing control in vertical attitude by signalling actuation of steel vanes in engine exhaust for pitch, roll and yaw trim. Elevons and rudder would have been similarly signalled for control in horizontal flight. Radar altimeter from Harpoon to sense altitude in both hover and, after spring loaded 90° rotation, in horizontal flight.

DIMENSIONS:

Wing span	2.21 m (7 ft 3 in)
Wing area	2.02 m² (21.74 sq ft)
Foreplane span	1.10 m (3 ft 7.5 in)
Foreplane area	0.46 m² (5 sq ft)
Body diameter (max)	0.36 m (1 ft 2 in)
Length overall	approx 3.58 m (11 ft 9 in)

WEIGHTS:

Fuel	42.6 kg (94 lb)
Max T-O weight	254 kg (560 lb)

PERFORMANCE (estimated):

Max cruising speed	400 knots (741 km/h; 460 mph)
Time to 1,525 m (5,000 ft)	8.8 s
Endurance	approx 30 min

LODED

LODED (LOng Duration Expendable Decoy) was designed by the Naval Research Laboratory as a low-speed ship protection system, and a slightly over half-scale prototype was flight tested in the early 1980s. This, combined with earlier wind tunnel tests, proved the vehicle's capability for low-speed loiter, moderate dash speed, and only minimal volume and logistic impact on the ship's operation. A full-scale vehicle was proposed, to provide mission durations in excess of 12 hours carrying an 18 kg (40 lb) payload, but this was not built. The following description applies to the scale prototype; details of the proposed full size LODED can be found on page 868 of the *1983–84 Jane's All the World's Aircraft*.

TYPE: Experimental expendable decoy.

AIRFRAME: Graphite reinforced glassfibre/epoxy fuselage spaceframe with plywood/PVC foam bulkheads and foam board closure panels. Engine cowling of moulded Kevlar/epoxy. Nose formed with Kevlar/epoxy laid up over a formed

LODED experimental drone built by the US Navy

Styrofoam shell. Wings and winglets formed of Kevlar/epoxy over hot wired Styrofoam cores and built-up Kevlar/graphite box spars. Forward and rear wings of equal area and span. Wings pivot about the 32 per cent chord location for pitch control (forward wings together), roll (rear wings differentially), and pitch trim (rear wings together). All control system components located inside fuselage for maximum aerodynamic efficiency and to allow ease of wing removal/installation and packaging. Wings and winglets utilise low Reynolds number Wortmann FX-63-137 aerofoil section. Winglets provide principal directional stability forces and augment pitch and stall stability while reducing drag at high lift coefficients. Geometric washout of 2° in each wing to provide gentle stall characteristics.

POWER PLANT: One 0.75 kW (1 hp) two-stroke engine, driving a two-blade wooden pusher propeller.

LAUNCH AND RECOVERY: Launched by ground take-off (tricycle landing gear) or pneumatic catapult. Conventional wheel landing in both cases.

GUIDANCE AND CONTROL: VHF pulse width AM command link. Individual servos driving forward and rear wing incidence adjustment for pitch, roll and trim commands. Pulse width modulated seven-channel telemetry link.

DIMENSIONS:
Wing span, each	1.73 m (5 ft 8 in)
Wing area, total	1.18 m² (12.76 sq ft)
Length overall	1.24 m (4 ft 1 in)
Fuselage: Max width	0.17 m (6.75 in)
Max depth	0.20 m (8 in)
Propeller diameter	0.28 m (11 in)

WEIGHTS:
Weight empty	5.9 kg (13 lb)
Max fuel	3.6 kg (8 lb)
Max payload	4.5 kg (10 lb)
Max launching weight	11.3 kg (25 lb)

PERFORMANCE:
Launching speed	33 knots (61 km/h; 38 mph)

QF-86

The Naval Weapons Center at China Lake, California, converted 31 North American F-86H Sabres into QF-86H

Naval Weapons Center QF-86F pilotless target aircraft *(US Navy)*

pilotless target aircraft, beginning in 1974. Modifications included an onboard TV camera, Sperry autopilot, a non-redundant proportional control system and associated telemetry. These were followed in 1979 by prototype conversion of three F-86Fs, and more than 100 QF-86Fs are being delivered at the rate of about 13 a year to support weapons systems test and evaluation. Used for both manned and unmanned target work, they are being modified by Northrop Services Inc, and became operational in 1982. Completion of this programme is due in 1991.

QF-4

The first (**QF-4B**) target conversion of the McDonnell Douglas F-4 Phantom II was undertaken by the Naval Air Development Center at Warminster, Pennsylvania, six examples being delivered to the Pacific Missile Test Center at Point Mugu, California, from spring 1972. Six more of this UHF configured QF-4B version were converted subsequently by the Naval Air Rework Facility at Cherry Point, North Carolina, in 1975–78. These aircraft, equipped for high-*g* manoeuvring, had provisions for photographic and electronic scoring and ECM.

To succeed the UHF QF-4B, an improved **QF-4N** version was developed by the Naval Weapons Center, differing primarily in having an NWC developed integrated target control system (ITCS) and a forward-looking TV camera for drone take-off and landing. Procurement of this ITCS configured QF-4 target aircraft is by conversion of retired F-4N Phantoms, deliveries beginning to the Pacific Missile Test Center in November 1985 and the NWC in June 1986. The

Naval Air Development Center QF-4B with onboard safety crew *(US Navy)*

QF-4N programme involves 90 targets, being delivered at approximately seven per year.

MR-RPV

The US Navy, as executive authority for this new medium-range reconnaissance RPV, issued a request for proposals in August 1986. The selected vehicle will also be procured by the US Marine Corps and USAF, who are collaborating in the programme.

Intended to operate at distances of 150–350 nm (278–648 km; 173–403 miles) from the point of launch, the MR-RPV is required to weigh no more than 998 kg (2,200 lb) and to have a minimum speed of 300 knots (556 km/h; 345 mph) and a ceiling of about 5,500 m (18,000 ft). It must be able to detect and identify targets by day or night, in a hostile jamming environment, and transmit data in real or near-real time. Navigation guidance will normally be pre-programmed, but must be capable of re-programming by remote control after launch.

Navy MR-RPVs must be launchable from Grumman A-6 aircraft or from the decks of 'Spruance' class destroyers, with a parachute/flotation bag system for recovery from water. Those for the USMC will be ground-launched, while USAF examples should be air launchable from the RF-4C and F-16. The US Navy has also stressed that ground control stations, data links and sensors should have either commonality or compatibility with those used in its Pioneer short-range reconnaissance RPV system. Initially, the USN and USMC will install a TV sensor package, but plans are eventually to introduce an electro-optical system being developed by USAF for its version of the MR-RPV.

The AROD airborne device being evaluated by the US Marine Corps in 1987 *(Jane's/Mike Keep)*

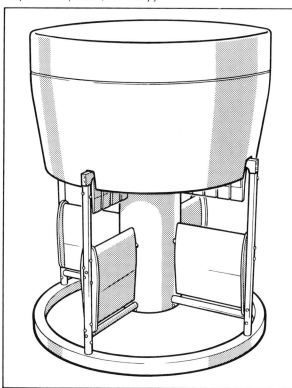

Three air vehicles were in contention in spring 1987: versions of the Beechcraft BQM-126A, Meteor Mirach 100 and Northrop NV-144 (which see). Beech is teamed in its entry with Martin Marietta and Singer, while the Meteor proposal (known as Mizar) is supported by Pacific Aerosystem and British Aerospace. During the year the USN was expected to select two finalists for a 21-month prototype demonstration programme leading to announcement of a winner in late 1988 and the start of production a year later. First deliveries will go to the USN and USMC (stated requirement for 31 systems, each with 10–12 RPVs). The USAF, which plans at least five squadrons of 20 MR-RPVs each plus a 100-vehicle reserve, expects to receive its first examples in FY 1993.

AROD

First flown in December 1986, AROD (airborne remotely operated device) is being developed by the US Marine Corps for short-range surveillance missions. Weighing less than 45.4 kg (100 lb), it is powered by a small two-cylinder petrol engine driving a two-blade vertically-mounted ducted fan to provide the necessary lift. Manoeuvring is achieved by conventional movable control surfaces. Onboard equipment includes a fibre optic data and control link and gyro stabilised miniature TV camera. Operational demonstration was expected in autumn 1987.

DEVELOPMENTAL SCIENCES
(Astronics Division of Lear Siegler Inc)
1930 South Vineyard Avenue, PO Box 50000, Ontario, California 91761

Since 1971 Developmental Sciences, which was acquired by Lear Siegler Inc in April 1984, has designed and built, under contract to various US agencies and manufacturers, a number of advanced RPVs for research and other purposes. More recently main activities have concentrated on supporting foreign and domestic operators of the SkyEye R4E RPV system.

DEVELOPMENTAL SCIENCES RPA-9 SCOUT

Developmental Sciences designed, built and flight tested this electrically propelled mini-RPV, under a USAF contract, on behalf of Northrop. It first flew in 1975, and development was subsequently continued by DS for several years as a company funded programme, with a new engine and autopilot. By 1978 the Scout had flown with two different power plants. One was an electric motor powered by lithium batteries, using a small petrol engine for launch only; the other was a low-cost 3.7 kW (5 hp) two-stroke engine, installed for harassment RPV development.

RPA-9 Scout, built for Northrop by Developmental Sciences

TYPE: Experimental mini-RPV.

AIRFRAME: Sweptback shoulder-wing monoplane, with servo-actuated trailing edge elevons and sweptback endplate fin at each wingtip. Wings, elevons and fins have Kevlar skins, with partial urethane foam support. Tapered body, of super-elliptical cross-section, built of bulkheads and Kevlar skin and having detachable nose-cap. Non-retractable tricycle landing gear.

POWER PLANT: See introductory paragraph.

LAUNCH AND RECOVERY: Conventional wheeled T-O and landing standard.

GUIDANCE AND CONTROL: As for RPA-12 SkyEye.

MISSION EQUIPMENT: DSI-PSA-WL-01 stability augmentation autopilot. Eight telemetry channels to monitor speed, altitude, autopilot functions and onboard sensors.

DIMENSIONS:

Wing span	2.715 m (8 ft 10.92 in)
Wing area	1.38 m² (14.86 sq ft)
Length overall	0.91 m (3 ft)
Height overall	0.20 m (8.04 in)

WEIGHTS:

Weight empty, equipped	15.4 kg (34 lb)
Payload	6.8 kg (15 lb)
Max T-O weight	25 kg (55 lb)

PERFORMANCE (at max T-O weight):

Max level speed	60 knots (111 km/h; 69 mph)
Stalling speed	32.5 knots (60 km/h; 37 mph)
Max rate of climb at S/L	91 m (300 ft)/min
Range	43 nm (80 km; 50 miles)
Endurance	1 h 15 min

DEVELOPMENTAL SCIENCES (NASA) OBLIQUE WING RPRA

Development of this RPRA (remotely piloted research aircraft) was sponsored by NASA's Ames Research Center; detail design and development was subcontracted to DSI. Guidelines called for a flying wing type of vehicle, with control achieved principally by use of the elevons, able to fly at wing yaw angles between 0° and 45°. A horizontal tail was added to provide longitudinal stability. Construction of the prototype began on 16 February 1973. First flight took place at NASA's Dryden Flight Research Center at Edwards AFB, California, on 6 August 1976. Two more successful flights were made in August and September. Each flight lasted between 40 and 60 minutes, and all test flight objectives were met, including yawing the wing to 45°.

TYPE: Remotely piloted research aircraft.

AIRFRAME: Mid-wing monoplane of elliptical planform. Special reflexed aerofoil section, constant over entire wing. No dihedral, anhedral, incidence or aerodynamic twist. Wing capable of in-flight sweeps of 15°, 30° and 45°. Glassfibre and epoxy resin construction. Outboard leading edge removable for installation and removal of payload. Wing 'dished' near centre to permit yawing of fuselage with respect to wing without breaking contour of the fuselage/wing mating surfaces. Trailing edge fitted with vertical stabiliser, ahead of normal fin and rudder, to provide 'weathercock' stability at larger wing yaw angles. Wingtips and stabiliser tip frangible to minimise damage during recovery. Control effected primarily by wide-span elevons on trailing edge, operable differentially (as ailerons) or in unison (as elevators). Tips, of glassfibre/epoxy resin/Ceconite construction, actuated

DSI/NASA oblique wing RPRV

electrically by directly coupled servos. Basically cylindrical fuselage, with moulded glassfibre/epoxy resin/aluminium skin. Transparent removable hemispherical nose cap. Central portion, housing the engine, parachute and other equipment, is a circular disc of constant thickness; spanwise slit through this accommodates propeller disc. Cruciform tail surfaces, carried on tubular boom designed to accommodate wing yawing motion and braced by two additional struts forming a Vee from propeller duct to tail. Struts carried through duct and continued upstream to fuselage nose. Angular sweptback fin and rudder and elliptical one-piece all-moving tailplane. Latter constructed of a thin layer of foam-filled glassfibre/epoxy material, and frangible (as is fin-tip) to minimise recovery damage. Horizontal tail actuated by separate servo commanded by same circuit as elevons' elevator functions. Thus, the tailplane could be removed and aircraft flown as a flying wing while still utilising elevator function of elevons. Non-retractable tricycle landing gear, with aluminium leaf-spring shock-absorption, for initial taxi and flight testing. Nosewheel and strut from a Cessna 150. No brakes. Streamlined fairings over mainwheels. Paraform 'chute (diameter 14.17 m; 46 ft 6 in) in rear of central 'cookie', deployed automatically if command signal lost. Aircraft also recoverable deliberately by this method in response to command signal from ground.

POWER PLANT: One 67 kW (90 hp) McCulloch 4318B O-100-1 flat-four engine, driving a two-blade fixed-pitch wooden pusher propeller turning within an annular duct. Duct designed to improve static thrust and thrust at low speeds, permitting a high cruise speed propeller to be used while still achieving satisfactory T-O and climb performance. It also reduced propeller tip noise and protected operators from turning propeller. Tubular supporting strut connecting fuselage nose to base of duct, serving also to deflect arresting cable in event of a low approach when using a horizontal-cable snag recovery system. Fuel tank in underside of forward fuselage.

ELECTRICAL SYSTEM: 1 kW Delco alternator and battery to power controls, TV, radio and autopilot.

MISSION EQUIPMENT: Proline command receiver, special FM data transmitter, Green Ray TV transmitter, ELT and radar transponder. Nose section contained the TV scanner and related zoom and tilt mechanisms; flight instrumentation and instrumentation camera; command receiver; yaw, roll and pitch gyros; TV signal transmitters; UHF tracking; battery; and vacuum pump.

DIMENSIONS:

Wing span	6.81 m (22 ft 4 in)
Wing area	9.29 m² (100 sq ft)
Length overall	5.89 m (19 ft 10 in)
Fuselage:	
Length	1.61 m (5 ft 3.5 in)
Diameter	0.46 m (1 ft 6 in)
Height overall	2.03 m (6 ft 8 in)
Tailplane span	2.29 m (7 ft 6 in)
Wheel track	2.60 m (8 ft 6.25 in)
Wheelbase	1.33 m (4 ft 4.5 in)
Propeller diameter	1.23 m (4 ft 0.5 in)
Payload volume	0.25 m³ (9 cu ft)

WEIGHTS:

Operating weight empty	412 kg (908 lb)
Fuel	27 kg (60 lb)
Max payload	68 kg (150 lb)
Max T-O weight	499 kg (1,100 lb)

PERFORMANCE (at max T-O weight):

Never-exceed speed	250 knots (463 km/h; 288 mph)
Max level speed at 1,525 m (5,000 ft)	150 knots (278 km/h; 173 mph)
Max cruising speed	100 knots (185 km/h; 115 mph)
Econ cruising speed	80 knots (148 km/h; 92 mph)
Stalling speed	60 knots (111 km/h; 69 mph)
Max rate of climb at S/L	305 m (1,000 ft)/min
Service ceiling	3,050 m (10,000 ft)
Endurance	1 h

DEVELOPMENTAL SCIENCES MARS ASTROPLANE

Among concepts studied by NASA in the late 1970s for future exploration of the planet Mars was one for a series of recoverable, remotely controlled aircraft able to photograph terrain, take atmospheric soundings, and acquire other useful data. Developmental Sciences completed a design study for such an aircraft in 1979–80, and built a one-tenth scale deployable model, as well as a full size fuselage section to demonstrate potential payload capacity. Built substantially of carbonfibre composites, the proposed Mars Astroplane had very high aspect ratio wings, hinged at six points to fold, Z-fashion, for storage inside a Viking type aeroshell container. The fuselage was also hinged at two points, and the aircraft was to be powered by a nose-mounted Sundstrand electric motor for cruising flight, powered by a lithium battery and driving a large-diameter foldable propeller. Alternatively, it could be powered by a non-air-breathing engine using hydrazine fuel. Variable thrust Viking lander rockets would be used for take-off and soft-landing. Wing span was 21 m (68 ft 10.75 in), length 6.35 m (20 ft 10 in), and maximum all-up weight 300 kg (661 lb), of which up to one-third would comprise the payload

DSI model of the proposed Mars Astroplane

of spectrometers, radiometers, imagers and other special equipment.

A considerably more detailed description of the Mars Astroplane can be found by referring to the 1979–80 edition of *Jane's All the World's Aircraft*; realisation of such an aeroplane depends upon future NASA funding for Mars exploration.

DEVELOPMENTAL SCIENCES RPMB

Developmental Sciences built and flew a small series of RPMBs (remotely piloted mini-blimps) in the second half of the 1970s, chiefly for urban area aerial photography in collaboration with the FAA and local law enforcement agencies.

The small scale prototype (referred to here for convenience as **RPMB 1**) was completed in 1976, and had a helium filled envelope of ripstop nylon and Mylar with inflatable tail surfaces. It was powered by a 0.19 kW (0.25 hp) piston engine and carried remote control avionics and a small ciné camera. Fifteen flights had been made by early 1977. The larger **RPMB 2**, which followed later that year, had an envelope of similar construction, but the tail surfaces were made of rigid composites, the horizontal surfaces being fitted with elevators; 'rudder action' was achieved by gimballing the 1.5 kW (2 hp) Quadra engine. Payload consisted of a TV camera and associated telemetry, and eight flights were made during the autumn of 1977.

Final version was the much larger **RPMB 3**, of similar configuration to RPMB 2 but with a 15 kW (20 hp) Herbrandson two-stroke engine driving a two-blade wooden Sensenich propeller, and an envelope of Neoprene coated Dacron. This mini-airship was completed in 1979.

GUIDANCE AND CONTROL (RPMB 3): Radio command guidance system. Pitch and yaw control provided by gimballing engine. If command link lost, engine shut down and helium dumped (dumping 8.5 m³; 300 cu ft made craft 9 kg; 20 lb 'heavy'). If engine failed, helium dumped in same way; if altitude hold malfunctioned, and vehicle escaped from 152 m (500 ft) to higher altitude, independent transducer triggered helium dump.

MISSION EQUIPMENT (RPMB 3): Dufresne 28V 650W alternator for electrical power; guidance and control equipment; servo motors; data link; payload (camera, bullhorn and spotlight); transponder and running lights; ballast.

Remotely piloted mini-blimp in its 4.88 m (16 ft) long version

DIMENSIONS:
Length overall:

1		4.88 m (16 ft)
2		7.92 m (26 ft)
3		11.94 m (39 ft 2 in)

Envelope max diameter:

1		1.22 m (4 ft)
2		2.74 m (9 ft)
3		3.40 m (11 ft 2 in)

Envelope volume:

1		not known
2		25.49 m³ (900 cu ft)
3		84.95 m³ (3,000 cu ft)

WEIGHTS:
Max payload:

1		1.6 kg (3.5 lb)
2		15.8 kg (35 lb)
3		20.5 kg (45 lb)

PERFORMANCE:
Max level speed:

1		17.5 knots (32 km/h; 20 mph)
2		22 knots (41 km/h; 25 mph)
3		43 knots (80 km/h; 50 mph)

DEVELOPMENTAL SCIENCES RPA-12 SKYEYE

Design of the original RPA-12 (remotely piloted aircraft) SkyEye began in February 1973, and the **SkyEye I-A** prototype flew for the first time on 26 April that year. Of tail-less sweptwing configuration, it had a pusher propeller mounted in an annular duct aft of the wing. Deletion of the duct, and addition of an angular fin near each wingtip, yielded the **SkyEye I-B** of 1974, the last two examples of which continued to serve until 1978.

These were followed by the **SkyEye II-E**, an expendable development of the I-B, and by the recoverable **SkyEye II-R**, which was six per cent larger than the II-E but had endplate fins at the wingtips and a lower radar signature. The II-R was basically similar to the I-B, but was of glassfibre and foam construction; the endplate fins were later deleted and a propeller duct added. The II-R also had a non-retractable tricycle landing gear. Both SkyEye II models were demonstrated to the US Army and various aerospace companies.

RPA/RPV-12 SkyEye I-A with early ducted propeller

SkyEye I-B with duct removed and movie camera in nose

SkyEye II-R in recovery net

A total of ten SkyEye Is and IIs were built under the RPA-12 designation, before being succeeded by the R4D; between them they made more than 20 flights. The following description applies to the SkyEye I-B:

TYPE: Experimental mini-RPV.
AIRFRAME: Sweptback high-wing monoplane, with servo-actuated elevons. Sweptback fin near each wingtip. Wings and fins of plywood with Styrofoam core. Cylindrical body of wooden bulkheads with epoxy/glassfibre skin. Non-retractable tricycle landing gear standard; this could be deleted for use with alternative launch system and parachute or net recovery.
POWER PLANT: One 9 kW (12 hp) McCulloch 101A piston engine, modified to reduce R/F interference, mounted in rear of fuselage. Two-blade wooden fixed-pitch pusher propeller. Fuselage fuel tank, capacity 3.8 litres (0.8 Imp gallon; 1 US gallon); provision for internal wing tanks to raise total capacity to 11.4 litres (2.5 Imp gallons; 3 US gallons).
GUIDANCE AND CONTROL: VHF radio command guidance system (15 W command output). Total-loss battery system; alternator added for flights of longer than 1 h.
MISSION EQUIPMENT: Variety of payloads demonstrated.
DIMENSIONS:

Wing span	3.50 m (11 ft 6 in)
Wing area	3.02 m² (32.5 sq ft)
Length: overall	1.70 m (5 ft 7 in)
fuselage only	1.50 m (4 ft 11 in)
Height overall	0.89 m (2 ft 11 in)
Wheel track	0.81 m (2 ft 8 in)
Wheelbase	0.58 m (1 ft 11 in)
Propeller diameter	0.61 m (2 ft)

WEIGHTS (A: conventional T-O/landing; B: launch T-O/parachute recovery):

Weight empty, equipped:

A	25 kg (55 lb)
B	27.2 kg (60 lb)

Max payload:

A	20.4 kg (45 lb)
B	18 kg (40 lb)
Max T-O/launching weight: A, B	56.5 kg (125 lb)

PERFORMANCE:

Max level speed:

A	90 knots (167 km/h; 104 mph)
B	120 knots (222 km/h; 138 mph)
Stalling speed: A, B	35 knots (65 km/h; 41 mph)

Max rate of climb at S/L:

A	548 m (1,800 ft)/min
B	670 m (2,200 ft)/min

Service ceiling:

A	3,960 m (13,000 ft)
B	4,575 m (15,000 ft)
Control-limit range: A, B	43 nm (80 km; 50 miles)

Max endurance at 55 knots (102 km/h; 63 mph):

A	6 h
B	9 h

DEVELOPMENTAL SCIENCES R4D SKYEYE

Visually reminiscent of the Aquila test vehicle, the R4D was essentially an upgraded version of the SkyEye II-R with an improved wing, a larger and flat-bottomed fuselage, no landing gear, and an improved flight control system. It also had a more powerful engine, increased payload capacity and higher launching weight. First flight was made in 1978, and a quantity of R4Ds was produced for an overseas customer.

TYPE: Tactical mini-RPV.

AIRFRAME: Predominantly of Kevlar skins with Nomex honeycomb core, giving a lightweight but robust airframe capable of high g loadings and of surviving rough handling in operation. Sweptback high-wing monoplane configuration, with servo actuated elevons and turned-down wingtips. Removal of wing and nosecone provides access to entire payload installation in nose and central bays. Four basic fuselage components: nose fairing, central body, cowling and propeller shroud. Three quickly removable flat-bottomed underfuselage panels for pallet-style installation and interchange of variety of payloads. Rudder and/or dive brakes optional.

POWER PLANT: One 11.9 kW (16 hp) or 16.4 kW (22 hp) Herbrandson 220 or 280 two-stroke flat-twin engine, driving a two-blade wooden pusher propeller turning within an annular duct. Fuel in two standard wing-root tanks, combined capacity 19 litres (4.2 Imp gallons; 5 US gallons). Optional tanks available to double this capacity for long-endurance missions.

LAUNCH AND RECOVERY: Two launch systems available: truck-mounted pneumatic launcher or simpler launch apparatus (also truck-mounted). With latter system, RPV is attached to launcher mounted on pickup truck; with RPV engine operating, truck is then accelerated to safe launch speed and RPV is released. Various recovery systems (e.g., skid landing gear) available, but usual method is by vertical barrier net in conjunction with air mattress. Emergency backup parachute system optional.

GUIDANCE AND CONTROL: VHF radio command guidance system. Aerodynamic control by elevons. Lear Siegler two-axis autopilot (three-axis optional when rudder fitted), and Tayburn Electronics data link with onboard encoder/decoder. Electrical power (battery, engine driven alternator, and regulator) available from 600–1,000W (28V DC); battery can provide 20 min of emergency power in event of alternator failure.

DIMENSIONS:

Wing span	3.78 m (12 ft 4.75 in)
Wing area	2.99 m² (32.2 sq ft)
Length overall	2.12 m (6 ft 11.5 in)
Body diameter (max)	0.355 m (1 ft 2 in)
Propeller duct diameter	0.69 m (2 ft 5.25 in)
Payload volume	more than 0.085 m³ (3 cu ft)

WEIGHTS:

Weight empty	45.4 kg (100 lb)
Fuel (standard)	13.6 kg (30 lb)
Payload	36.3 kg (80 lb)
Max launching weight	99.3 kg (219 lb)

PERFORMANCE (22 hp engine):

Max level speed at S/L	130 knots (241 km/h; 150 mph)
Stalling speed	39 knots (73 km/h; 45 mph)
Max rate of climb at S/L	600 m (1,970 ft)/min
Service ceiling	6,100 m (20,000 ft)
Endurance: standard fuel	6 h
auxiliary fuel	8 h
g limits	± 6

DEVELOPMENTAL SCIENCES R4E SKYEYE

From its success with the R4D, and its work on the US Army Aquila programme (see under LMSC in this section), DS began in 1980 to develop a family of R4E SkyEyes to respond to customers' needs for a variety of missions, payloads and vehicle sizes.

The R4E has an entirely different aerodynamic configuration to that of the R4D, and can perform day and night missions which include real-time surveillance, reconnaissance, tactical weather observation, artillery and naval gunfire and close air support, laser designation and rangefinding, battle damage assessment, coastal and maritime patrol, elint/sigint/comint, ECM, communications relay, and weapons delivery and emplacement. Operational suitability in many of these roles has already been demonstrated successfully.

The system is completely mobile, being transportable by ground vehicles, military transport aircraft or naval vessels. A typical ground-based SkyEye unit consists of four to six RPVs, a mobile command and control shelter, a mobile launch system, and a personnel/equipment transport vehicle.

Prototype SkyEye R4D

The following versions have been announced; 'dash' numbers indicate approximate engine horsepower:

R4E-5. Used as a trainer for the larger R4Es. One-half the size of the R4E-30; carries a non-gimballed TV system and basic flight instruments, including autopilot. Powered by 3 kW (4 hp) engine. In service.

R4E-10. Designed as a portable, quick-deployment system able to provide a meaningful surveillance capability. Modular pallet concept allows system to be manned by a crew of three and transported in a single truck, trailer or large helicopter to the launch site, from where it can be airborne in a matter of minutes to perform a pre-programmed mission. Meanwhile the crew can depart the area with its vehicle, while maintaining contact and receiving video transmission from the RPV.

R4E-30. Developed originally for a strike mission, and evaluated by US Army as a platform for delivering 2.75 in rockets, Viper rockets, and (eventually) 'smart' weapons. Powered by 22.5 kW (30 hp) two-cylinder two-stroke engine with two-blade fixed-pitch (optionally v-p) propeller. Useful load, including fuel, of 86 kg (190 lb); max endurance with a 22.7 kg (50 lb) payload is more than 8 hours. A squadron of six R4E-30s, together with all support equipment and manuals, was supplied to the Royal Thai Air Force in 1982 and is in service for surveillance and other missions.

R4E-40. Same basic size vehicle as R4E-30, but with 28.3 kW (38 hp) engine and increased fuel capacity (useful load, including fuel, 113 kg; 250 lb). Four delivered to US Army in late 1984, with a further four funded in mid-1985. Joint DS/US Army operations included reconnaissance patrols along the Honduran/Nicaraguan border after launch from airfields at Puerto San Lorenzo and Palmerola in central and southern Honduras. Missions have also included night launch and recovery, and the use of both daylight and LLL TV payloads, FLIR sensors, and a panoramic camera. In late 1985 it was reconfigured to accommodate either a turreted daylight video camera or a turreted common module FLIR.

R4E-30 SkyEye, as supplied to Royal Thai Air Force

SkyEye R4E-40 with Texas Instruments turreted FLIR

R4E-50. Enhanced version of R4E-40: see Addenda for details.

R4E-70. Version for OTH weapon delivery, characterised by a much longer and slimmer fuselage pod than other R4E models.

The following description applies principally to the R4E-40, except where otherwise indicated:

TYPE: Multi-mission mini-RPV.

AIRFRAME: Cantilever high-wing monoplane with a fuselage pod, twin tailbooms, twin sweptback fins (one with rudder), and an enclosed tailplane with central elevator. Inboard wing panels are sweptback, with ailerons on their trailing edges; outer panels have swept leading edges, non-swept trailing edges, and are set at an anhedral angle. The engine is mounted at the rear of the fuselage pod, driving a pusher propeller, and there is an extendable landing skid beneath the fuselage. Airframe construction is primarily of graphite (carbonfibre) and Kevlar reinforced epoxy, and is fully sealed for long life in hot and humid climates. Fuselage of R4E-70 is much longer and slimmer than on other models. The SkyEye can be fitted with a rail or pod under each wing, in line with the tailbooms, for the carriage of external stores (eg, chaff).

POWER PLANT (R4E-40): One Developmental Sciences modified Kawasaki 440 cc two-cylinder two-stroke engine (nominal rating 28.3 kW; 38 hp), driving a two-blade fixed-pitch wooden propeller (variable-pitch propeller optional). Bladder fuel tank in each wing.

LAUNCH AND RECOVERY: All American Engineering HP-3403 hydraulic/pneumatic catapult launcher. (R4E-5 can also use a car-mounted launcher.) The HP-3403 is self-contained, can be truck-mounted, and can launch a vehicle within ten minutes of being started, so eliminating both the recurring expense of a rocket boost and its associated infra-red, noise and visual signatures. System contains enough engine fuel for 20 launches. The RPV uses a simple extendable-skid landing system which allows a pilot, after brief training, to land the RPV safely by monitoring the TV picture from the RPV's nose camera. The RPV is flown in the landing pattern to a short field; full pitch-up is then applied while the RPV limits elevator position to provide an approach speed safely above stalling speed. A specially designed shock attenuation system compensates for not flaring the RPV, and the vehicle skids to a straight stop in a few hundred feet. As a backup to the skid landing, for use in rough terrain or in an emergency, a low altitude (less than 61 m; 200 ft) 12.8 m (42 ft) diameter cruciform parachute (housed in the wing centre-section between the fuel tanks) is deployed.

GUIDANCE AND CONTROL: Radio/TV command guidance system, with fully equipped three-axis autopilot for stability and precise control, even in very rough air. Developmental Sciences guidance and control unit includes vertical gyro, yaw rate gyro, barometric altitude transducer, vertical accelerometer, airspeed transducer, and compass. Aircraft can be operated in four different modes, in-flight selected from the command console: (1) rate mode, commanding rate of climb/descent and turn, used for target tracking and other tasks requiring continuous manoeuvring of the RPV; (2) attitude mode (used, for example, to align vehicle weapons with a target, or for landing); (3) automatic (pre-programmed) mode; and (4) manual mode, in which uplink commands are applied directly to the RPV's control surfaces. (Manual is an electrically redundant mode, used in case of autopilot failure; because of SkyEye's low speed and high intrinsic stability, it can be operated safely without autopilot.) The type of data link used depends upon customers' specific requirements, and both analog and digital links can be specified. Avionics and data link equipment are housed in a rear fuselage bay, together with the electrical system equipment, which comprises a 980W engine-driven alternator (2kW alternator optional) for 28V DC power, and an emergency battery which provides 5 min flying time in the event of alternator failure.

MISSION EQUIPMENT: The large payload volume and weight capacity permit the accommodation of a wide variety of payloads, carried individually or in combinations. Demonstrated examples of payloads carried by the R4E-40 include gyro stabilised daylight and low light level TV systems in combination with panoramic cameras or communications repeaters; a standard US Army common module gyro stabilised FLIR (Texas Instruments AIR-360/3) in a gimballed 'chin' turret, in combination with infra-red linescanners (Texas Instruments RPV-700); nose-mounted TV with underwing rocket launchers (up to six 10 kg rockets or tubes for 2.75 in rockets); and a turreted (360°) daylight video camera. Other payloads can include multiple meteorological sensors, a Martin Marietta (Orlando Aerospace) laser detector/tracker pod, two 33 kg (73 lb) underwing pods of fuel or ejectable items such as chaff, leaflets, flares or communications jammers.

DIMENSIONS:

Wing span:	
5	2.67 m (8 ft 9 in)
10	3.35 m (11 ft)
30, 40	5.36 m (17 ft 7 in)
70	6.35 m (20 ft 10 in)
Wing area: 30, 40	3.63 m² (39.1 sq ft)
Length overall:	
5	1.85 m (6 ft 1 in)
10	2.16 m (7 ft 1 in)
30, 40	3.72 m (12 ft 2.5 in)
70	5.77 m (18 ft 11 in)
Length of fuselage: 30, 40	2.59 m (8 ft 6 in)
Body diameter (max):	
5	0.20 m (8 in)
10	0.305 m (1 ft)
Height:	
5, 10	0.47 m (1 ft 6.5 in)
30, 40	1.04 m (3 ft 4.8 in)
70	0.95 m (3 ft 1.3 in)
Propeller diameter:	
5	0.51 m (1 ft 8 in)
10	0.61 m (2 ft)
30, 40	0.79 m (2 ft 7 in)

WEIGHTS:

Weight empty, equipped:	
30	119 kg (263 lb)
40	127 kg (280 lb)
Fuel (standard):	
30	44 kg (97 lb)
40	45.5 kg (100 lb)
Max payload: 40	63.5 kg (140 lb)
Max launching weight:	
5	22.7 kg (50 lb)
10	77 kg (170 lb)
30	204 kg (450 lb)
40	236 kg (520 lb)
70	308 kg (680 lb)

PERFORMANCE:

Max level speed ('clean'):	
5	70 knots (130 km/h; 81 mph)
10	100 knots (185 km/h; 115 mph)
30	125 knots (232 km/h; 144 mph)
40	115 knots (213 km/h; 132 mph)
70	160 knots (297 km/h; 184 mph)
Max rate of climb at S/L:	
30, 40	305 m (1,000 ft)/min
Service ceiling:	
5	1,525 m (5,000 ft)
10	3,050 m (10,000 ft)
30, 40 (AUW of 190.5 kg; 420 lb)	6,100 m (20,000 ft)
40 (AUW of 227 kg; 500 lb)	4,575 m (15,000 ft)
70	6,100 m (20,000 ft)
Max range:	
5	2.7 nm (5 km; 3.1 miles)
10	21 nm (40 km; 25 miles)
30	81 nm (150 km; 93 miles)
40	135 nm (250 km; 155 miles)
70	162 nm (300 km; 186 miles)
Typical command and control range:	
40	80 nm (148 km; 92 miles)
Endurance:	
5 (max)	30 min
10 with 13.5 kg (30 lb) payload, 30 with 54.5 kg (120 lb), 40 with 82.5 kg (182 lb), and 70 with 181 kg (400 lb)	3 h
30 with 22.7 kg (50 lb) payload	8 h
40 with 63.5 kg (140 lb) payload, at S/L	7 h 42 min
40 with 63.5 kg (140 lb) payload, at 4,875 m (16,000 ft)	6 h 24 min
40 with 27 kg (60 lb) payload	9 h
g limits	±6

DEVELOPMENTAL SCIENCES US NAVY ACTIVE EXPENDABLE DECOY (AED)

DSI began working on this programme, with the Naval Research Laboratory and other US Navy agencies, in 1976. The AED is powered by a booster/sustainer engine, and carries an active payload. It is basically of long and narrow cylindrical shape, with three foldaway/flip-out tail control surfaces and a one-piece pivoting wing, which deploy after launch from a container. Cruising flight, and boost launch from a folded position, were demonstrated successfully in 1978 in the Mojave Desert and at the Naval Weapons Center, China Lake, California. Development had ended by 1986.

DEVELOPMENTAL SCIENCES GUNSIGHT

Gunsight is a low-cost target for tracking and weapon-firing use. Development began in 1981–82, and continued until 1986 (programme inactive 1987). Latest details received (1983) are as follows:

POWER PLANT: 15 kW (20 hp) flat-twin piston engine initially; being replaced by an 18.5 kW (25 hp) engine in 1982.

LAUNCH AND RECOVERY: Rocket launch; parachute recovery.

MISSION EQUIPMENT: Two-axis autopilot. Visual (smoke), infra-red (flares) and R/F (three Luneberg lenses) augmentation available.

DIMENSIONS:

Wing span	1.17 m (3 ft 10 in)

Developmental Sciences' Gunsight (left) and Locomp

Length overall	2.03 m (6 ft 8 in)
Body diameter	0.20 m (8 in)
Span over tail fins	0.65 m (2 ft 1.75 in)
WEIGHTS:	
Mission equipment	9.1 kg (20 lb)
Max launching weight	36 kg (80 lb)
PERFORMANCE (with 15 kW; 20 hp engine):	
Never-exceed speed at S/L	
	300 knots (555 km/h; 345 mph)
Max level speed at S/L	
	240 knots (444 km/h; 276 mph)
Service ceiling	4,575 m (15,000 ft)
Endurance at S/L	40 min

DEVELOPMENTAL SCIENCES LOCOMP

Locomp, also in the feasibility demonstration phase from about 1982, is a multi-purpose system for operation at high subsonic speeds. This programme also was inactive in 1987.

POWER PLANT: Single turbojet engine.
LAUNCH AND RECOVERY: Air or ground launch; recoverable from land or water (floats with 50 per cent fuel or less).
DIMENSIONS:

Wing span	1.37 m (4 ft 6 in)
Length overall	2.31 m (7 ft 7 in)
Body diameter	0.33 m (1 ft 1 in)
Payload volume	0.057 m³ (2 cu ft)

WEIGHTS:

Weight empty (incl 52 kg; 115 lb equipment)	
	136 kg (300 lb)
Max launching weight	200 kg (440 lb)
PERFORMANCE:	
Max level-flight Mach No. at S/L	0.80
Max level-flight Mach No. at 6,100 m (20,000 ft)	0.82
Endurance at max Mach No. at S/L	37 min
Endurance at max Mach No. at 6,100 m (20,000 ft)	1 h

E-SYSTEMS INC (Greenville Division)

PO Box 1056, Greenville, Texas 75401

E-SYSTEMS L450F

USAF designation: XQM-93

E-Systems built this single-seat aircraft to meet military requirements for a high-altitude long-endurance reconnaissance aircraft, capable of carrying data-gathering equipment or electronic relay equipment (similar to that of a communications satellite) to a height of more than 13,715 m (45,000 ft), and having a 24-hour endurance.

The first prototype made its first flight, with a pilot, during February 1970 but was lost on its third flight on 23 March that year. The second prototype (N2450F) differed in having increased fuel tankage and deletion of speed brakes from the upper and lower wing surfaces.

On 24–25 January 1972 this prototype, converted to unmanned configuration for USAF evaluation and designated XQM-93 (serial number 70-1287), made a non-stop flight of more than 21 hours at Edwards AFB, California. The flight, then believed to be an endurance record for RPVs, was made to determine the feasibility of flying RPVs for long periods of time, and was part of the USAF's Compass Dwell programme in which the XQM-93 was flown competitively with the Martin Marietta Model 845A. The evaluation was completed in early 1972, neither vehicle being selected for production.

On 23 and 27 March 1972 the L450F, flown by test pilot Don Wilson, established six new international altitude records and ten time-to-height records at Majors Field, Greenville, Texas.

The basic airframe of the L450F is that of a Schweizer SGS 2-32 sailplane; this was modified extensively by Schweizer, to

The E-Systems XQM-93 (L450F) in USAF markings

E-Systems drawings, to cater for the installation of engine, fuel tank, landing gear and electronics equipment. Modification involved strengthening of the wing spars and areas of the forward and rear fuselage, use of heavier skins, and an increase in the surface area of the fin and rudder. The non-retractable tricycle landing gear, with cantilever spring steel main legs, was based on that of the Grumman Ag-Cat. 28V 6kW electrical power was available as standard. The piloted version had a bubble canopy and conventional flying controls, including a modified Bendix PB-60 autopilot system.

The XQM-93 unmanned version differed from the piloted version in having the bubble canopy and pilot's seat removed and replaced by an interface unit. As used for the 24-25 January 1972 flight, it carried a more advanced autopilot system than the piloted version.

Complete ground control and monitoring by telemetry allowed control of the pilotless version in a variety of modes, including take-off, constant heading/constant pitch angle, constant altitude/constant heading, constant airspeed/constant heading, reciprocal heading loiter, automatic preset heading and landing.

Applications include data/communications relay, electronic reconnaissance, time-of-arrival measurements, ocean surveillance, ecological data collection, and stand-off jamming. The study of potential military and civil applications, especially the latter, has continued in recent years.

POWER PLANT: One Pratt & Whitney Canada PT6A-34 turboprop engine, derated to 354 ekW (475 ehp) and driving a Hartzell three-blade metal propeller. Fuel contained in wing cells and a single aft fuselage cell.

DIMENSIONS (XQM-93):
Wing span	17.37 m (57 ft)
Length overall	9.02 m (29 ft 7 in)
Height overall (excl antenna fairing on top of fin)	
	3.25 m (10 ft 8 in)
Tailplane span	3.20 m (10 ft 6 in)
Wheelbase	2.03 m (6 ft 8 in)
Payload volume	1.25 m³ (44 cu ft)

WEIGHTS:
Weight empty	1,089 kg (2,400 lb)
Max payload	499 kg (1,100 lb)
Max T-O weight:	
manned	2,086 kg (4,600 lb)
unmanned	2,404 kg (5,300 lb)

PERFORMANCE (at max T-O weight):
Cruising speed at 13,715 m (45,000 ft)	
	200 knots (370 km/h; 230 mph)
Best glide ratio	28
Stalling speed	61 knots (114 km/h; 71 mph)
Max rate of climb at S/L	914 m (3,000 ft)/min
Min time to 12,200 m (40,000 ft)	21 min
Service ceiling	more than 15,240 m (50,000 ft)
T-O run	366 m (1,200 ft)
Endurance	more than 24 h
g limits	+3.8/−1.52

E-SYSTEMS (Melpar Division)

7700 Arlington Boulevard, Falls Church, Virginia 22046

Primary business areas of Melpar Divison are electronic combat weapons and reconnaissance systems (ECWRS), remotely controlled intelligence systems (RCIS), information systems, electronic warfare and communications products, and physical security sensors. In the ECWRS area, the Division has since the early 1970s developed an extensive family of mini-RPVs, all of modular construction, enabling a variety of mostly interchangeable payload packages to be carried and capable of pre-programmed, real-time continuous or intermittent control. They can be classified into two broad configuration groups, with designations which indicate the maximum launching weight of the aircraft in pounds. Although none of those listed was in production in 1987, any of them could still be produced to meet a specific requirement; and the Division continues to be a major producer of sensors and other equipment for other unmanned aircraft.

E-SYSTEMS E-45, E-55 and E-100X

Melpar's first mini-RPVs followed a pod-and-twin-tailboom configuration, starting with the **E-45**, which was developed under a DARPA contract as a multi-role feasibility testbed and flew for the first time in June 1974. Primary sensor was a miniature TV camera, installed on a Melpar developed gimbal mounting. Twelve E-45s were built, five being variously modified later for 1976 demonstration in the US Air Force's **Axillary** (formerly RPAODS: remotely piloted aerial observation designation system) harassment vehicle study. These underwent assorted changes to their wing and tail configurations, and included a capability for radar homing to indicate their suitability for defence suppression if carrying a small explosive charge.

Later that year the E-45s were upgraded to **E-55** standard, with an uprated engine and increased payload capacity, primarily to flight test real-time reconnaissance, jamming, targeting and homing packages. The E-55 underwent West German (**Quälgeist**) evaluation as a harassment drone in 1977, and two years later three were modified to **E-55S**, with side-force panels above and below each wing. These enabled the aircraft to yaw with wings level, so that the ground controller's CRT could receive a level-horizon picture from the RPV without the need to gyro-stabilise its onboard TV camera. The E-55S was successfully demonstrated in 1979 in a US Army programme called **Superfly**.

Last in the twin-boom series was the **E-100X** of 1978–79, which was essentially an increased-span E-45/55 with a higher powered engine and increased payload capacity.

The following description applies generally to all twin-boom models, except where indicated:

TYPE: Experimental mini-RPV.
AIRFRAME: High-wing twin-tailboom monoplane, with pod-

E-Systems E-55 in 'Superfly' programme configuration

shaped central nacelle. Marked dihedral on standard outer wing panels of E-45/55 (but none on E-55S). This span increased on Axillary E-45s and E-100X by no-dihedral extensions. Side force generation panel above and below each wing of E-55S, lower ones being frangible. Twin sweptback endplate fins and rudders; tailbooms bridged by central tailplane with full span elevator. Underside of fuselage reinforced to serve as landing skid.

POWER PLANT: One 1.5 kW (2 hp) single-cylinder two-stroke engine in E-45, 2.8 kW (3.7 hp) Roper single-cylinder two-stroke in E-55, 6.7 kW (9 hp) Rosspower four-cylinder two-stroke in E-100X, in each case driving a two-blade pusher propeller. Fuel capacity 3.4 litres (0.75 Imp gallon; 0.9 US gallon) in E-45 and E-55, 3.8 litres (0.8 Imp gallon; 1 US gallon) in E55S, and 11.4 litres (2.5 Imp gallon; 3 US gallon) in E-100X.

LAUNCH AND RECOVERY (all): Launched either by vehicle-mounted launcher, using jettisonable take-off dolly, or by catapult. Recovery by skid landing or retrieval net system.

GUIDANCE AND CONTROL (all): Either by van mounted real-time tracking radar, or by standard non-tracking radio control link. Radar system capable of controlling RPV effectively for approx 43 nm (80 km; 50 miles), but extendable to 130 nm (241 km; 150 miles) by pre-programming flight and using airborne relay for video downlink. Aircraft controllable either manually or by combination of pre-programmed flight and manual landing. Melpar five-axis autopilot for dead reckoning or Omega navigation. Aerodynamic control effected by ailerons, elevator, rudders, and (E-55S) side-force panels.

MISSION EQUIPMENT: Primary E-45 sensor was Melpar TV surveillance system for remote manual control, target identification, and navigation assistance away from launch site. Additional payloads for E-55 and E-100X included miniature TV reconnaissance system, or packages for photographic reconnaissance, electronic jamming, tactical strike support and communications relay.

DIMENSIONS:
Wing span:
| 44, 55/55S | 2.41 m (7 ft 11 in) |
| 100X | 3.28 m (10 ft 9 in) |

Wing area:
| 45, 55/55S | 0.68 m² (7.36 sq ft) |
| 100X | 1.33 m² (14.33 sq ft) |

Length overall:
| 45, 55/55S | 2.36 m (7 ft 9 in) |
| 100X | 2.74 m (9 ft) |

Height overall:
45, 55	0.51 m (1 ft 8 in)
55S	0.61 m (2 ft)
100X	0.57 m (1 ft 10.5 in)

Body diameter (max):
| 45, 55/55S | 0.20 m (8 in) |
| 100X | 0.27 m (10.75 in) |

Tail unit span:
| 45, 55/55S | 0.71 m (2 ft 4 in) |
| 100X | 0.66 m (2 ft 2 in) |

WEIGHTS:
Weight empty:
45	10.9 kg (24 lb)
55/55S	11.3 kg (25 lb)
100X	14.5 kg (32 lb)

Payload:
45	6.8 kg (15 lb)
55/55S	13.6 kg (30 lb)
100X	23.6 kg (55 lb)

Fuel:
| 45, 55/55S | 2.7 kg (6 lb) |
| 100X | 8.2 kg (18 lb) |

Max launching weight:
45	20.5 kg (45 lb)
55/55S	24.9 kg (55 lb)
100X	45.4 kg (100 lb)

PERFORMANCE:
Cruising speed:
45	43 knots (80 km/h; 50 mph)
55/55S	52 knots (97 km/h; 60 mph)
100X	75 knots (139 km/h; 86 mph)

Stalling speed:
45	35 knots (65 km/h; 40 mph)
55/55S	39 knots (72 km/h; 45 mph)
100X	42 knots (78 km/h; 49 mph)

Max rate of climb at S/L:
45	229 m (750 ft)/min
55	198 m (650 ft)/min
55S	137 m (450 ft)/min
100X	305 m (1,000 ft)/min

Ceiling:
45, 55	3,050 m (10,000 ft)
55S	2,745 m (9,000 ft)
100X	over 3,050 m (10,000 ft)

Endurance:
45	5 h
55/55S	4 h
100X	over 5 h

E-SYSTEMS E-75, E-90, E-130, E-150, E-175, E-200, E-260 and E-310

The first in Melpar's developing family of single-tailboom minis was the **E-75**, which in 1977–78 became a candidate in the US Air Force's **LCEHV** (low cost expendable harassment vehicle) programme. This was followed in October 1977 by the first flight of the **E-90**, a version with uprated engine and wider payload potential. The **E-150**, which first flew on 4 August 1978, was a (one-off?) hybrid, based on the E-75 but having a blunter nose shape; extended wings, tailboom and tailplane;

E-75, one of the smaller single-boom minis in the E-Systems range

auxiliary finlets; and a long-legged, shock-absorbing twin-skid landing gear with a small castoring wheel at the front of each skid. It was designed specifically to carry a 27.2 kg (60 lb) stabilised TV camera.

In 1979–81, Melpar reverted to the general layout of the E-75/90 by building three prototypes of the **E-130**, which became the basic standard air vehicle of the early 1980s. The E-130 was distinguished by a rectangular side-force panel beneath each wing at mid-span; an improved autopilot, capable of real-time data link update as well as pre-programmed control; VLF/Omega or Navstar/GPS navigation; and alternative methods of ground launch (truck top, trailer mounted pneumatic catapult, or rocket assisted rail launch) and recovery (belly skid or parachute/parafoil landing, net retrieval, or arrester hook and cushion). The **E-200** of 1979, capable of carrying more than twice the E-130's payload, was a testbed vehicle, based on the E-130 airframe but with extended-span wings and no side-force panels.

The underwing panels reappeared on the **E-175**, which was a scaled-up and slightly more powerful version of the E-130. It was developed primarily for expendable strike or EW missions, but a recoverable reconnaissance version, fitted with a panoramic camera, is thought to have been produced for Egypt in about 1983. Further scaling up in 1984–85 led to the **E-260** and **E-310**, two recoverable models (without side-force panels) able to carry various reconnaissance or other packages in interchangeable nose modules. Typical payloads could include stabilised, unstabilised or LLL TV, FLIR, IRLS, pan cameras or sigint equipment.

The following description can be taken to apply broadly to all of the foregoing models, except as indicated:

AIRFRAME: Cantilever high-wing monoplane. Non-swept constant chord wings, with dihedral on E-75 and E-90, without anhedral or dihedral on other models; wing incidence depends on mission configuration. Wings fitted with electrically actuated ailerons; no flaps. Side-force generator panel beneath each wing at approx mid span on E-130 and E-175. Tailboom and tail surfaces of E-75/90 stiffened by cardboard tubes coated internally with phenolic resin; on E-130 and later models, a formed and machined aluminium backbone joins the firewall, propulsion unit, tailboom and wing spars. Fuselage is of rotationally moulded polyethylene or similar material, reinforced on underside to form landing skid (except on E-150). Firewall provides for structural mounting of equipment package. Wings and horizontal tail surfaces are shaped foam cores covered with glassfibre reinforced skin. Nose modules are removable and have

E-175 in flight, showing underwing side-force panels

interchangeable configurations; wings and horizontal tail surfaces are also removable, and all removable items facilitate transportation.

POWER PLANT: One single-cylinder two-stroke engine (2.6 kW; 3.5 hp Roper) in E-75; two-cylinder two-stroke in all subsequent models (Herbrandson or similar), with ratings of 9.7 kW (13 hp) in E-90 and E-150, 13.4 kW (18 hp) in E-130 and E-175, 18 kW (24 hp) in E-200, and 18.6 kW (25 hp) in E-260 and E-310. Two-blade pusher propeller in all cases. Fuel capacities 5.7 litres (1.25 Imp gallons; 1.5 US gallons) in E-75 and E-90, 15 litres (3.3 Imp gallons; 4 US gallons) in E-130; 9.5 litres (2.1 Imp gallons; 2.5 US gallons) in E-150; 19 litres (4.2 Imp gallons; 5 US gallons) in E-175; 8.7 litres (1.9 Imp gallons; 2.3 US gallons) in E-200; 33.3 litres (7.3 Imp gallons; 8.8 US gallons) in E-260; and 30.3 litres (6.7 Imp gallons; 8 US gallons) in E-310.

LAUNCH AND RECOVERY: Launching of all models can be performed from the top of a moving vehicle, and on later models also by a 6 m (20 ft) pneumatic catapult or by rocket assistance. Recovery methods for E-130 and later models include parachute or parafoil, arrester hook, skid landing, or flying the RPV into a recovery net which can stop the aircraft without damage within 12 m (40 ft). Fully automated recovery is feasible by this last technique.

GUIDANCE AND CONTROL (E-130 and later models): Radio command control for launch and recovery. In-flight guidance by Melpar three-axis autopilot with dead reckoning capability. Aerodynamic control by ailerons, elevator, rudder, side-force panels (where applicable) and throttle. Sensor inputs are angle of attack, magnetic heading, yaw/pitch/roll rates, and altitude. The autopilot is capable of real-time data link update from the ground operator, or can be pre-programmed to carry out an autonomous mission. The same telemetry system can provide data to the control station for monitoring vehicle performance, as well as providing data from the payload package(s). Omega (VLF) or Navstar/GPS are the two recommended navigation systems, but Loran, inertial, area correlation or beacon techniques may be employed.

MISSION EQUIPMENT: A variety of interchangeable nosecones, each with a different equipment configuration, allows for versatility in a number of recoverable or expendable missions. For remote real-time reconnaissance, Melpar manufactures a miniature TV camera system in a gimballed mount which can be positioned during flight. Remotely controlled camera functions are from horizon to $-45°$ in pitch, $±90°$ in yaw, and CAMERA ON/OFF; the camera has a 500 line resolution. Electrical power is generated by an engine driven alternator with an emergency battery backup. For electronic warfare, three types of Melpar onboard jammer are available: (1) barrage – wide-band noise and tone, (2) spot – narrow-band noise and tone with remote running or onboard look-through, and (3) dart (delay and repeat transmitter), which combines the best features of barrage and spot jamming at low cost. Other possible payloads can include FLIR, IRLS, still or ciné cameras, communications relay and other equipment.

DIMENSIONS:
Wing span:

75, 90, 130	3.05 m (10 ft)
150	3.96 m (13 ft)
175, 200	3.66 m (12 ft)
260	4.42 m (14 ft 6 in)
310	4.30 m (14 ft 1.25 in)

Wing area:

75	1.02 m² (11 sq ft)
90	1.11 m² (12 sq ft)
130	1.34 m² (14.4 sq ft)
150	1.45 m² (15.6 sq ft)
200	2.56 m² (27.6 sq ft)
175, 260, 310	not known

Length overall:

75	2.41 m (7 ft 11 in)
90	2.29 m (7 ft 6 in)
130	2.77 m (9 ft 1 in)
150	2.22 m (7 ft 3.5 in)
175	2.54 m (8 ft 4 in)
200	3.35 m (11 ft)
260	3.23 m (10 ft 7 in)
310	3.77 m (12 ft 4.5 in)

Height overall:

75, 90	0.51 m (1 ft 8 in)
130	0.57 m (1 ft 10.5 in)
150	0.89 m (2 ft 11 in)
200	0.71 m (2 ft 4 in)
175, 260	not known
310	0.66 m (2 ft 2 in)

WEIGHTS:
Weight empty:

75	15.9 kg (35 lb)
90	24.9 kg (55 lb)
130	33.1 kg (73 lb)
150	34 kg (75 lb)
175	47.6 kg (105 lb)
200	39.9 kg (88 lb)
260	68 kg (150 lb)
310	90.7 kg (200 lb)

Payload (typical):

75	13.6 kg (30 lb)
90	9.1 kg (20 lb)
130	15.9 kg (35 lb)
150, 310	27.2 kg (60 lb)
175	18.1 kg (40 lb)
200	40.8 kg (90 lb)
260	24.9 kg (55 lb)

Fuel:

75	4.5 kg (10 lb)
90, 150	6.8 kg (15 lb)
130, 200	9.8 kg (21.6 lb)
175	13.6 kg (30 lb)
260	24.9 kg (55 lb)
310	22.7 kg (50 lb)

Max launching weight:

75	34 kg (75 lb)
90	40.8 kg (90 lb)
130	59 kg (130 lb)
150	68 kg (150 lb)
175	79.4 kg (175 lb)
200	90.7 kg (200 lb)
260	117.9 kg (260 lb)
310	140.6 kg (310 lb)

PERFORMANCE:
Cruising speed:

75	70 knots (130 km/h; 81 mph)
90	69 knots (128 km/h; 80 mph)
130	78 knots (145 km/h; 90 mph)
150	56 knots (105 km/h; 65 mph)
175	104 knots (193 km/h; 120 mph)
200	74 knots (137 km/h; 85 mph)
260, 310	67 knots (125 km/h; 78 mph)

Stalling speed:

75	40 knots (74 km/h; 46 mph)
90, 200	44 knots (81 km/h; 50 mph)
130	48 knots (89 km/h; 55 mph)
150	46 knots (86 km/h; 53 mph)
175	not known
260	54 knots (100 km/h) 62 mph)
310	49 knots (90 km/h; 56 mph)

Max rate of climb at S/L:

75, 150, 175	not known
90	488 m (1,600 ft)/min
130	305 m (1,000 ft)/min
200	610 m (2,000 ft)/min
260, 310	300 m (984 ft)/min

Ceiling:

75, 150, 175, 260, 310	not known
90, 200	3,660 m (12,000 ft)
130	3,350 m (11,000 ft)

Range:

75, 150	not known
90	191 nm (354 km; 220 miles)
130	208 nm (386 km; 240 miles)
175, 260	260 nm (483 km; 300 miles)
200	139 nm (257 km; 160 miles)
310	97 nm (180 km; 112 miles)

Endurance:

75, 90, 130, 175	4 h
150	2 h
200	3 h
260, 310	over 5 h

EGLEN HOVERCRAFT INC

In the latter half of the 1970s, this company was responsible for prototyping and/or production of two small drones designed by the US Air Force Flight Dynamics Laboratory (the Eagle and Falcon), and also built the small delta-winged Matador of its own design. Manufacturing rights in the Falcon and Matador were acquired in the early 1980s by Simulators Limited Inc (which see).

EGLEN (USAF) EAGLE

First prototype of the Eagle was built by the FDL, with Eglen completing a second in 1976. Powered by a 9.7 kW (13 hp) piston engine, it carried a fully gimballed TV relay system in the nose, behind a transparent dome. Its subsequent fate is not known.

Eglen Eagle twin-boom mini-RPV

DIMENSIONS:
Wing span	4.88 m (16 ft)
Propeller diameter	0.61 m (2 ft)

WEIGHTS:
Payload	36.3–40.8 kg (80–90 lb)
Max T-O weight	90.7 kg (200 lb)

PERFORMANCE:
Not known

FAIRCHILD INDUSTRIES INC

Washington Dulles International Airport, 300 West Service Road (PO Box 10803), Chantilly, Virginia 22021–9998

FAIRCHILD SAILWING

Basic design of the folding sailwing used in this RPV was undertaken at Princeton University, sponsored by Fairchild Industries. It utilised a specially shaped fabric wing glove over a rigid leading edge and tip rib, cable tensioned along the trailing edge. The wings were wire-braced, and could be folded back alongside the fuselage to facilitate transport, handling and storage. The design was extensively tested in a NASA wind tunnel, numerous manned and unmanned test flights subsequently proving the sailwing equal aerodynamically to conventional rigid wings, with excellent immunity from stalling. Later versions were fitted with ailerons.

The basic fuselage comprised a flat-sided honeycomb beam, with streamlined fairings on each side enclosing the controls, equipment, and a 22.7 kg (50 lb) payload. The tail unit was conventional, with wire-braced fixed surfaces, rudder and balanced elevators. Non-retractable tricycle landing gear was standard.

An off-the-shelf 8.9 kW (12 hp) McCulloch piston engine, driving a two-blade fixed-pitch wooden pusher propeller, was used to power the engineering model. A 28V 840W alternator was fitted in some versions. A full range of command, autopilot and telemetry downlink systems was integrated with the vehicles, and a variety of payloads were flown, including photographic, electro-optical, infra-red, early warning and communications relay systems.

Vehicles of the Sailwing type were built by Fairchild Space and Electronics Company and flown in such defence programmes as **Black Fly**, **Dragon Fly**, **Minipop** and **Lookout**. A variant of the basic design, evaluated by the US Army for its 1976 **RPAODS** programme, was primarily of non-metallic construction, to minimise radar signature, and incorporated a three-axis autopilot and Vega C-band command and control system.

The following data apply to the basic Sailwing:

DIMENSIONS:
Wing span	4.48 m (14 ft 8.5 in)
Wing area	3.13 m² (33.7 sq ft)
Length overall: incl nose probe	3.87 m (12 ft 8.5 in)
excl nose probe	3.63 m (11 ft 10.75 in)
Height, bottom of fuselage to top of propeller disc	1.07 m (3 ft 6 in)
Fuselage diameter	0.46 m (1 ft 6 in)
Propeller diameter	0.66 m (2 ft 2 in)

WEIGHT:
Max T-O weight	113 kg (250 lb)

PERFORMANCE:
Not known

FAIRCHILD ATM-100 ADVANCED TACTICAL MINI-DRONE

The ATM-100 (Advanced Tactical Mini-drone) was designed by Fairchild Republic for both recoverable and expendable missions. Design began in August 1981. Three prototypes were built, and the first of these made its initial flight in August 1982 at the US Navy's Calverton test facility. Designed as a harassment RPV against hostile radars and communications systems, it was intended to be capable of carrying a warhead, but the company terminated the programme in 1985.

TYPE: Experimental tactical mini-RPV.
AIRFRAME: Cantilever mid-wing monoplane, with foreplanes; square section fuselage; upper and lower fixed fins at rear,

Fairchild Sailwing flown in US Army RPAODS programme

Fairchild ATM-100 prototype tactical drone

forward of which are smaller rudder surfaces above and below fuselage. Symmetrical section wings, with full span ailerons; cambered, all-moving canard surfaces. Wings have 1° 30′ incidence and 13° sweepback at quarter-chord. Control surface movement assisted by electric servos. Wings and foreplanes of injection moulded polyurethane with Kevlar/epoxy skin; fuselage of injection moulded polystyrene. Rearward retracting nosewheel and Y shape skid under each outer wing; landing gear would have been deleted on expendable versions.

POWER PLANT: One 13.4 kW (18 hp) Herbrandson Dyad 220C two-cylinder two-stroke engine, mounted at rear of fuselage and driving a three-blade fixed-pitch pusher propeller. Single fuel tank in fuselage, capacity 10.4 litres (2.3 Imp gallons; 2.75 US gallons). Rocket-assisted take-off planned for production versions.

LAUNCH AND RECOVERY: Prototypes took off under own power from three-wheeled dolly on concrete runway, and were equipped with landing gear (see 'Airframe' paragraph). Production versions intended to have rocket-assisted launch, requiring no rail, and (on re-usable version) a recovery parachute.

GUIDANCE AND CONTROL: Kraft Systems radio command guidance system on prototypes. Production versions intended to have Doppler radar navigation system, with digital central processing unit. Humphrey heading and altitude reference system. KBG Corporation rate sensors and analog autopilot.

MISSION EQUIPMENT: Expendable version intended to carry radar interferometer for target acquisition and terminal guidance, plus a Chaparral missile warhead in fuselage 41 cm (16 in) aft of nose. Recoverable (reconnaissance) version capable of being equipped with a low light level TV camera/transmitter.

DIMENSIONS:

Wing span	2.21 m (7 ft 3 in)
Wing area	1.10 m² (11.8 sq ft)
Foreplane span	0.81 m (2 ft 8 in)
Foreplane area	0.16 m² (1.7 sq ft)
Length overall	2.29 m (7 ft 6 in)
Fuselage width and depth	0.20 m (8 in)
Height overall	0.91 m (3 ft)
Propeller diameter	0.61 m (2 ft)

WEIGHTS:

Mission equipment (max)	22.7 kg (50 lb)
Fuel load (max)	9.1 kg (20 lb)

Max launching weight (incl 5.4 kg; 12 lb rocket motor)	78 kg (172 lb)

PERFORMANCE:

Max level speed at 1,525 m (5,000 ft)	195 knots (362 km/h; 225 mph)
Max cruising speed at 3,050 m (10,000 ft)	108 knots (201 km/h; 125 mph)
Stalling speed, engine idling	61 knots (113 km/h; 70 mph)
Max rate of climb at S/L	610 m (2,000 ft)/min
Service ceiling	3,350 m (11,000 ft)
T-O run (prototype, incl dolly)	214 m (700 ft)
Range with max fuel, no reserves	326 nm (603 km; 375 miles)

FLIGHT SYSTEMS INC (FSI)

1901 Dove Street, PO Box 2400, Newport Beach, California 92660

FSI has been producing drones for the US Department of Defense since 1975, and currently (1987) holds contracts to convert more than 200 aircraft into unmanned aerial target vehicles. These include the North American F-86 and F-100, Convair F-106 and Northrop F-5A.

FSI QF-86E SABRE

FSI demonstrated two remotely controlled Sabre jet fighters to the US Army in 1975, the converted aircraft being Canadair-built Sabre 5s, structurally similar to the US-built F-86E. Deliveries began in mid-1977, and 51 target conversions had been delivered by March 1985, with low-quantity production continuing in 1986–87.

The QF-86Es are actively supporting US Army air defence system requirements at White Sands missile range, and can deploy stores, initiate jamming and provide other countermeasures, all under remote control.

TYPE: Full scale aerial target.

POWER PLANT: One Orenda 10 turbojet engine, rated at 28.15 kN (6,325 lb st). Fuel capacity 1,571 litres (345 Imp gallons; 415 US gallons) internal, plus provision for two 454 or 757 litre (100 or 166 Imp gallon; 120 or 200 US gallon) underwing drop tanks.

LAUNCH AND RECOVERY: Conventional runway T-O and landing, on retractable tricycle landing gear. Aircraft programmed to come to a halt, or continue and make safe T-O and climbout, if ground control link is lost during T-O run.

GUIDANCE AND CONTROL: Radio command guidance system. Primary mode of operation is NOLO (no local operator), over full range of pre-programmed flight manoeuvres including T-O and landing; but provision for onboard human pilot is retained (eg for manned practice presentations, or maintenance or ferry flights). Remote control exercised from one fixed and one mobile ground station, both manufactured by Vega Precision Laboratories; or by IBM drone formation control system.

MISSION EQUIPMENT: Onboard avionics and instrumentation comprise three basic installations: autopilot, with FSI avionics; Vega command/telemetry data system; and FSI interface coupler for processing uplink command and downlink telemetry data to and from drone aircraft. A fourth installation, the IBM drone formation control system, is optional. Radar altimeter optional, for simulated low-level attack presentations. Ancillary equipment, according to mission, may include scoring gear, infra-red flare dispenser, chaff dispensers or ECM pods. Television added as optional T-O and landing aid.

DIMENSIONS:
Wing span	11.31 m (37 ft 1.2 in)
Length overall	11.43 m (37 ft 6 in)
Height overall	4.48 m (14 ft 8.4 in)

WEIGHTS:
Basic weight empty	4,921 kg (10,850 lb)
T-O weight 'clean'	6,123 kg (13,500 lb)
T-O weight with two 120 US gallon drop tanks	6,894 kg (15,200 lb)

PERFORMANCE:
Max level speed above 11,000 m (36,000 ft)	Mach 0.92 (527 knots; 977 km/h; 607 mph)
Service ceiling	13,715 m (45,000 ft)
Max range at 9,145 m (30,000 ft) with two 120 US gallon drop tanks	600 nm (1,112 km; 691 miles)
Max endurance, conditions as above	2 h
g limit	+8

FSI (NORTH AMERICAN) QF-100 SUPER SABRE

Conversion of US Air Force/Air National Guard F-100 fighter-bombers for remotely piloted operation as QF-100 aerial targets is performed under contract from the US Air Force Sacramento Air Logistics Center, McClellan AFB, California. This full scale aerial target (FSAT) programme is for a multi-service target to provide air-to-air and ground-to-air missile evaluation and combat crew training. The QF-100 succeeded the Sperry-converted Convair QF-102/PQM-102 target (which see) in these roles.

The full scale engineering development and initial production programme was conducted by Sperry Corporation, and involved delivery of 100 Super Sabres (nine prototype and 91 'production') in four different configurations. Of these, configuration No. 2, converted from the single-seat F-100D, is the standard US Air Force target version; No. 1 incorporates

additional cockpit controls to permit evaluation of system performance from within the cockpit; No. 3 is the same configuration as No. 2, except that it is converted from the two-seat F-100F; No. 4 incorporates a drone formation control system (DFCS) for multiple-target missions involving up to six QF-100s. Subsequent conversions have been carried out at FSI's Aircraft Modification and Test Center at Mojave, California.

Deliveries by Sperry began on 13 March 1981 to Tyndall AFB, Florida, where the first unmanned flight was made on 19 November 1981. Initial operational capability with Tactical Air Command was achieved in late 1983.

In May 1984 the QF-100 follow-on production contract was awarded to FSI, which is delivering a total of 209 targets over a five-year period from mid-1985.

While sharing a common conversion and operational scheme with the PQM-102 series, the QF-100 utilises an SDP-175 digital flight control computer instead of the PQM-102 analog flight control stabilisation system (FCSS), thus achieving ease of testing and flexibility for future growth of operational modes.

TYPE: Full scale aerial target.
POWER PLANT: One Pratt & Whitney J57-P-21A turbojet, rated at 75.4 kN (16,950 lb st) with afterburning.
LAUNCH AND RECOVERY: Normal runway T-O and landing. Automatic T-O and landing, utilising the IBM DFCS, will be installed on the Eglin AFB Gulf range as part of the latter's control update system.
GUIDANCE AND CONTROL: Dual Vega command guidance and telemetry systems. Fully redundant digital tracking and control system for command/telemetry link, in conjunction with AN/FPS-16 ground-based range radar. Simultaneous control of multiple targets has been demonstrated. Sperry digital flight control computer (FCC) system incorporates air data sensors, SDP-175 processor, analog/digital and digital/analog converters, a power supply, and necessary interface electronics. FCC provides eight longitudinal/vertical and four lateral/directional modes, and interface between aircraft systems and command/telemetry system. Automatic modes are provided for take-off, loss of command carrier, take-off abort, and other safety modes. Redundant power systems and dual autopilot channels. Digital FCC permits automatic checkout of many primary autopilot

QF-100 full scale aerial target converted by Flight Systems Inc

functions; it also provides a flexible system for incorporating target system functions, or for adaptation to other target programmes. Control is exercised by a mobile ground station for take-off and recovery, and by a fixed ground site for guidance to, over and from the target range. Manoeuvre programmer can be pre-programmed for multiple manoeuvres, in any required sequence, and provides backup for FCC system.

MISSION EQUIPMENT: Incorporates remotely operated smoke, braking and explosive destruct systems; Digidops miss distance scoring system standard. Two types of scoring camera operational, covering forward and aft areas to provide missile approach angle, velocity and miss distance. Manoeuvre destruct and explosive destruct systems incorporated. Visual augmentation (smoke) system, operable at any altitude or power setting. Radar and infra-red augmentation not required, due to size of aircraft. LVSS (laser vector scoring system), one of several systems tested, can provide a directional parameter to help further in evaluating missile performance. A DLQ-3B ECM pod and ALE-40 infra-red/chaff pod are incorporated to provide realistic evaluation of missile performance against anticipated countermeasures. Drone formation control system incorporated to permit formation flight of two or more targets, to provide a realistic challenge for missiles equipped with seeker heads.

DIMENSIONS:

Wing span	11.82 m (38 ft 9.33 in)
Wing area	35.79 m² (385.2 sq ft)
Length overall, incl probe	16.54 m (54 ft 3 in)
Height overall	4.95 m (16 ft 2.66 in)

WEIGHT:

Mission operational T-O weight	14,060 kg (31,000 lb)

PERFORMANCE:

Max speed at altitude	Mach 1.3 (745 knots; 1,381 km/h; 858 mph)
Operating height range	60–15,240 m (200–50,000 ft)
Range, nominal (guidance radar range-limited)	120 nm (222 km; 138 miles)
Normal mission endurance	40–55 min
g limits	+8/−2

FSI (CONVAIR) QF-106 DELTA DART

The Sperry Defense Systems Division of Honeywell Inc was appointed prime contractor in July 1986 to supply QF-106 full scale aerial targets to the US Air Force. In the following month Sperry awarded FSI a $7.25 million major subcontract to convert six F-106As to prototype QF-106 configuration. The contract contains options to convert up to 192 more of these aircraft for target use over the following five years.

Further details of the conversion had not been received at the time of going to press. The following basic details apply to the manned F-106A:

POWER PLANT: One 109 kN (24,500 lb st) Pratt & Whitney J75-P-17 afterburning turbojet.

DIMENSIONS:

Wing span	11.67 m (38 ft 3.5 in)
Length overall	21.56 m (70 ft 8.75 in)

WEIGHT:

Max T-O weight	over 15,875 kg (35,000 lb)

PERFORMANCE:

Max level speed at 11,000 m (36,000 ft)	1,324 knots (2,455 km/h; 1,525 mph)

Service ceiling	17,375 m (57,000 ft)
Range	1,000 nm (1,850 km; 1,150 miles)

FORD AEROSPACE AND COMMUNICATIONS CORPORATION (Aeronutronic Division)
Ford Road, Newport Beach, California 92660

Under various DARPA contracts beginning in March 1972, Ford (or Philco-Ford, as it was then) designed, developed and built a series of low-cost mini-RPVs that were evaluated for battlefield reconnaissance, target acquisition and laser designation roles. Known as Praeire and Calere (respectively the Latin verbs 'to precede' and 'to give heat'), they differed only in the sensor system carried. The day-only missions were performed by the TV/laser-equipped Praeires, while the Caleres, carrying a miniature FLIR, could accomplish the same missions by day or night and in reduced visibility. Each was designed for two-person control by a pilot/navigator and a sensor operator.

FORD PRAEIRE I/CALERE I

These original air vehicles (two of each were ordered) were small, high-wing high-dihedral monoplanes with a fixed 'tailsitter' landing gear. They were built of wood and fabric, and powered by a nose-mounted two-cylinder engine driving a two-blade propeller. First flight was made in 1973, and in the summer of that year a **Praeire I** successfully designated targets for laser homing bombs delivered by tactical aircraft. The RPV was gyro-stabilised, and controlled within line-of-sight by a Motorola radio command guidance system. An electric field autopilot permitted out-of-sight flight to the limit of the data link. Mission equipment consisted of (1) a non-stabilised wide-angle TV camera with zoom lens, (2) a stabilised narrow-angle TV camera, and (3) a TWL-50 laser target designator. **Calere I** was identical except that items (2) and (3) were replaced by a Texas Instruments FLIR imager and a larger (TWL-100) designator.

DIMENSION:

Wing span	3.05 m (10 ft)

WEIGHTS:

Payload: Praeire I	11.3 kg (25 lb)
Max T-O weight: Praeire I	34 kg (75 lb)
Calere I	38.6 kg (85 lb)

PERFORMANCE:

Cruising speed	52 knots (96 km/h; 60 mph)
Range	approx 10.4 nm (19.3 km; 12 miles)

FORD PRAEIRE II/CALERE II and III

The Praeire/Calere II series was developed to further the technologies associated with mini-RPVs and to incorporate the lessons learned with Praeire I. Particular attention was given to the radar back-scatter characteristics, with low observables seen as an important aspect of survivability, together with minimum physical size and manoeuvring capability. Viewing coverage of the sensor, and its protection during take-off and landing, were also prime considerations. The resulting design featured a configuration entirely different from Praeire I, with a sharply dihedralled shoulder wing, a pod and boom fuselage and slender tail surfaces, all built of glassfibre, aluminium and

Ford Praeire IIB, showing transparent nose turret for TV sensor

polystyrene foam plastics. The 3.7 kW (5 hp) engine was installed in a small, pylon-mounted pod behind the wings, driving a two-blade pusher propeller, and the aircraft took off and landed on a fixed tricycle landing gear. The ogival fuselage nose section rotated 180° after take-off, bringing the transparent dome to the underfuselage position to give full viewing coverage for the sensor.

The Praeire/Calere II vehicles were demonstrated to all three US services, with payloads including TV, laser and FLIR. They had a max payload capacity of 13.6 kg (30 lb), although individual sensors weighed much less: the TV/laser installation, for example, was 8.6 kg (19 lb) and the FLIR only about 2.9 kg (6.5 lb). Electronic warfare (interception and jamming) payloads were also developed, and a **Praeire IIB** (6 kW; 8 hp Kolbo engine) demonstrated an endurance capability of nearly 6 hours with a high performance data link. Sale of a quantity of Praeire IIBs to Israel was approved in 1977.

In 1976, Ford test flew two prototypes of a **Calere III**, again under DARPA contract, as part of the **LANDSS** programme (lightweight advanced night/day surveillance system). This had a reduced wing span of 2.74 m (9 ft) and a max T-O weight of 27.2 kg (60 lb); payloads again comprised miniature FLIR and laser designation systems.

The following details apply to the Praeire IIB long-range version:

DIMENSIONS:

Wing span	3.96 m (13 ft)
Length overall	3.35 m (11 ft)
Propeller diameter	0.56 m (1 ft 10 in)

WEIGHTS:

Weight empty	40.4 kg (89 lb)
Payload	8.6 kg (19 lb)
Fuel	12.7 kg (28 lb)
Max T-O weight	61.7 kg (136 lb)

PERFORMANCE:

Max level speed at 1,525 m (5,000 ft)	
	75 knots (138 km/h; 86 mph)
Cruising speed	48 knots (88 km/h; 55 mph)
Stalling speed	35 knots (65 km/h; 40 mph)
Ceiling	3,050 m (10,000 ft)
Endurance	up to 6 h

GRUMMAN CORPORATION

Bethpage, New York 11714-3580 (Mail Stop B24-05)

GRUMMAN DESIGN 754

This unusual VTOL RPV design was developed in response to current US Navy RFPs (requests for proposals) for a medium-range/long-endurance surveillance air vehicle for use with its carrier battle and surface action groups, although it would be equally capable of an overland role. Its four primary applications are seen as: (1) airborne early warning; (2) detection and identification of targets up to 100 nm (185 km; 115 miles) from the parent ship; (3) battlefield surveillance; and (4) elint or ECM duties.

To avoid the need for additional deck equipment such as launch and recovery systems, Grumman opted for a self-launching VTOL design having a single turbojet for direct lift, plus a smaller cruise (turbofan) engine which would also contribute a proportion of the vertical thrust required during take-off and landing. Although quite large for an RPV, Design 754 would be operable from the helicopter pad of 'Spruance' class destroyers or larger ships, and possibly also from smaller vessels such as frigates. Hovering and cruising flight have been demonstrated successfully using a small scale model (wing span 2.13 m; 7 ft) powered by two ducted fan piston engines.

The following description applies to the full size Design 754:

TYPE: Medium-range variable geometry VTOL RPV.

AIRFRAME: Shoulder-wing monoplane, with cigar-shaped fuselage and mid-mounted tailplane. High aspect ratio sweptback wings (20° on leading edges) with short, fixed root sections, the outer portions folding backward and down for take-off, landing and storage, and locating inboard of the under-tailplane sweptback fins and rudders when fully folded. Retractable tricycle (wheel or skid) landing gear. Cruciform deflector vanes beneath fuselage.

POWER PLANT: Cruise engine is a 5.92 kN (1,330 lb st) Garrett F109 turbofan, mounted in an underfuselage pod. Rear of this pod is fitted with a vectoring nozzle which diverts efflux through 90° to augment thrust from lift-jet. Latter engine is either a 26.73 kN (6,010 lb st) Rolls-Royce RB162-81 or a 40.03 kN (9,000 lb st) Rolls-Royce XJ-99 turbojet, mounted within fuselage at CG with its axis at 20° forward of vertical, and capable of ±15° of tilt about this axis. Providing some 85 per cent of the total T-O thrust, the lift-jet is used for only about 30 s during the T-O and landing phases, between which times it is shut down and its dorsal intake doors closed.

Grumman Design 754 for a shipborne VTOL reconnaissance UMA

LAUNCH AND RECOVERY: Aircraft takes off from ship's deck or helicopter platform with wings folded back to their 90° position, retracting ventral deflector vane 'trapeze' and transitioning to wings fully spread approx 30 s after T-O, once clear of any nearby obstacles. Fully automatic recovery, using parent ship's radar to position RPV on initial approach. More precise positioning for touchdown effected by modified form of carrier ILS. In final half-minute before touchdown, lift engine is restarted, vectored thrust from cruise engine being added when airspeed drops to 55 knots (102 km/h; 63 mph). Landing gear and 'trapeze' then lowered, wings swept back, touchdown made at approx 1.52 m (5 ft)/s, and aircraft secured by harpoon decklock.

GUIDANCE AND CONTROL: Guided by parent ship's radar for first 200 nm (370 km; 230 miles), thereafter by pre-programmed inertial guidance, with data uplink/downlink via HF radio, satellite relay, or relay RPV. Pitch and roll control in cruising flight effected by ventral deflector vane 'trapeze'; yaw control in hover by ducting bleed air from lift engine to vents at nose and tail.

MISSION EQUIPMENT: (1) for AEW mission, UHF conformal radar with antennae buried in wing leading edges and tailplane trailing edges, having wide-angle beam steerable within 60° to left and right of aircraft's longitudinal axis. Onboard digital data link to process and return information. (2) For target location and identification up to 100 nm (185 km; 115 miles) from parent ship, a nose-mounted inverse synthetic aperture radar (ISAR) is proposed. (3) Joint STARS radar and video downlink for battlefield surveillance role. (4) Provision for elint, ECM or other payloads as required.

DIMENSIONS:

Wing span	15.54 m (51 ft)
Length overall:	
wings spread	8.38 m (27 ft 6 in)
wings folded	10.57 m (34 ft 8 in)
Height overall, excl landing gear	2.44 m (8 ft 0 in)
Tailplane span	5.03 m (16 ft 6 in)

WEIGHTS:

Mission equipment	680 kg (1,500 lb)
Fuel	1,724 kg (3,800 lb)
Max T-O weight	4,445 kg (9,800 lb)

PERFORMANCE (estimated):

Max level speed at S/L	133 knots (246 km/h; 153 mph)
Cruising speed at altitude	210 knots (389 km/h; 242 mph)
Max rate of climb at S/L	152 m (500 ft)/min
Mission altitude:	
normal	8,230 m (27,000 ft)
maximum	11,275 m (37,000 ft)
Range with 680 kg (1,500 lb) payload	
	2,800 nm (5,190 km; 3,225 miles)
Endurance	14 h

GYRODYNE COMPANY OF AMERICA INC

St James, Long Island, New York 11780

Gyrodyne (the name means an aerodyne with its engine power driving both rotor(s) for lift and propeller(s) for thrust) was formed in August 1946, and embodied this concept in its little Model 2B coaxial helicopter which first flew in 1949. It was followed in November 1955 by the XRON–1 Rotorcycle, a more conventional (but still coaxial) open-seat one-man

helicopter developed under US Navy contract for use by the US Marine Corps. On 2 April 1958 that contract was amended to provide for the design, development and production of a small drone helicopter to operate from the deck of a destroyer as the airborne torpedo-carrying component of the DASH (Drone Anti-Submarine Helicopter) weapon system.

GYRODYNE QH-50

The initial USN contract authorised Gyrodyne to make minimum modifications to a YRON–1 Rotorcycle to make it completely controllable from the ground by means of off-the-shelf and 'breadboard' electronic equipment, to investigate its suitability as a drone. A specialised DASH vehicle was authorised in a follow-on contract of 31 December 1958. Gyrodyne, as weapon system manager, was responsible not only for the drone helicopters but also for the on-ship equipment for controlling them in flight, and development of special deck handling equipment.

Nearly 800 QH-50s were built eventually, and they remain the most widely used drone rotorcraft so far produced. Many were placed in storage after withdrawal from USN service, and the QH-50 airframe is currently (1987) the basis of at least two contemporary RPH programmes: the Aerodyne Systems CH-84 Pegasus and the Dornier Argus/Priamos (which see). During their earlier career, QH-50s were used operationally for surveillance duties as well as their primary ASW function. Other flight test demonstrations proved their capability to transport, deliver and retrieve cargo; lay down smokescreens; perform rescue missions; carry out night illumination of targets; and drop sonobuoys and flares. The command/control equipment was installed variously on board ship, in a piloted aircraft and in a mobile ground vehicle, in all of which the 'hands off' transfer of the QH-50, in flight, from one station to another, was demonstrated.

Variants built or projected were designated as follows:

QH-50A (originally DSN-1). Initial version (nine built), incorporating standard Rotorcycle piston engine (54 kW; 72 hp Porsche YO-95-6 flat-four), transmission and rotor control system, but with redesigned fuselage and landing gear; tip brake directional controls on each rotor blade, to eliminate need for tail rotor; and seat for safety pilot. More advanced electronics for pilotless operation, including on/off channels for weapon arming and release. First at-sea landing (with safety pilot) made on 1 July 1960, on USS *Mitscher*; followed on 12 August 1960 by first free flight of a completely unmanned drone helicopter, at NATC Patuxent River, Md; and on 7 December 1960 by first successful drone helicopter flight from a ship at sea (USS *Hazelwood*). Several reconditioned in 1965 and equipped with new avionics for use as air-to-air missile targets, in which role they served at Pacific Missile Range, Point Mugu, California, from November 1965 until February 1966.

QH-50B (originally DSN-2). Modified QH-50A (three built), ordered as interim development model for QH-50C and first flown in 1961. Powered by two 54 kW (72 hp) Porsche YO-95-4 piston engines. Flown in piloted configuration only; used to develop and test equipment for QH-50C.

QH-50C (originally DSN-3). Initial operational model (373 built), first flown on 25 January 1962 and delivered to USN (two to each destroyer) from 15 November that year. Production ended December 1965. Powered by single 224 kW (300 shp) Boeing T50-BO-8A turboshaft engine coupled directly to transmission. Avionics, integrated with shipboard command/control system, provided for operation in all flight regimes. First US warship to receive operational aircraft, on 7 January 1963, was USS *Buck*. In addition to ASW mission, QH-50Cs and Ds equipped with TV systems were used by USN for surveillance and target spotting under **Project Snoopy**. Operating from a destroyer off the coast of Viet-Nam, the drone's TV camera relayed real-time data to the shipboard monitor to provide guidance for firing of ship's guns at detected land targets.

QH-50D. Improved version of QH-50C (370 built for USN and 24 for Japan Maritime Self-Defence Force), first flown in 1965 and delivered from January 1966. Uprated Boeing T50-BO-12 turboshaft (246 kW; 330 shp), greater fuel capacity, Gyrodyne all-weather glassfibre rotor blades, contributing to increased range and payload. Some used in Project Snoopy role (see QH-50C paragraph). Others used in DARPA programmes **Nite Panther** and **Nite Gazelle**, initiated in January 1968. Former provided for installation and flight test of Cohu day/night TV cameras, motion and still cameras, Korad laser rangefinder/target designator, moving target indicator radar, covert illuminator, and other sensing and detection equipment. Nite Gazelle programme similarly tested weapon installations, including Minigun, high-velocity gun, grenade launcher, bomblet dispensers, bombs, and Martin Marietta LARS (laser-aided rocket system) missiles. 'Nite' versions equipped with high-accuracy tracking mount and could carry additional 303 litres (66.6 Imp gallons; 80 US gallons) of fuel in auxiliary tank. One (piloted) QH-50D test flown with four-blade coaxial rotors to prove feasibility of a 'heavy lift' drone version.

QH-50E. Modified QH-50D (one only), re-engined with 236 kW (317 shp) Allison T63-A-5A turboshaft. First droned flight 11 September 1969.

QH-50F. Proposed production version of QH-50E, with 276 kW (370 shp) Allison T63 engine. Not built.

QH-50H. Discontinued project for twin-engined (two 370 shp T63) version of QH-50F, with increased diameter rotors.

A Gyrodyne QH-50D equipped with day TV camera, laser rangefinder and XM129 grenade launcher

TYPE: Multi-purpose drone helicopter.

AIRFRAME: Semi-rigid rotor system, each of the coaxial contra-rotating rotors having two tapered blades of laminated wood (glassfibre on QH-50D). Two-stage reduction gear, with freewheel unit and clutch. Steel tube 'fuselage' chassis, with inverted V tail surfaces. Non-retractable skid landing gear. Seat for safety pilot during flight test stages.

POWER PLANT: As detailed in 'variant' paragraphs. Standard fuel capacities: QH-50A, 27.6 litres (6.1 Imp gallons; 7.3 US gallons); QH-50B, 56.4 litres (12.4 Imp gallons; 14.9 US gallons); QH-50C, 127.2 litres (28 Imp gallons; 33.6 US gallons); QH-50D/E/F, 196.8 litres (43.3 Imp gallons; 52 US gallons); QH-50H, 454.2 litres (100 Imp gallons; 120 US gallons).

LAUNCH, RECOVERY, GUIDANCE AND CONTROL: For take-off, deck control officer used a transmitter with manoeuvre stick control of cyclic roll, pitch and flat turns, and knob control of altitude and heading. Digital signals sent from transmitter to relay assembly for assignment to an audio frequency coder. Digital audio command signals then transmitted by UHF line-of-sight data link. Drone's transistorised FM radio receiver eliminated carrier frequency and applied audio frequency to drone's decoder, which extracted digital messages, decoded command information and provided analog voltages, as well as on/off switch closure for torpedo

arming and release mechanisms. Analog voltages combined with sensor inputs from roll, pitch and displacement gyros and altitude control, then fed to electronic control amplifier. This in turn controlled pitch, roll, yaw and collective servo clutches in drone's electro-mechanical actuator. When in-flight drone appeared on radar scope, control was transferred to a second transmitter in ship's combat information centre (CIC). CIC tracked drone by radar, adjusting course, speed and altitude as necessary to position it over submarine target whose location was known from sonar information. CIC controller was then able to actuate arming and weapon release switches, afterwards returning drone to vicinity of launch vessel. When deck control officer sighted returning drone, he took over its control and brought it in for landing.

ARMAMENT: Two Mk 44 homing torpedos, or one Mk 46 torpedo and one sonobuoy.

DIMENSIONS (by QH-50 suffix letter):

Rotor diameter (each):	
A to F	6.10 m (20 ft)
H	8.53 m (28 ft)
Rotor disc area (each):	
A to F	29.2 m² (314.2 sq ft)
H	57.2 m² (615.8 sq ft)

Fuselage length:

A	1.96 m (6 ft 5 in)
B	2.03 m (6 ft 8 in)
C	3.94 m (12 ft 11 in)
D	2.33 m (7 ft 7.75 in)
E, F	2.68 m (8 ft 9.5 in)
H	5.27 m (17 ft 3.5 in)

Height overall:

A	2.39 m (7 ft 10 in)
B	2.51 m (8 ft 3 in)
C, D, E, F	2.96 m (9 ft 8.5 in)
H	3.02 m (9 ft 11 in)

WEIGHTS:

Weight empty, equipped:

A	252 kg (555 lb)
B	369 kg (813 lb)
C	499 kg (1,100 lb)
D	427 kg (941 lb)
E, *F	409 kg (901 lb)
*H	590 kg (1,300 lb)

Ordnance (ASW):

A	120 kg (265 lb)
B	236 kg (520 lb)
C	393 kg (866.5 lb)
D, E, *F	416 kg (918 lb)
*H	825 kg (1,820 lb)

Ordnance (Nite Gazelle):

D, E, *F	136 kg (300 lb)
*H	340 kg (750 lb)

Normal max T-O weight:

A	401 kg (885 lb)
B	658 kg (1,450 lb)
C (ASW and Snoopy)	1,035 kg (2,281 lb)
D (ASW)	1,055 kg (2,327 lb)
D (Snoopy, Panther, Gazelle)	1,111 kg (2,450 lb)
E (ASW)	1,006 kg (2,217 lb)
*F (ASW)	1,037 kg (2,287 lb)
*H (ASW)	1,778 kg (3,920 lb)
*H (Snoopy, Panther, Gazelle)	2,359 kg (5,200 lb)

PERFORMANCE (at normal max T-O weight):

Max level speed at S/L:

A	58 knots (107 km/h; 67 mph)
B	70 knots (130 km/h; 81 mph)
C, D, E, *F	80 knots (148 km/h; 92 mph)
*H (ASW)	160 knots (296 km/h; 184 mph)

Max vertical rate of climb at S/L (ISA):

A	152 m (500 ft)/min
B	198 m (650 ft)/min
C	427 m (1,400 ft)/min
D (ASW)	731 m (2,400 ft)/min
D (Snoopy, Panther, Gazelle)	518 m (1,700 ft)/min
E (ASW)	488 m (1,600 ft)/min
*F (ASW)	762 m (2,500 ft)/min
*H (ASW)	1,173 m (3,850 ft)/min
*H (Snoopy, Panther, Gazelle)	427 m (1,400 ft)/min

Service ceiling:

B	2,620 m (8,600 ft)
C	4,940 m (16,200 ft)
D	4,785 m (15,700 ft)

Hovering ceiling OGE:

A	975 m (3,200 ft)
C	3,385 m (11,100 ft)
D	3,110 m (10,200 ft)

Mission radius:

A	26 nm (48 km; 30 miles)
B	32 nm (59 km; 37 miles)
C	28 nm (52 km; 32 miles)
†D, E, *F, *H	40 nm (74 km; 46 miles)

Range (non-ASW) with max standard fuel:

A	270 nm (500 km; 311 miles)
B	394 nm (730 km; 454 miles)
C	310 nm (574 km; 357 miles)
D	393 nm (728 km; 452 miles)
E	400 nm (741 km; 460 miles)
*F	355 nm (658 km; 409 miles)
*H	900 nm (1,668 km; 1,036 miles)

*Design estimate
† Typical mission at 305 m (1,000 ft) altitude, command/control line of sight

HYNES HELICOPTER (Division of Hynes Aviation Industries Inc)

PO Box 697, Frederick, Oklahoma 73542

In 1984 Hynes began adapting the airframes of its H-2 and H-5 commercial helicopters to remotely piloted operation, so as to offer a 'rent-a-drone' capability to manufacturers of avionics, weapons and other aircraft equipment. The programme is known as TERT, signifying the RPH's suitability for test and evaluation, educational, R & D and tactical missions. First result of this programme was a September 1984 contract from the US Army Missile Command for four H-5Ts, with options on a further six. Hynes Aviation was put up for sale in spring 1987.

HYNES H-2T and H-5T

In general, these RPH versions use the standard airframes, power plants and systems of the passenger carrying H-2 and H-5, but modifications can be made to the cabin and avionics, or weapons and other equipment installed, to meet specific customer requirements. For example, the H-5Ts built for the US Army in 1986 had glassfibre fairings over the fuselage to simulate the Soviet Mi-24 'Hind-D' helicopter. It is not thought that any H-2Ts were completed.

In order to improve payload capability in hot and high conditions, Hynes initiated two engine test programmes with the H-5T in 1986. One involved fitting a turbocharger to the existing IVO-540 piston engine; the other was to replace that engine with a Soloy conversion using a 313 kW (420 shp) Allison 250-C20B turboshaft.

TYPE: Remotely piloted helicopters.
AIRFRAME: Three-blade main rotor with inboard flapping hinges and coincident flap and lag hinges. Blades are semi-rigid at hub and fully articulated at 40 per cent span to eliminate ground resonance. Inboard portion of each blade is built around a steel spar, outboard portion has an extruded aluminium leading edge spar and polyurethane core; aluminium skin is bonded to core and riveted to spar. Blades do not fold, but can be separated quickly at inboard/outboard junction for easy storage. Two-blade all-metal anti-torque tail rotor. Rotors driven via automatic centrifugal clutch and planetary reduction gears; bevel gear take-off from main transmission to tail rotor driveshaft. Fuselage is a stressed skin all-metal structure with conical tail

Hynes H-5T target representation of a 'Hind-D' helicopter

section and small fixed horizontal stabiliser. Tail rotor on swept-up boom extension. Non-retractable tricycle landing gear (single mainwheels and twin nosewheels) with optional mainwheel braking is standard, but skid gear or pontoons are optional.

POWER PLANT: One 134 kW (180 hp) Avco Lycoming IVO-360-A1A flat-four engine in H-2T; 227.4 kW (305 hp) Avco Lycoming IVO-540-B1A flat-six in H-5T. Rubber bag type fuel tank under engine, capacity 117 litres (25.8 Imp gallons; 31 US gallons) in H-2T, 163 litres (35.8 Imp gallons; 43 US gallons) in H-5T.

LAUNCH AND RECOVERY: Conventional helicopter T-O and landing. Automatic emergency flight termination system standard.

GUIDANCE AND CONTROL: No details supplied.

MISSION EQUIPMENT: A 12V (H-2T) or 24V (H-5T) DC electrical power source can power a wide range of equipment, according to individual customer requirements. Other DC or AC sources can be provided if required.

DIMENSIONS:
Main rotor diameter:
2T   7.24 m (23 ft 9 in)
5T   7.82 m (25 ft 8 in)
Tail rotor diameter:
2T, 5T   1.30 m (4 ft 3 in)
Main rotor disc area:
2T   41.16 m² (443 sq ft)
5T   48.07 m² (517.4 sq ft)
Length overall, rotors turning:
2T   8.56 m (28 ft 1 in)
5T   9.53 m (31 ft 3 in)
Length of fuselage:
2T   6.53 m (21 ft 5 in)
5T   8.38 m (27 ft 6 in)
Height overall:
2T   2.13 m (7 ft)
5T   2.44 m (8 ft)
Wheel track:
2T   1.93 m (6 ft 4 in)
5T   2.03 m (6 ft 8 in)

Wheelbase:
2T   1.73 m (5 ft 8 in)
5T   1.88 m (6 ft 2 in)

WEIGHTS (designed):
Weight empty:
2T   386–431 kg (850–950 lb)
5T   680–771 kg (1,500–1,700 lb)
Max fuel:
2T   27.2 kg (60 lb)
5T   49 kg (108 lb)
Max payload:
2T   295–363 kg (650–800 lb)
5T   317–544 kg (700–1,200 lb)
Max T-O weight:
2T   680–748 kg (1,500–1,650 lb)
5T   998–1,225 kg (2,200–2,700 lb)

PERFORMANCE (estimated at max T-O weight):
Max cruising speed:
2T   76 knots (142 km/h; 88 mph)
5T at 915 m (3,000 ft)   91 knots (169 km/h; 105 mph)
Rate of climb at 1,525 m (5,000 ft):
2T   183 m (600 ft)/min
5T   305 m (1,000 ft)/min
Service ceiling:
2T   3,050 m (10,000 ft)
5T   3,660 m (12,000 ft)
Hovering ceiling IGE:
2T   1,830 m (6,000 ft)
5T   2,440 m (8,000 ft)
Hovering ceiling OGE:
2T   1,220 m (4,000 ft)
5T   1,830 m (6,000 ft)
Range with max fuel:
2T   217 nm (402 km; 250 miles)
5T   191 nm (354 km; 220 miles)
Max endurance:
2T, 5T   more than 3 h

HYNES (BELL) UH-1H DRONE

In the summer of 1986, Hynes was working on an R & D programme to drone a UH-1H for an unnamed foreign country. This customer has a large supply of surplus UH-1Hs, for which drone conversions are required. The Hynes demonstrator was to embody a modified version of the H-2T/H-5T control system.

ILC DOVER (Division of ILC Industries Inc)

PO Box 266, Frederica, Delaware 19946

ILC Dover designs and manufactures a range of unmanned non-rigid aerostats of the tethered, aerodynamically-shaped balloon type. It also performs varied R & D programmes on high-altitude long-endurance platforms and inflatable-wing RPVs, hybrid heavy-lift vehicles, and many other inflatable technology products.

ILC DOVER APTERON

This small, lightweight RPV was built in about 1979 to prove the feasibility of a 'flying wing' vehicle using an inflatable aerofoil. Preliminary studies indicated that the principle could be applied successfully to much larger vehicles: for example, one with a 23 m (75 ft) wing span and 130 m² (1,400 sq ft) wing area could support a 90.7 kg (200 lb) payload and be capable of operation at altitudes of up to 21,340 m (70,000 ft). Such a vehicle would be compact, easily transportable, and quickly erected. The soft fabric structure would be essentially radar-transparent, further enhancing its mission capabilities.

TYPE: Experimental inflatable wing mini-RPV.
AIRFRAME: 'Flying wing' monoplane, with moderate sweepback. Reflex-section fabric wing, inflated by compressed air prior to flight. To maintain inflation pressure irrespective of barometric or ambient temperature changes during flight, fuselage accommodates a small tank of freon gas. Wing fitted with elevons of Mylar covered balsa wood; fuselage is aerofoil-shaped and built of plywood. Non-retractable tricycle landing gear.
POWER PLANT: One 0.4 kW (0.5 hp) piston engine, driving a two-blade pusher propeller.
LAUNCH AND RECOVERY: Conventional T-O and landing.
GUIDANCE AND CONTROL: Radio command guidance system. Elevons for pitch and roll control.

ILC Dover Apteron inflatable wing mini

DIMENSION:
Wing span	1.55 m (5 ft 1 in)

WEIGHTS:
Weight empty	1.8 kg (4 lb)
Payload	1.4 kg (3 lb)

PERFORMANCE:
Not known

ILC DOVER HYBRID HEAVY-LIFT VEHICLES

Several concepts of hybrid heavy-lift vehicle have been prepared which combine the principles of aerostatic and aerodynamic lift to derive a total system lift greater than that attainable by either principle alone.

ILC DOVER HIGH ALTITUDE PLATFORMS

ILC Dover has developed conceptual designs for several high-altitude aerostat RPV platforms. These vehicles are designed to fly at altitudes in the order of 21,350 m (70,000 ft), where they can take advantage of optimum wind fields to reduce power requirements.

These systems have been evaluated in two configurations. One concept carries its own power source and can be fully mobile, while another maintains a fixed location and has microwave power transmitted up from the ground. Both concepts utilise advanced laminar flow hull shapes fabricated from lightweight reinforced film laminate materials.

Configurations ranging in size from 70,792 to 141,584 m³ (2.5 to 5.0 million cu ft) have been investigated. Future development of the concept would start with a scale vehicle in the order of 7,079 to 28,317 m³ (0.25 to 1.0 million cu ft).

ILC DOVER AG-60 BALLOON

ILC's AG-60 balloon is designed for any general use where a highly visible ground marker is required for such applications as aerial spraying and surveying. Its envelope is made from heat sealed white urethane coated nylon, and incorporates three inflatable fins forming an inverted 'Y' to ensure stable flight in wind velocities from 0 to 39 knots (72 km/h; 45 mph) on a 91 m (300 ft) nylon tether. It is equipped with an automatic self-closing fill port to provide easy inflation, and a pressure relief valve to prevent overpressurisation. Handled easily by one operator, it can be transported, flown and retrieved from a standard open pickup truck.

DIMENSIONS, ENVELOPE:
Length overall	3.05 m (10 ft)
Max diameter	1.17 m (3 ft 10 in)
Volume, gross	1.70 m³ (60 cu ft)

WEIGHT:
Unfilled	1.4 kg (3 lb)

ILC DOVER SSP SERIES

The SSP (stable sensor platform) is a non-rigid tethered aerostat based upon the design of the successful Family II D7 developed by DARPA for the surveillance and communications relay requirements of the US Department of Defense. It consists of an elliptically shaped envelope, containing a lenticular-shaped ballonet, and incorporating three fins forming an inverted 'Y'.

ILC's SSP series aerostats range in size from 85 to 1,076 m³ (3,000–38,000 cu ft). A typical and popular model is the

SSP-6ooo, which has a pressure control system that maintains the envelope's design shape, with redundant valves to relieve pressure resulting from superheat, atmospheric pressure drop, or increase in altitude. A battery-powered electric blower, with more than five days' sustained in-flight capability, maintains pressure during descent, atmospheric pressure increase, or temperature drop. The fins are air-inflated and coupled to the ballonet, so that the complete aerostat is maintained at the same pressure.

An effective low-cost mooring system is available for the SSP series.

DIMENSIONS, ENVELOPE:

Length overall	15.35 m (50 ft 4.25 in)
Max diameter	4.98 m (16 ft 4 in)
Tail fin span:	
horizontal	5.06 m (16 ft 7.25 in)
vertical	6.10 m (20 ft)
Max helium volume	170 m³ (6,000 cu ft)
Max ballonet volume	28.33 m³ (1,000 cu ft)
Nominal helium volume at S/L	147.25 m³ (5,200 cu ft)
Nominal ballonet volume at S/L	22.65 m³ (800 cu ft)

WEIGHTS:

Gross lift, 95% helium purity	144 kg (317 lb)
Free lift	14.5 kg (32 lb)
Aerostat weight	72.6 kg (160 lb)
Net lift	56.7 kg (125 lb)

PERFORMANCE:

Max design altitude	1,525 m (5,000 ft)
Max wind velocity, operational	
	45 knots (83 km/h; 52 mph)

ILC DOVER 250,000 CU FT AEROSTAT

This large-volume aerostat can lift a payload of 454 kg (1,000 lb) to an altitude of 3,660 m (12,000 ft). The shape of its envelope is a modification of the Class 'C' developed by the US Air Force as a radar surveillance platform. The envelope incorporates a large ballonet, and has four tail fins in cruciform configuration: these not only provide pitch and yaw stability, but generate additional lift as wind speeds increase. The avionics or other payload is carried beneath the envelope, and a pressurised cover is available to protect the payload and decrease aerodynamic drag. Pressure control is maintained by a system of valves and blowers which add or dump air from the ballonet, tail fins, and pressurised load cover. This pressure maintenance is totally automatic, controlled by pressure switches and logic circuits, but manual control from the ground via onboard telemetry can be used to override any pre-set limits. Onboard power supplies can be matched to the payload requirements but, typically, a 6 kW generator will meet radar payload and pressure system requirements.

DIMENSIONS, ENVELOPE:

Length overall	53.34 m (175 ft)
Max diameter	17.31 m (56 ft 9.5 in)
Tail fin span	24.62 m (80 ft 9.5 in)
Volume: gross	7,079 m³ (250,000 cu ft)
ballonet	3,030 m³ (107,000 cu ft)

PERFORMANCE:

Design altitude, with 454 kg (1,000 lb) payload	
	3,660 m (12,000 ft)
Max wind velocity:	
operational	60 knots (111 km/h; 69 mph)
moored	90 knots (167 km/h; 103 mph)

KAMAN AEROSPACE CORPORATION

PO Box 2, Old Windsor Road, Bloomfield, Connecticut 06002–0002

A pioneer of RPH development, Kaman flew its first remotely controlled helicopter, an HTK-1 with a safety pilot on board, in September 1953. First pilotless flight of a droned helicopter followed in July 1957, and the company subsequently droned a number of helicopters for various DoD programmes, including such widely differing types as the Bell H-13, Kaman H-43 and Vertol H-21.

Its most recent purpose-designed RPH was the STAPL, the test programme for which was completed in early 1980. Currently, under US Army contract, Kaman continues to provide helicopter drone kits for use in defence programmes. These kits provide complete radio remote control from the ground for take-off, performance of mission, return and landing. Kaman designs and manufactures the kits, installs and flight tests them, and provides the ground controller to fly the target missions.

Drone kits to convert surplus Bell UH-1 helicopters into **QUH-1** target aircraft have been produced for use at Fort Bliss, Texas, in testing candidate designs for forward area air defence weapons systems. Additional kits, also for installation in UH-1s, have been used at White Sands missile range, New Mexico, in trials of a variety of missile and gun system combinations. Fabrication of drone kits is expected to continue until at least 1989.

KAMAN STAPL

Kaman began design of the STAPL (Ship Tethered Aerial PLatform) under contract to the US Office of Naval Research in September 1972, and testing of two demonstrators, as well as their mobile launch/recovery platform and control system, began in 1974. The aircraft, of autogyro configuration, were each equipped with an automatic flight control system and data recording equipment. After initial flight testing with only a single central fin and rudder, a horizontal stabiliser was added, with additional fins at the tips. The test programme ended in spring 1980.

AIRFRAME: Welded steel tube fuselage; skid type landing gear. Sheet metal vertical fin, with aerodynamically balanced rudder. Variable incidence horizontal stabiliser, actuated electrically, and endplate auxiliary fins, of plywood construction. Bensen two-blade teetering and autorotating rotor, with non-folding metal blades. No rotor brake.

POWER PLANT: One 67 kW (90 hp) McCulloch 4318G piston engine, driving a Bensen two-blade fixed-pitch propeller. Single fuselage fuel tank, capacity 22.4 litres (5 Imp gallons; 6 US gallons).

LAUNCH AND RECOVERY: Tethered T-O and landing.

GUIDANCE AND CONTROL: Kaman AFCS, powered by two 12V batteries, providing three-axis stabilisation and automatic flight path control. Redundancy incorporated for mission reliability.

DIMENSIONS:

Rotor diameter	6.63 m (21 ft 9.01 in)
Rotor disc area	34.56 m² (371.5 sq ft)
Length, excl rotor	3.27 m (10 ft 8.75 in)
Height to top of rotor head	1.92 m (6 ft 3.5 in)
Propeller diameter	1.22 m (4 ft)

Kaman STAPL ship tethered aerial platform

WEIGHTS:
Weight empty	172 kg (380 lb)
Fuel	17.7 kg (39 lb)
Max payload	34 kg (75 lb)
Max T-O weight	224 kg (494 lb)

PERFORMANCE:
Not known

LOCKHEED AERONAUTICAL SYSTEMS COMPANY (Burbank Division)

Burbank, California 91520

LOCKHEED D-21/GTD-21B

This high-speed reconnaissance drone owed its existence to the Gary Powers U-2 affair of 1960. Lockheed's A-12 design (forerunner of the SR-71 'Blackbird'), which had been selected in August 1959 as the U-2's successor in a joint CIA/USAF programme known as Oxcart, received a setback from the incoming US government's decision in 1961 to prohibit manned overflights of the Soviet Union. The D-21 was therefore proposed as a pilotless, expendable and politically less embarrassing alternative, to be air-launched by the A-12 itself from a safe stand-off distance. Both programmes were undertaken by the company's Advanced Development Projects department – the celebrated 'Skunk Works' – and a total of 38 D-21s was built between 1964–67. In the Lockheed development programme, two single-seat A-12s were converted as launch aircraft, the 'Q-bay' behind the pilot being modified to accommodate a launch control officer (LCO) for the drone.

The D-21 itself bore a family resemblance to the A-12 in both appearance and construction, with possibly even greater application of 'stealth' techniques than its piloted predecessor to mask its radar and infra-red signatures. Early reports that it was originally carried aloft semi-recessed under the A-12's belly

have not been confirmed. Be that as it may, the method Lockheed eventually adopted was to mount the drone pick-a-back fashion on a pylon above the A-12's rear fuselage, between the inward canted fins. On reaching launch speed (reportedly about Mach 3.15), the LCO ignited the D-21's ramjet and an explosive charge separated the drone from the pylon. This system went tragically wrong on 30 July 1966 when the D-21, failing to clear the shock wave, struck the tail of the A-12, resulting in the loss not only of both aircraft but also of the LCO. Lockheed Vice-President 'Kelly' Johnson immediately terminated the A-12/D-21 launch programme.

When next heard of some two years later, the D-21 had undergone redesign of the engine air inlet, which now had a fixed centrebody 'spike' instead of a movable one. Air launch was more conventional, being made by airdrop from the inboard underwing pylon of a B-52 bomber. To offset the correspondingly lower and slower launch conditions, a large booster rocket was strapped beneath each drone to accelerate it to cruising speed and altitude. Two B-52Hs of the 4200th Test Wing at Beale AFB were assigned as carriers, and a small number of operational missions were flown in the USA and the Far East under the USAF's Senior Bowl programme, until the 1972 Viet-Nam peace talks and the banning of overflights of mainland China combined to end further deployment of the D-21. When the 17 survivors were placed in store at Davis-Monthan AFB in 1976–77, their basic designation had acquired a GT prefix, together with a B suffix that presumably reflected the inlet modification.

Lockheed-California D-21 supersonic reconnaissance drone

General arrangement of the Lockheed-D21
(Michael A. Badrocke)

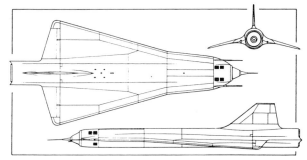

Type: Expendable reconnaissance drone.

Airframe: Low/mid-wing monoplane, of basically delta planform with curved leading edge chines inboard, extending forward to lip of air inlet. Pitot boom or antenna on each chine, near root. Conical camber on outer wing leading edges; elevons on trailing edges. Blended wing/body design, with circular section fuselage, broadly resembling that of nacelle and outer wing of A-12. Large conical centrebody 'spike' in nose air inlet. Extended exhaust nozzle, to mask IR signature. Single low aspect ratio fin with inset rudder, well forward of exhaust nozzle; no horizontal tail surfaces. Extensive use of titanium alloys and composite materials, including (apparently) a radar absorbent 'blanket' covering on large central areas of wing/body above and below.

Power Plant: One Marquardt RJ43-MA-11 ramjet (approx 53.4 kN; 12,000 lb thrust). Forward and rear rows of bypass doors. Circular inlet in nose, with large movable (later fixed) centrebody 'spike'. Fixed geometry exhaust nozzle, with internal honeycomb-like plug beyond neck area. Large booster rocket attached to underside of drone to assist launch from B-52.

Launch and Recovery: Air-launched from A-12 at speed of approx Mach 3.15 at very high altitude; or at lower speed and altitude from B-52, with rocket booster to accelerate drone to operational cruise speed and altitude before being jettisoned. Drone non-recoverable; payload data capsule ejected before end of mission, for C-130 or helicopter MARS retrieval.

Guidance and Control: Radio command control system for launch phase. Operational part of mission probably pre-programmed (no details known).

Mission Equipment: Panel beneath forward fuselage on each side, aft of air inlet, giving access to air-conditioned bay(s) for reconnaissance sensor package. Data capsule ejected via these panels at conclusion of mission.

Dimensions:
Wing span   5.79 m (19 ft)
Length overall   13.16 m (43 ft 2 in)

Weight:
Max launching weight (excl rocket booster)
                       approx 9,072 kg (20,000 lb)

Performance (estimated):
Max level speed
        Mach 4.0 (2,300 knots; 4,260 km/h; 2,645 mph)
Absolute ceiling   above 30,500 m (100,000 ft)
Max range   1,085 nm (2,010 km; 1,250 miles)

LOCKHEED AERONAUTICAL SYSTEMS COMPANY (Georgia Division)

86 South Cobb Drive, Marietta, Georgia 30063

Lockheed-Georgia took over from Lockheed Missiles and Space Company (which see) responsibility for the current Solar HAPP design study now being examined by NASA. In early 1987 Georgia received a US Army contract to design and develop a UMA capable of launching 'smart' weapons, as part of a classified DARPA R & D programme. Team members include Honeywell Defense Systems, Tecknowledge and Titan. A six-month concept/design study was to be followed by a 2½ year development/test phase, and then by a further 2½ years of system integration and demonstration.

Artist's impression of a future Solar HAPP vehicle

LOCKHEED/NASA SOLAR HAPP

In October 1984 NASA's Langley Research Center awarded Lockheed Missiles and Space Co a third contract for a Solar High Altitude Powered Platform (Solar HAPP), with a new mission and revised design. Earlier (1981-83) contracts with LMSC had covered operational needs, systems and structures, with a potential mission to monitor crops in California for the US Department of Agriculture. The UMA proposed under the earlier contracts was a 'flying wing' design with an integral central payload pod.

During the course of the 1984 contract, the Solar HAPP programme was transferred to Lockheed-Georgia, where the study was completed. The final report was with NASA Langley for further consideration in 1987.

As currently envisaged, the payload pod is underslung, and twin tailbooms/tail unit added. There are solar cells on each side of the overwing vertical stabilisers and on the top and bottom surfaces of the outer wing panels; the latter would be hinged upward during daylight, as in the illustration, to absorb maximum solar energy, and downward at night to improve cruise performance. The electric motor would be powered directly by the solar cells during the day. Surplus energy collected during daylight would be used to separate water by electrolysis into hydrogen and oxygen storage cells, re-combining the gases during nocturnal flight to produce electrical power for the motor and water for recycling the following day.

The 1984 contract covered the study of payload options, and simulation of a potential mission to monitor experimental crops in southern Arizona. The sensor payload would operate in the near-infra-red, far-infra-red and ultraviolet spectra, sending back real-time images to assist farmers in making quick economic and crop decisions. Images transmitted would be much sharper than those from orbiting satellites.

Solar HAPP (also known unofficially as 'Solar Star') would be aero-tow launched in still air, spiralling upward in 4 hours to its operational altitude, where winds are light, and loitering over a designated area using an onboard reference system. Changes of location could be directed by radio command. The

UMA could remain airborne for up to a year; first flight is possible by 1993.

TYPE: Very long endurance UMA.

AIRFRAME: Extremely long span monoplane, with Liebeck L1003 aerofoil section, having outer panels that hinge upward through 90°. No anhedral, dihedral, incidence or sweep. Wing structure comprises a spanwise graphite/epoxy tube truss, with chordwise stiffeners of birch and spruce, covered with Teflon fabric and wire-braced externally. Rectangular vertical stabilising panel above wing on each side at approx one-third span. Aileron, with proportional tab, inboard of each outer hinge point. Twin hexagonal fins and rudders, bridged at top by a fixed incidence tailplane with elevator and proportional tab, carried on slender tubular tailbooms attached to main wing structure. Tail surfaces of similar construction to wings. Mission pod 'fuselage', suspended below and forward of wing at centreline on large-area pylon, is a non-pressurised structure of graphite/epoxy with Teflon covering. Aerodynamic control surfaces powered electrically by Sundstrand actuators. Non-retractable monowheel on centreline.

POWER PLANT: One 20 kW (26.8 hp) Sundstrand electric motor, mounted in overwing fairing at centreline and driving a Lockheed constant-speed pusher propeller with spinner. Two storage cells (one hydrogen, one oxygen), combined capacity 100 litres (26.4 US gallons; 22 Imp gallons).

SYSTEM AND EQUIPMENT: Solar photovoltaic electrical system (capacity approx 150 kW). INS and GPS navigation equipment. Artificial intelligence sensor payload(s).

DIMENSIONS:

Wing span:	
tips up	57.80 m (189 ft 7.5 in)
tips down	98.30 m (322 ft 6 in)
Wing area:	
tips up	180 m² (1,937.5 sq ft)
tips down	287 m² (3,089.2 sq ft)
Length overall	28 m (91 ft 10.5 in)
Fuselage pod:	
Length	10.76 m (35 ft 3.5 in)
Max diameter	1.99 m (6 ft 6.25 in)
Height overall: tips down	10 m (32 ft 9.75 in)
Propeller diameter	10 m (32 ft 9.75 in)

WEIGHTS (estimated):

Max payload	113 kg (250 lb)
Max fuel load (H₂ and O₂)	43.4 kg (95.6 lb)
Max T-O and landing weight	797 kg (1,757 lb)

PERFORMANCE (estimated):

Max level speed	60 knots (111 km/h; 69 mph)
Max cruising speed at 21,300 m (70,000 ft)	52.5 knots (97 km/h; 60 mph)
Econ cruising speed at 21,300 m (70,000 ft)	43 knots (79 km/h; 49 mph)
Stalling speed at S/L, power off	15 knots (27 km/h; 17 mph)
Max rate of climb at S/L	134 m (440 ft)/min
Service ceiling	30,000 m (98,500 ft)
Endurance, with no in-flight failures	up to 1 year

LOCKHEED MISSILES AND SPACE COMPANY INC (LMSC)

1111 Lockheed Way (PO Box 504), Sunnyvale, California 94086

The 9.75 m (32 ft) span Sunrise I, built for LMSC by Astroflight in 1974

LMSC's entry into the field of RPVs came in 1971 with the development of the small twin-boom RTV-1. As the company gained experience, it began working with the US Army and Air Force, and DARPA, to develop design criteria for RPV systems, particularly those with gross weights below 91 kg (200 lb), and to assess the survivability of RPVs in a battlefield environment. Two such studies for the US Army were FASTAR (family of Army surveillance and target acquisition requirements) and RPAODS (remotely piloted aerial observer and designator system), the latter leading directly to the Aequare and Aquila programmes. Along the way LMSC has developed other company funded mini-RPVs of its own design and, at the opposite end of the size spectrum, has recently undertaken a feasibility design study for NASA of the 98.3 m (322.5 ft) wing span Solar HAPP described under the Lockheed-Georgia entry.

LMSC RTV-1 and RTV-2

This company funded mini was designed as a hard-flying testbed for autopilot concepts, data links and various sensor payloads, flying most of its missions at heights below 610 m (2,000 ft). It first flew in about 1972 and was originally powered by a 20.9 kW (28 hp) Hirth two-stroke snowmobile engine, replaced in the rebuilt RTV-2 by a 26.1 kW (35 hp) marine Wankel unit driving a two-blade pusher propeller. A pod-and-twin-tailboom configuration was adopted, the tailplane having a single, centrally located fin and rudder, and the aircraft took off and landed conventionally on a tricycle undercarriage. Early development work included a GCS which allowed the operator to 'dial' flight instructions to the RPV instead of 'flying' it with a remote control stick.

DIMENSIONS:

Wing span	3.96 m (13 ft)
Length overall	3.05 m (10 ft)

WEIGHT:

Max T-O weight	159 kg (350 lb)

PERFORMANCE (approx):

Cruising speed	130 knots (241 km/h; 150 mph)
Range	17.4 nm (32.2 km; 20 miles)
Endurance	1 h

LMSC's first mini-drone in its RTV-2 form

LMSC AEQUARE

First flown in mid-1975, Aequare (Latin for 'to equalise') was built under a 1973 DARPA contract for an air-launched mini-RPV system (airframe, data link, sensors and GCS) intended for target acquisition and designation missions in a high-threat environment. It was also required to be operable in adverse weather conditions. The glassfibre airframe was manufactured by Windecker Industries.

In the target designation mode, video data from the air vehicle was relayed to the GCS via the launch aircraft, which loitered at a safe height and distance from the target. The operator steered the sensor and RPV to search, locate and lock on to a target, which was then illuminated by the laser beam. Another aircraft could then zero in on the target and destroy it with a terminally guided weapon, while the Aequare could fly on to designate another target or loiter to provide reconnaissance support, after which it could be parachute-recovered or expended as desired. Flight demonstrations to USAF included use in connection with laser guided bombs. Between 15 and 20 air vehicles were ordered under the USAF/ASD contract, plus one GCS; the demonstration programme ended in March 1976.

POWER PLANT: One 9.3 kW (12.5 hp) McCulloch MC-101 single-cylinder piston engine, driving a three-blade wooden pusher propeller in an annular duct.

LAUNCH AND RECOVERY: Air-launched at 7,620 m (25,000 ft) from F-4 Phantom, under starboard wing of which it was carried with wings folded inside a modified SUU-42 flare dispenser pod. A CTV-2 pod containing the command/telemetry/video data link was carried under the fighter's port wing. Upon launch, end cap of carrier pod was released by explosive charge, deploying a drogue parachute on which pod descended to 4,270 m (14,000 ft). Barometric device then released main 'chute, which pulled pod clear of RPV. Wings of Aequare then pivoted forward into flight position, and engine was started. Provision also made for ground launch by rocket. RPV airframe expendable, but parachute system provided for recovery of payload package.

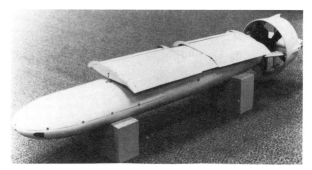

Lockheed Aequare with wings folded and aligned with fuselage for pod storage

GUIDANCE AND CONTROL: After launch of pod, carrier aircraft climbed to 10,670 m (35,000 ft) to act as relay between RPV and ground control station. On release from pod, RPV was pre-programmed to enter level, powered flight and to set up real-time data link with ground controller. Remainder of flight normally controlled from ground station, but could be pre-programmed if desired.

MISSION EUIPMENT: Recoverable payload compartment in lower fuselage for Ford Aerospace stabilised TV (non-stabilised in initial tests) and laser target designator, Aacom data link equipment, Lockheed autopilot, and X- and C-band beacons.

DIMENSIONS:

Wing span	2.29 m (7 ft 6 in)
Length overall	2.26 m (7 ft 5 in)

WEIGHT:

Max launching weight	63.5 kg (140 lb)

PERFORMANCE:

Max level speed	100 knots (185 km/h; 115 mph)
Range	174 nm (322 km; 200 miles)
Endurance in target area	2 h

LMSC RSVP

The RSVP (rotating surveillance vehicle platform) was a company-funded proposal of *circa* 1976 to meet a requirement of the US Army's Air Mobility Research and Development Command for a 'pop-up' RPV to enhance OTH surveillance and communications capabilities in forward patrol areas. As the illustration shows, it had an egg-shaped body on a four-stalk landing gear, and a four-blade rotor for vertical take-off and landing. The daylight TV/laser designator payload utilised the Honeywell package developed for the fixed-wing Aquila, and provision was made to exchange this for a night imaging sensor. Few other details are known, except that the suitcase-sized GCS incorporated a real-time CRT readout. It is believed that about three air vehicles were built.

DIMENSIONS:
Rotor diameter	3.05 m (10 ft)
Height overall	0.91 m (3 ft)

WEIGHT:
Max T-O weight	approx 13.6 kg (30 lb)

PERFORMANCE:
Max level speed	30 knots (55 km/h; 34 mph)

The experimental RSVP miniature rotorcraft

LMSC HARASSMENT VEHICLE

This drone/RPV was an independent development by LMSC; flight tests were a joint undertaking by LMSC and the USAF's Aeronautical System Division. Designed as an expendable vehicle to harass enemy air defences, its purpose was to support manned aircraft missions, equipped with electronic gear and munitions. In USAF's **LCEHV** (low-cost expendable harassment vehicle) programme, it was flight tested at the US Army's Yuma Proving Ground, Arizona, during the first quarter of 1977. On its first flight the air vehicle remained aloft for more than 2 hours, travelling more than 108 nm (200 km; 124 miles) over a closed course at altitudes up to 2,895 m (9,500 ft). In subsequent flights it demonstrated autonomous pull-outs from nearly vertical dive angles, and autopilot-controlled dive to ground impact.

AIRFRAME: Built of compression moulded glassfibre sheet.
POWER PLANT: One 6.3 kW (8.5 hp) Kolbo D-274 two-stroke piston engine with Lockheed capacitive discharge ignition system.
LAUNCH AND RECOVERY: Ground launch from pneumatically powered rail launcher; skid landing recovery.
GUIDANCE AND CONTROL: Designed for pre-programmed operation, with mission data stored in onboard memory before launch, directing autopilot and other equipment during flight; but operated during some flight demonstrations as RPV controlled from manned GCS to test alternative flight modes and to recover equipment for repeated tests. Omega navigation device developed by Develco Inc.

DIMENSIONS:
Wing span	2.74 m (9 ft)
Length overall	2.13 m (7 ft)

WEIGHTS:
Payload	11.3–18 kg (25–40 lb)
Max launching weight	45.3–54.4 kg (100–120 lb)

PERFORMANCE:
Endurance	5–6 h

Expendable mini built by LMSC for a 1970s harassment vehicle competition

LMSC LOW-COST MINI-RPV

Brief details were published of a new non-recoverable LMSC mini-RPV in late 1981. Using low-cost materials and constructional techniques, it had a blunt-nosed circular-section body, with space for approx 29.5 kg (65 lb) of sensors or warhead, and was powered by a rear-mounted 26 kW (35 hp) piston engine. The high-mounted constant-chord wings were sharply sweptback, with elevons extending aft of the trailing edge, the two-blade 'pusher' propeller turning in the gap between them. A dependent endplate fin and rudder was attached to each wingtip. The RPV was equipped with two pairs of D/F antennae and had a gross weight of 91 kg (200 lb). This experimental programme did not extend beyond 1982.

LOCKHEED MISSILES AND SPACE COMPANY INC (LMSC) (Austin Division)

PO Box 17100, Austin, Texas 78760

LMSC YMQM-105A Aquila and its truck mounted launch rail

LMSC AQUILA

US Army designation: YMQM-105

Known briefly at first as **Little r**, the Aquila (Latin for eagle) mini-RPV was developed to provide real-time target acquisition, first round fire for effect, artillery adjustment, laser target designation and aerial reconnaissance. US Army interest in such a vehicle was first expressed in 1974, and resulted in an XMQM-105 programme (first flight December 1975) to quantify the performance, operations and training characteristics for such a system. The Army awarded LMSC contracts for a TADAR (target acquisition, designation and aerial reconnaissance) full scale development programme, beginning on 31 August 1979. Under these contracts, Lockheed was to supply 28 YMQM-105 Aquila air vehicles (first flight July 1982), together with ground control stations (GCS), a remote ground terminal (RGT), hydraulic catapult launchers, Dornier net recovery units, payload subassemblies, maintenance shelters, training simulators and training manuals. The Aquila programme was transferred from LMSC at Sunnyvale, California, to Lockheed-Austin in mid-1983.

During 1985, an early operational capability Aquila system was fielded by the US Army, operated by Army personnel in full scale force-on-force exercises to develop operational techniques. At the end of 1985, the Army restructured the programme to include a month-long capability demonstration in January 1986 and to reschedule the remainder of operational testing to November 1986. During the testing in January 1986, Aquila successfully demonstrated its capability to perform to its design specifications, and was used to designate tank targets for live Copperhead anti-tank rounds fired from artillery howitzers. Other capabilities demonstrated included: finding a target and determining its specific type and identity at specified ranges and conditions; locking on and tracking a moving target automatically; maintaining a laser spot on a moving target to provide a marker for laser guided munitions; retrieving the Aquila automatically; launching the Aquila at a central launching facility, passing it in flight to a forward facility, and reversing this process for recovery.

By early 1986 some 330 test flights of the FSD Aquila had been completed: 306 were completely successful, 15 ended with parachute recoveries, and nine crashed. Operational Test 2, at Fort Hood, Texas, was completed by the US Army in spring

Aquila being retrieved in vertical ribbon net

1987. During this test period 310 flight hours were achieved in 143 flights, during which 20 Copperheads and more than 150 rounds of other types of ammunition were fired at the RPVs, and handoffs to other GCSs were made over ranges of up to 24 nm (45 km; 28 miles). The US Army's planned purchase includes 376 air vehicles and 88 ground stations. It was hoped that a production go-ahead would be given in autumn 1987, but the proposed budget was again cut by the House Armed Services Committee.

Sensors for the target acquisition/designation role consist of a stabilised daylight TV camera combined with a laser rangefinder/designator. The air vehicle and its payload are controlled from the GCS; video imagery and target location information are returned via an anti-jam data link. The target acquisition system can be used for conventional artillery as well as for such laser homing munitions as Copperhead, Hellfire and other laser guided projectiles, both cannon and aircraft launched. Real-time TV pictures and damage assessment data can be relayed to a ground station many miles behind the battlefront.

Command and control of the tactical system entail four basic functions: (1) automatic launch and navigation of the air vehicle over enemy territory, and return for recovery; (2) control of an onboard video camera by ground operators to acquire and auto-track targets; (3) accurate determination of target co-ordinates; and (4) processing and transmission of target data to fire direction centres, for use by artillery batteries.

TYPE: Recoverable tactical mini-RPV.

AIRFRAME: Mid-mounted sweptwing tail-less blended fuselage monoplane, built by Hitco from moulded and pre-impregnated Kevlar epoxy laminates with graphite/epoxy laminates for increased strength, shaped and treated for low radar signature. Leading edge sweepback 28°. Differentially operated elevons on trailing edges of wings. Airframe dismantles into three major subsections (centrebody and the two wings).

POWER PLANT: One Herbrandson Dyad 280B two-stroke flat-twin piston engine (17.9 kW; 24 hp at 8,000 rpm), driving a two-blade fixed-pitch wooden pusher propeller within an annular duct. Exhaust is directed upward to minimise IR signature. Collapsible, quick-disconnect bladder fuel cell; fuel is a 50:1 (by volume) petrol/oil mixture.

LAUNCH AND RECOVERY: Launched from All American Engineering HP-30 hydraulically actuated catapult mounted on a 5-ton truck. Primary recovery system uses infra-red sensors to retrieve the air vehicle automatically, guiding it into a hydraulically deployed Dornier vertical ribbon net raised on back of M814 truck and capable of being lowered quickly after recovery in order to maintain low profile. Entire ground system can be set up for launch in less than 1 h and taken down in 30 min. For test and training flights, YMQM-105 has an 11.51 m (37 ft 9 in) diameter nylon parachute for emergency backup recovery, from which air vehicle is suspended inverted to protect mission equipment, providing survivability for avionics and payload. Parachute deploys automatically if control link is lost for more than 20 min.

GUIDANCE AND CONTROL: Flight is defined by pre-programmed waypoints stored in air vehicle's LMSC flight control electronic package (FCEP) and ground system's Norden System GCS computer. At any time during mission, air vehicle operator can change waypoints or command RPV to go into any of several loiter or jinking modes. If data link transmission is interrupted, RPV continues its flight according to last set of instructions and position data received. At any time when within line of sight, RPV can receive a burst transmission with position update and, if desired, onboard computer can be reloaded with new instructions. Final waypoint is recovery area. In addition to FCEP, flight control subsystem includes a Singer-Kearfott attitude reference assembly (ARA), two air data transducers, three servo-actuators, a power supply, and a near IR source landing aid. FCEP provides computation capability for navigation, guidance and control of the RPV as well as signals for controlling the payload air data terminal and built-in test functions. ARA is a strapdown inertial sensor package, key components of which are a three-axis rate gyro assembly, three-axis accelerometer assembly, and a small computer to provide co-ordinate transformation calculations. System requires periodic position update by burst transmission; this allows the onboard computer to calculate and compensate for gyro and accelerometer errors and calculate a new wind estimate. Computer also points the steerable data link antennae, transfers control from one GCS to another following handoff, and initiates pre-programmed link loss and reacquisition logic following dead reckoning or inadvertent link loss. Air data transducers provide barometric altitude and airspeed information to the FCEP, where it is combined with outputs from the ARA to provide signals to the servo-actuators controlling elevons and throttle and updates to the onboard FCEP computer. Airborne data terminal (ADT) receives command signals from, and returns status and video signals to, the RGT.

The Aquila FSD programme utilises a Harris Inc modular integrated communication and navigation system (MICNS) as its jam-resistant data link. This J-band system provides command uplink, telemetry and video downlinks, and navigation of the RPV relative to the ground station, all in a hostile jamming environment. Location of target with respect to RPV is determined from the mission payload gimbal angles while it is tracking the target; the laser measures slant range. The ARA provides heading and local vertical reference to the onboard computer, which calculates target position relative to local vertical. This vector is transmitted to the GCS and combined with RPV position and the surveyed location of the ground station to determine co-ordinates of the target. GCS is the control centre of the RPV system. Telemetry and video data from the air vehicle are processed and displayed; command data are generated and relayed to the air vehicle via the ground station.

SYSTEM: Electrical power for onboard subsystems provided by a 1.5 kW 28V DC engine-driven alternator via a power conditioning unit.

MISSION EQUIPMENT: Mission payload subsystem (MPS) is mounted in lower forward fuselage. MPS is a Westinghouse three-axis stabilised daylight TV camera, incorporating a laser rangefinder/designator, autotracker (controlled by a microprocessor), and three-fields-of-view optics. Line of sight stabilisation and tracking are provided throughout lower hemisphere and up to 15° elevation above air vehicle's horizontal reference plane. Azimuth rotation is continuous while observing targets. The TV camera, laser, laser receiver and control electronics are stationary, with image stabilisation provided by a gimballed mirror system. The boresighted laser provides range to target and designation. A turret mounted Kevlar shroud protects the gimballed portion of the MPS, and contains a multi-faceted window through which the optical line-of-sight is projected. The turret is environmentally sealed. A stabilised, gimbal mounted FLIR MPS (still under development in 1987) has been ordered from Ford Aerospace (Aeronutronic Division), to extend RPV operations to 24 hour day/night and restricted visibility conditions. Ford's main subcontractor is Honeywell (Electro-Optics Division), which will provide the mini-FLIR and dual-mode autotracker.

DIMENSIONS:

Wing span	3.88 m (12 ft 8.75 in)
Length overall	2.08 m (6 ft 10 in)
Propeller diameter	0.66 m (2 ft 2 in)

WEIGHTS (A: TADARS Aquila, B; extended range Aquila):

Payload:	
daylight TV + laser designator	28.1 kg (62 lb)
FLIR	25 kg (55 lb)
Max payload: A	36.5 kg (80.5 lb)
B	52 kg (114.5 lb)
Max fuel weight:	
A	15 kg (33 lb)
B	40.5 kg (89 lb)

Usable load:
A   51.5 kg (113.5 lb)
B   71 kg (156.5 lb)
Max launching weight:
A   120 kg (265 lb)
B   150 kg (331 lb)
PERFORMANCE (A and B except where indicated):
Max level speed   113 knots (210 km/h; 130 mph)
Cruising speed
      73–94 knots (135–175 km/h; 84–109 mph)
Loiter speed   70 knots (130 km/h; 81 mph)
Service ceiling   4,500 m (14,765 ft)
Endurance, excl 40 min reserves:
A   3 h
B   10 h

LMSC ALTAIR

Lockheed's Austin Division announced the Altair on 5 June 1985 as an international version of the US Army's Aquila. Intended to provide a highly survivable means of providing real-time imaging for target acquisition and artillery adjustment, it utilises the same basic airframe and power plant as the Aquila and made its first flight in the summer of 1987. Principal difference is elimination of the Aquila's laser target designation system; also, the data link in the Altair is less resistant to jamming than that in the Aquila.

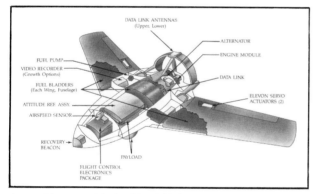

Internal features of the Lockheed Altair

The Altair is designed to carry a Lockheed adaptive modular payload (LAMP) with a stabilised platform. Initially, the payload choice will consist of a solid state TV or FLIR camera for full day/night imaging capability.

Growth options for Altair include launch from helicopters or ships' platforms. Increased flight endurance, using electronic engine control and additional fuel tanks in the wings, is being developed, and LMSC expects to be able to achieve a mission endurance of up to 11 hours (3 h being the limit of the US Army requirement for Aquila).

DIMENSIONS AND PERFORMANCE:
As for extended range Aquila
WEIGHTS:
Weight empty   45 kg (99 lb)
Max payload   approx 30 kg (66 lb)

LTV AEROSPACE AND DEFENSE (Vought Missiles and Advanced Programs Division)
PO Box 650003, Dallas, Texas 75265–0003

LTV (VOUGHT) VTS-6

The VTS-6 (Vought Target System 6) was LTV's contender for the US Navy's SLAT (supersonic low altitude target) competition in 1984, eventually won by the Martin Marietta Orlando YAQM-127A (which see). Based on LTV's earlier, successfully demonstrated low volume ramjet (LVRJ) vehicle, it was proposed with Northrop payload and recovery systems and a CSD propulsion system.

The air-launched LVRJ demonstrated speeds of more than 1,737 knots (3,220 km/h; 2,000 mph), a range of more than 87 nm (161 km; 100 miles), high- and low-altitude flight, and pop-up manoeuvring to a terminal dive simulating an attack on a surface vessel. The VTS-6 was intended to have the same 38 cm (15 in) body diameter, but be slightly longer than the 4.57 m (15 ft) LVRJ in order to accommodate the parachute recovery system, a scoring unit, and other specialised equipment for the target role.

MARTIN MARIETTA DENVER AEROSPACE
PO Box 179, Denver, Colorado 80201

MARTIN MARIETTA MODEL 845A

Under an April 1971 USAF contract, Martin Marietta built two prototypes of this medium-altitude, long-endurance surveillance RPV for evaluation in the **Compass Dwell** programme. Components for a third were manufactured, but used only as spares. Design, based on the modified airframe of a Schweizer SGS 1-34 sailplane, began in May 1971, and the prototypes made their first flights on 7 April and 6 June 1972. They were subsequently evaluated at Edwards AFB in competition with the E-Systems XQM-93 (which see). Flight testing of the Martin RPV, which ended on 1 July 1972, included a flight of 27 h 54 min on 30 June/1 July 1972. One prototype was later transferred to the USAF Museum at Wright-Patterson AFB, Ohio.

Martin Marietta Model 845A

TYPE: Medium-altitude long-endurance surveillance RPV.

AIRFRAME: Shoulder-wing monoplane, with Wortmann FX-61-163/FX-60-126 root/tip sections. Dihedral 3° 30'. Plate type spoiler above and below each wing. No flaps. Sweptback fin and rudder; non-swept fixed incidence tailplane. Electric actuation of ailerons, spoilers, elevators and rudder. Entire airframe of aluminium alloy construction. Non-retractable tricycle landing gear, with single wheel on each unit (main units from Grumman Ag-Cat, nose unit from Piper Aztec).

POWER PLANT: One 149 kW (200 hp) Avco Lycoming TIO-360-A3B6 turbocharged flat-four fuel-injection engine, driving a Hartzell three-blade variable-pitch propeller. Fuel in fuselage tank and integral forward and rear wing tanks. Electric de-icing of propeller blades.

LAUNCH AND RECOVERY: Conventional runway T-O and landing.

GUIDANCE AND CONTROL: Remote guidance by APW-26 radio command control unit. Onboard equipment included engine controls, and Sperry three-axis autopilot with airspeed/pitch attitude/roll angle commands and heading hold function. ARN-97 TALAR for runway approach guidance. DC electrical system, powered by 28V 125A engine driven generator, for control surface actuation, avionics, and propeller de-icing.

DIMENSIONS:

Wing span	18.01 m (59 ft 1.25 in)
Wing area	15.51 m² (167 sq ft)
Length overall	7.74 m (25 ft 4.75 in)
Height overall	2.90 m (9 ft 6 in)
Wheel track	1.77 m (5 ft 9.5 in)
Wheelbase	1.74 m (5 ft 8.5 in)
Propeller diameter	1.98 m (6 ft 6 in)

WEIGHTS:

Basic operating weight empty	918 kg (2,024 lb)
Max payload	136 kg (300 lb)
Max zero-fuel weight	1,054 kg (2,324 lb)

PERFORMANCE:

Never-exceed speed	130 knots (240 km/h; 149 mph)
Stalling speed	52 knots (97 km/h; 60 mph)
Unstick speed	70 knots (130 km/h; 81 mph)
Max rate of climb at S/L	204 m (670 ft)/min
T-O run	957 m (3,140 ft)
Landing run	457 m (1,500 ft)
Endurance with max fuel	more than 27 h

MARTIN MARIETTA ORLANDO AEROSPACE

PO Box 5837, Orlando, Florida 32855

MARTIN MARIETTA SLAT

US Navy designation: YAQM-127A

A full scale engineering development contract for SLAT (supersonic low-altitude target) was awarded to Martin Marietta by the US Navy in September 1984, after consideration also of entries from LTV (Vought) and Teledyne Ryan. The contract called for delivery of 15 pre-production targets by 1987, with the flight test programme to take place during FYs 1987–88. It is then planned to carry out limited operations at the Pacific Missile Test Center in FY 1989, using targets remaining from the flight test programme. Initial procurement of 30 production targets is planned for FY 1990, followed by a three-year production option for 100 targets per year with IOC for Fleet training coming in FY 1991.

Martin Marietta's partners in this programme are Marquardt (main rocket/ramjet sustainer engine), Morton Thiokol (solid propellant booster rocket), and Northrop (avionics, payload integration, recovery system, and related ground support equipment).

The air vehicle is a derivative of the cancelled advanced strategic air launched missile (ASALM), which made seven test flights during 1978–80. Primary payload will be an I-band seeker simulator, radar cross-section augmentation (1-10 m²; 11-108 sq ft in G, E/F and I/J-bands), and scoring equipment. First flight of a YAQM-127A was expected in 1987. The target will be pre-programmed, with a remote command override. It is required to be capable of subsonic launch from an F-4 or

Artist's impression of the Martin Marietta Orlando YAQM-127A sea skimming target

QF-4 aircraft at 305 m (1,000 ft) altitude, be capable of recovery from land and water, and have a design life of four flights. It should also demonstrate capability for air launch from a DC-130 aircraft, and compatibility for such launch from the A-6 Intruder, F/A-18 Hornet and P-3 Orion, under the same conditions. Launch speed will be in the order of 200 knots (370 km/h; 230 mph), the SLAT then entering a shallow dive to level out at about 9 m (30 ft) above the surface after reaching its maximum speed of Mach 2.5, to simulate a sea skimming missile. It will be recoverable by parachute and re-usable. Range requirement, all fuel expended, is 55 nm (102 km; 63 miles).

DIMENSIONS:
Length overall	5.47 m (17 ft 11.5 in)
Body diameter (max)	0.54 m (1 ft 9.25 in)

WEIGHT (estimated):
Max launching weight	1,088 kg (2,400 lb)

MCDONNELL DOUGLAS ASTRONAUTICS COMPANY
PO Box 516, St Louis, Missouri 63166

MCDONNELL DOUGLAS MINI-RPV

Developed under a company-funded programme, this MDAC mini was originally conceived to meet DARPA and US Army requirements for a small, low-cost battlefield reconnaissance and laser target designation vehicle. Missions envisaged included shipboard launch and recovery, battlefield and broad ocean area reconnaissance and surveillance, artillery spotting and fire adjustment, and laser rangefinding. The MDAC vehicle was designed to maximise low observability and so enhance survivability in a battlefield environment.

A 'feasibility' engineering model was successfully flight tested in 1973; the data apply to this model, of which two examples were built. An operational prototype vehicle, designed to carry a Honeywell TV camera/laser designator package, was flight tested in 1974, and was reportedly flown against simulated and real defences at Eglin AFB, Florida, in the summer of 1975.

POWER PLANT: One 7.5 kW (10 hp) Louis Ross four-cylinder piston engine.

DIMENSIONS:
Wing span	3.05 m (10 ft)
Length overall	2.18 m (7 ft 2 in)

WEIGHT:
Max launching weight	54.4 kg (120 lb)

PERFORMANCE:
Max cruising speed at 3,050 m (10,000 ft)	60 knots (111 km/h; 69 mph)
Max endurance	6 h

NATIONAL AERONAUTICS AND SPACE ADMINISTRATION (NASA)
600 Independence Avenue SW, Washington, DC 20546

NASA HYPER III

This aircraft was the first to be designed and flown by NASA to obtain operating experience of remotely piloted research

NASA Hyper III remotely piloted research vehicle

aircraft. Design began in August 1968, and the Hyper III flew for the first time in December 1969, after being air dropped from a helicopter at 3,050 m (10,000 ft) above the dry lake bed at Edwards. The aircraft's performance was generally satisfactory, but for a number of reasons no further flights were made.

TYPE: Remotely piloted lifting-body research vehicle.

AIRFRAME: Narrow chord tapering wings (Wortmann FX-61-163 section), of riveted aluminium sheeting. No dihedral, incidence, sweepback or moving control surfaces. Steel tube and aluminium fuselage, of narrow delta planform, with glassfibre nose and fabric covering. Twin fins and rudders, each canted outward at approx 40°. Hydraulically actuated hinged elevons on horizontal tail surfaces. Non-retractable tricycle landing gear.

POWER PLANT: None.

LAUNCH AND RECOVERY: Air launched from helicopter. Emergency parachute recovery system, using a drogue parachute, a decelerator parachute and three T-10 personnel parachutes.

GUIDANCE AND CONTROL: Uplink command by five-channel Kraft radio. Downlink telemetry via 12-channel FM-FM system to pilot displays in ground station.

DIMENSIONS:
Wing span	4.57 m (15 ft)
Wing area	3.29 m² (35.41 sq ft)
Length overall	9.75 m (32 ft)
Height overall	2.29 m (7 ft 6 in)
Wheel track	3.28 m (10 ft 9 in)
Wheelbase	5.18 m (17 ft)

WEIGHT:
Basic operating weight	431 kg (950 lb)

PERFORMANCE:

Max diving speed	150 knots (277 km/h; 172.5 mph)
Stalling speed	60 knots (111 km/h; 69 mph)
Launch ceiling	3,660 m (12,000 ft)
Landing run	152 m (500 ft)
Gliding range	10 nm (18.5 km; 11.5 miles)

NASA MINI-SNIFFER

The Mini-Sniffers were a series of simple, low-cost vehicle platforms designed for high-altitude atmospheric research in remote areas, to measure air turbulence and atmospheric trace gas and to determine the constituents of particles in the atmosphere. Three versions were built:

Mini-Sniffer I. Prototype vehicles (two built). Design began in October 1973, and the first flight was made in August 1974, with an interim air-breathing engine. Fifteen flights were made at altitudes up to 6,100 m (20,000 ft), primarily to validate airframe, aerodynamic and guidance control data, and to develop launch/recovery techniques.

Mini-Sniffer II. Mission vehicle, fitted with a hydrazine-burning engine to permit flights to altitudes of up to 27,430 m (90,000 ft). First flight with this engine was made in November 1976. New configuration, with modified outer wings and twin-tailboom rear assembly replacing canard surface of Sniffer I.

Mini-Sniffer III. Final version, which made one flight to 6,100 m (20,000 ft) but was not funded for further missions. Upturned wingtips and other detail changes to airframe.

TYPE: Remotely piloted research vehicles.

AIRFRAME: Mid-wing monoplane, built entirely of foam plastics, glassfibre and wood. Wings have 20° sweepback at quarter chord, and 13% thickness/chord ratio. No dihedral or incidence on Sniffer I; variable dihedral on outer panels of Sniffer II. Elevons on wing trailing edges. Ground-adjustable foreplane on Sniffer I, deleted from Sniffer II. Endplate fins and rudders at wingtips of Sniffer I, replaced on Sniffer II by twin tailbooms supporting twin fins and rudders and central tailplane.

POWER PLANT: Sniffer I powered initially by a 5.2 kW (7 hp) McCulloch 91 piston engine, driving a two-blade pusher propeller; fuel capacity (fuel/oil mixture) 7.5 litres (1.7 Imp gallons; 2 US gallons) in integral glassfibre tank in fuselage. Changed in Sniffer II to an approx 14.9 kW (20 hp) Akkerman 235 with variable-pitch feathering propeller and increased fuel capacity (hydrazine monopropellant) of 26.5 litres (5.8 Imp gallons; 7 US gallons) in aluminium tanks.

LAUNCH AND RECOVERY: Conventional runway T-O and landing.

GUIDANCE AND CONTROL: Alternator on Akkerman engine provides electrical power during climb and cruise; 28V nickel-cadmium battery for use during unpowered flight. Kraft (in Sniffer I) or Resdel (Sniffer II) uplink control. SCI-680-PCM 16-channel data telemetry system. Vega radar transponder. NASA autopilot. Sun and magnetic sensors for wing levelling, airspeed hold and heading hold.

MISSION EQUIPMENT (Sniffer II): Payload instrumentation developed by Wallops Flight Center and National Oceanic and Atmospheric Administration to measure nitric oxide, chlorine, freon 11 and 12, free oxygen, and the hydroxyl radical. Intended also for use by Langley Research Center to make accurate measurements of fine turbulence which cannot be obtained with faster aircraft. Equipped with lightweight wire impact particle grab samplers developed by Ames Research Center, and a real-time telemetered particulate density sensor, the Mini-Sniffer could make low-speed manoeuvres through aerospace vehicle wakes or other suspected particle concentrations. Radiation sensor payloads developed by Atomic Energy Commission to allow multiple and prompt monitoring of nuclear activity.

DIMENSIONS:

Wing span:	
I	5.49 m (18 ft)
II	6.71 m (22 ft)
Wing area: I	3.30 m² (35.5 sq ft)
Length overall: I	3.05 m (10 ft)
Height overall: I	0.86 m (2 ft 10 in)
Wheel track: I, II	1.14 m (3 ft 9 in)
Propeller diameter:	
I	0.66 m (2 ft 2 in)
II	1.83 m (6 ft)
Payload compartment volume:	
I, II	0.033 m³ (1.16 cu ft)

Flying scale models of NASA's Mini-Sniffer I (right) and II for atmospheric sampling

WEIGHTS:

Max payload: I, II	22.7 kg (50 lb)
Max T-O weight:	
I	65.8 kg (145 lb)
II	88.9 kg (196 lb)

PERFORMANCE (Sniffer II):

Max level speed at 21,340 m (70,000 ft)	
	160 knots (296 km/h; 184 mph)
Stalling speed	26 knots (49 km/h; 30 mph) IAS
Max rate of climb at S/L	792 m (2,600 ft)/min
Service ceiling	27,430 m (90,000 ft)
Range with max payload	
	434 nm (805 km; 500 miles)

NASA LRV-2

In October 1982 NASA's Dryden Flight Research Center began a one-year flight demonstration programme with a modified Volmer VJ-24W Sunfun powered hang glider adapted for remotely piloted flight. This aircraft, known as the LRV-2 (Low Reynolds number Vehicle No. 2), was used to investigate the possibility of pilotless aircraft operating for long periods at extremely high altitudes as low-cost 'satellites' for relaying communications signals or monitoring Earth resources.

AIRFRAME: Strut braced monoplane, of aluminium tube construction with Dacron covered wings and tail surfaces.
POWER PLANT: One 7.5 kW (10 hp) two-stroke piston engine, driving a two-blade propeller. Fuel capacity 5.7 litres (1.25 Imp gallons; 1.5 US gallons).
LAUNCH AND RECOVERY: Conventional runway T-O and landing.
GUIDANCE AND CONTROL: Radio command control, via onboard lightweight autopilot, from fixed base or truck-mounted GCS.
MISSION EQUIPMENT: Gondola 'trike' unit suspended below mainframe, carrying nose-mounted TV camera, radar tracking beacon and telemetry downlink.

*DIMENSIONS:

Wing span:	
VJ-24W	11.13 m (36 ft 6 in)
LRV-2	9.75 m (32 ft)
Wing area: VJ-24W	15.14 m² (163 sq ft)
Length overall	5.64 m (18 ft 6 in)
Height overall	1.75 m (5 ft 9 in)

*WEIGHTS:

Weight empty	75 kg (165 lb)
Max T-O weight	156 kg (345 lb)

*PERFORMANCE:

Cruising speed	24 knots (45 km/h; 28 mph)
Stalling speed	13 knots (25 km/h; 15 mph)
Ceiling: LRV-2	6,100 m (20,000 ft)

*Standard VJ-24W with 11.2 kW (15 hp) engine except where stated

NASA PROJECT DAST

Project DAST (Drones for Aerodynamic and Structural Testing), is (or was: no news of the programme has been forthcoming since 1985) conducted jointly by NASA's Langley and Dryden Flight Research Centers, utilising modified Firebee IIs as testbeds for high-risk evaluation of various research wing configurations. Primary object of the programme was to demonstrate the ability of advanced flight control systems to control wing flutter.

A flight vehicle and the first aeroelastic research wing (ARW-1) were damaged during a flight in June 1980. The wing was modified, rebuilt and mated to another modified Firebee, with which flight testing resumed on 3 November 1982, following air launch from a B-52 carrier. A 220 litre (48.3 Imp gallon; 58 US gallon) belly fuel tank was fitted, to extend flight time by nearly 100 per cent.

Design studies were then complete and fabrication under way for ARW-2, which, in addition to flutter suppression, was intended to study manoeuvre load alleviation, gust load alleviation, and relaxed static stability. Vehicle control is via a rudder and differentially moving horizontal tail surfaces. All wing control surfaces are used for the flutter and load control functions. The ARW-2, which has a high aspect ratio, low sweep angle, and a wing section designed for transonic flight, is similar to wings proposed for use on energy-efficient transports. Flight tests were to study the effectiveness of various load control systems when operating simultaneously. Studies were also under way towards developing an energy absorbing system to allow an alternative recovery mode, in which the approx 1,134 kg (2,500 lb) vehicle would descend to ground impact on a 30.5 m (100 ft) diameter parachute.

FAA/NASA CID

In a joint FAA/NASA programme designated CID (controlled impact demonstration), a Boeing 720 commercial transport was converted in 1984 to become the largest remotely piloted aircraft ever flown. At a gross weight of 91,625 kg (202,000 lb), and carrying 45,425 litres (9,992 Imp gallons; 12,000 US gallons) of fuel, its primary purpose was to test the fire-retarding efficacy of a new AMK (anti-misting kerosene) fuel combining standard Jet A fuel with an ICI additive known as Avgard FM-9. Instrumentation and data acquisition systems were developed by NASA Langley; NASA Ames-Dryden designed and implemented the remote piloting flight control system and also integrated experiment and system hardware. Other onboard experiments were carried to evaluate such features as crash forces, new seat designs, and fireproofing materials. The aircraft was deliberately crashed on to a prepared runway site at Edwards AFB, California, on 1 December 1984, impacting at a speed of 146 knots (271 km/h; 168 mph).

NORTHROP CORPORATION (Ventura Division)

1515 Rancho Conejo Boulevard, Newbury Park, California 91320

Northrop Ventura (formerly Radioplane) undertook the design, development and construction of its first radio controlled target drone in the mid-thirties. Since then it has become a leader in the field of pilotless aircraft. More than 80,000 drones have been delivered to the US military services and 25 allied nations. It has more than 2,000 employees engaged in aerial target design and production.

Since 1971, Ventura Division has also been responsible for aerial target services at the NATO Missile Firing Installation (NAMFI) on the island of Crete.

NORTHROP BASIC TRAINING TARGET (BTT)

US military designations: MQM-33 and MQM-36

In continuous production for 40 years, this small target aircraft originated as the Radioplane RP-19, flying for the first time in July 1945. It entered production for USAF as the OQ-19, with a change from wooden to metal wings during the life of the OQ-19A and to the present vertical tail configuration with the OQ-19C. In 1964 the OQ-19B (which had a vertical gyro for out of sight operation) and OQ-19D (which didn't) were redesignated **MQM-33A** and **-33B** respectively. In 1955 a modified version of the OQ-19 appeared as the RP-71 surveillance drone, with a 68.6 kW (92 hp) McCulloch O-100-2 engine, twin JATO launch boosters and onboard still or TV cameras. From 1959 a total of 1,445 examples of this were produced for the US Army (as **MQM-57A Falconer**) and foreign customers (NATO designation **AN/USD-1**). There was even an autogyro version, the **NV-101** prototype, modified from an OQ-19B and first flown in December 1963.

US Navy counterparts of the original OQ-19 series were designated KD2R-1 to -4. Engine and systems improvements in the KD2R-5 (notably an improved autopilot and altitude hold unit) justified the new US designation **MQM-36A**. They also boosted the target's success in the export market, where today the aircraft is in worldwide use, having been manufactured for the armed forces of 25 countries including the United States. In some of these versions it is still known as the **KD2R-5** or by the name **Shelduck**. Nowadays the current production model is known simply as the **BTT** or Basic Training Target, which has an uprated engine, larger battery, and a wider variety of equipment kits and wing stores not standard on the MQM-36A. A modified version of the BTT, with a Northrop developed G-band command control system, was still in production in 1987 for the US Army National Guard as the **MQM-33C**.

During its recent service career the target has been used as a training device for 20 mm, 23 mm, 35 mm, 40 mm, 57 mm, 3 in, 5 in, Vulcan and Bitubes anti-aircraft gunnery, as well as a target for surface-to-air missiles such as Blowpipe, Chaparral, Rapier, RBS-70, Redeye, Seacat, Sea Sparrow, Shahine, Stinger and Tigercat. The BTT system has been integrated with a Northrop developed portable tracking system.

Over its 40-year production run, the BTT in all its versions has become a strong contender for the highest number of aircraft of one basic design ever produced: more than 65,000 have been manufactured so far, and production plans extend into the 1990s. The following description applies to the current standard BTT:

TYPE: Remotely controlled recoverable target.
AIRFRAME: High-wing monoplane, of aluminium alloy construction. No dihedral. Wing incidence 1° at root, −2° at tip. Ailerons and elevator servo-operated by D-9 actuators.
POWER PLANT: One 59.7 kW (80 hp) Northrop O-11-3 flat-four two-stroke engine, driving a two-blade fixed-pitch wooden propeller. Steel integral fuel tank in mid-fuselage, capacity 44 litres (9.7 Imp gallons; 11.6 US gallons). Refuelling point in fuselage forward of wing.
LAUNCH AND RECOVERY: Surface launch from land or ship, by either rotary catapult or zero-length launcher. Recovery by parachute released by radio command. Engine is stopped and parachute deploys automatically in event of serious damage by gunfire, or loss of radio control or electrical power.
GUIDANCE AND CONTROL: AN/ARW-79 radio command guidance system, with automatic altitude hold. Visual or radar tracking (radar or FM type tracking systems or equivalent).
MISSION EQUIPMENT: 28 V battery for all electrical power. Optional augmentation devices include two wingtip radar

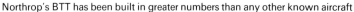

Northrop's BTT has been built in greater numbers than any other known aircraft

reflector pods, visual and infra-red flare kits, towed gunnery sleeves with real-time scoring, and six towed infra-red targets. An acoustic scoring system and auxiliary decoder can provide three spare command and control links in addition to the single spare channel of the basic system. An altitude hold control, a precision barometric sensor which detects variations in altitude and provides control corrections to secure constant flight altitude, can also be provided.

DIMENSIONS:

Wing span	3.50 m (11 ft 6 in)
Wing area	1.74 m² (18.7 sq ft)
Length overall	3.85 m (12 ft 7.5 in)
Height overall	0.76 m (2 ft 6 in)
Propeller diameter	1.12 m (3 ft 8 in)

WEIGHTS:

Weight empty	123 kg (271 lb)
Max launching weight	181 kg (400 lb)

PERFORMANCE:

Max level speed at S/L and max cruising speed	
	195 knots (360 km/h; 224 mph)
Stalling speed	58 knots (108 km/h; 67 mph)
Max rate of climb at S/L	1,341 m (4,400 ft)/min
Service ceiling	more than 8,230 m (27,000 ft)
Range at S/L with max fuel	
	183 nm (338 km; 210 miles)
Average flight duration	55 min

NORTHROP CHUKAR I and II

US Navy designations: MQM-74A and MQM-74C

This drone was designed to meet requirements for a small, lightweight 400 knot (742 km/h; 461 mph) target for anti-aircraft gunnery, surface-to-air missile and air-to-air missile training and weapons systems evaluation. Four delta-winged NV-105 prototypes were built in 1964, but the straight-tapered wing form of the 1965 NV-105A was subsequently preferred, and some 1,800 were built as **MQM-74A**s for the US Navy and others (including Israel) between 1966–72. A modified version, with special augmentation, was used as a standard target at the NATO Missile Firing Installation (NAMFI) in the Mediterranean, and other **Chukar I** recipients included the Royal Navy and Italian Navy. The Italian Meteor Gufo (which see) was based on the Chukar's design. The Chukar (pronounced 'chucker') is named after an Indian rock partridge found in the western USA.

The **MQM-74C**, which replaced the A model in 1974, is an improved version (developed via an experimental MQM-74B) to meet USN requirements for a 500 knot (926 km/h; 576 mph) target. More than 1,400 MQM-74Cs have been delivered to the US Navy, making more than 3,200 of the MQM-74 series Chukars manufactured in all. Other **Chukar II** customers include the UK, West Germany, Greece, Iran, Italy, Japan, Netherlands, Saudi Arabia and Spain. Japan's Chukar IIs are used as RPVs, and can carry a Martin Marietta Orlando laser detector/tracker pod at each wingtip. Production of the Chukar II is continuing.

Modified versions of the MQM-74C have been tested and operated as reconnaissance, electronic warfare and strike RPVs under the US Navy's Persistent Anti-Radiation Missile (**PARM**) and US Air Force's **TEDS** programmes. Under US Navy contract, Northrop is producing a version known as the **BQM-74C** (described separately), for use by the US Navy as a cruise missile simulator and standard aerial training target.

Chukar II is also in service at the NATO Missile Firing Installation on Crete, where it is used to train crews of radar and non-radar directed anti-aircraft guns, active and semi-active radar guided, visual and infra-red guided surface-to-air and air-to-air missiles which include Hawk, Redeye, Chaparral, Standard Sparrow, Sea Sparrow, Sidewinder, Seacat and Tigercat. Meteor of Italy provides Chukar II services at the Salto di Quirra range in Sardinia.

TYPE: Turbojet powered recoverable target.

AIRFRAME: Shoulder-wing monoplane, of aluminium construction. No dihedral. Detachable wings, each with electrically actuated aileron. Tapered circular section body, with underslung air intake duct. Inverted Y tail unit, with 30° anhedral on tailplane, electrically actuated elevators and fixed vertical fin.

POWER PLANT: One 0.54 kN (121 lb st) Williams WR24-6 (YJ400-WR-400) turbojet in MQM-74A, or 0.80 kN (180 lb st) WR24-7-2 (J400-WR-401) in MQM-74C. Fuel tank in centre of fuselage, capacity 39.75 litres (8.75 Imp gallons; 10.5 US gallons) in MQM-74A, 61.3 litres (13.5 Imp gallons; 16.2 US gallons) in MQM-74C.

LAUNCH AND RECOVERY: Zero-length launching by means of two JATO rockets and a ZL-5 launcher. Normal recovery by automatic drone pull-up followed by main parachute deployment, initiated automatically in emergencies such as interruption of continuous radio signal or loss of parachute command channel. Alternative method consists of direct main parachute deployment and is initiated automatically on loss of electrical power. Main parachute housed in fuselage immediately aft of wing, with automatic disconnect on impact.

GUIDANCE AND CONTROL: Radio command guidance system. Out-of-sight control by automatic stabilisation and command, with radar tracking; in-sight control with visual acquisition aids. Proportional feedback stabilisation and control system for pitch and bank. Engine throttle position, altitude hold initiation and recovery system initiation controlled by audio tone signals. Components include receiver, decoder, autopilot, aileron and elevator servos,

Chukar II built by NEC for the Japanese defence forces

Northrop MQM-74A Chukar I naval gunnery target

altitude hold and airspeed pressure transducers. Command control antenna in upper forward fuselage.

MISSION EQUIPMENT (target): Electrical power from engine-driven alternator through a rectifier-regulator. 28V nickel-cadmium battery secondary power source used during glide. Onboard acquisition and tracking aids include fore and aft Luneberg lenses for passive radar augmentation, four wingtip-mounted Mk 28 Mod 3 infra-red flares, pyrotechnic infra-red plume augmentors, active L-band augmentation, and a smoke system to improve visual detection. Main payload compartment is in front fuselage between control equipment bay and fuel tank. Improved manoeuvrability package (IMP) successfully flight tested in 1976 has closed loop control device installed in flight control system, enabling Chukar II to perform constant g manoeuvres at any of five selected levels up to and including $6g$. A low cost infra-red tow target, for use with the Chukar II system, is in production. One can be attached to each wingtip and towed approx 30 m (100 ft) behind the Chukar. A re-usable active RF augmentation tow target system is in use for various RF guided missile systems. Production of active tow targets began in 1979.

DIMENSIONS (A: Chukar I, B: Chukar II):

Wing span:
A	1.69 m (5 ft 6.7 in)
B	1.76 m (5 ft 9.4 in)

Wing area:
A	0.56 m² (6 sq ft)
B	0.74 m² (8 sq ft)

Length overall:
A	3.46 m (11 ft 4.1 in)
B	3.87 m (12 ft 8.4 in)

Body diameter (max): A, B 0.35 m (1 ft 1.9 in)

Height overall:
A	0.70 m (2 ft 3.7 in)
B	0.71 m (2 ft 4.1 in)

WEIGHTS:

Weight empty:
A	105.7 kg (233 lb)
B	128.4 kg (283 lb)

Fuel:
A	32.7 kg (72 lb)
B	50.3 kg (111 lb)

Max launching weight:
A without boosters	143 kg (316 lb)
B without boosters	182 kg (401 lb)
A with boosters	193 kg (425 lb)
B with boosters	223 kg (492 lb)

PERFORMANCE (at typical in-flight weight):

Max level speed at S/L:
A	400 knots (742 km/h; 461 mph)
B	475 knots (880 km/h; 547 mph)

Max level speed at 6,100 m (20,000 ft):
A	425 knots (787 km/h; 489 mph)
B	515 knots (954 km/h; 593 mph)

Max rate of climb at S/L:
A	1,676 m (5,500 ft)/min
B	1,780 m (5,840 ft)/min

Service ceiling: A, B 12,200 m (40,000 ft)

Range at max level speed:
A at S/L	143 nm (264 km; 164 miles)
B at S/L	205 nm (380 km; 236 miles)
A at 6,100 m (20,000 ft)	237 nm (439 km; 273 miles)
B at 6,100 m (20,000 ft)	330 nm (611 km; 380 miles)

g limits:
A	+7
B	+10

NORTHROP NV-130

Northrop and Beech were selected by the US Air Force in 1975 to develop and produce flight demonstration examples of a tactical expendable drone system (**TEDS**). First flight of a Northrop NV-130 prototype was made on 22 January 1976. A total of 11 flights was made during the validation flight test programme. Systems definition and computer simulations were completed in early 1977.

The ECM effectiveness of the NV-130 was validated successfully, but funds for full scale development were not forthcoming.

Three MQM-74C targets were modified as flying prototypes for TEDS, plus a fourth for ground and payload performance trials. Fuselage, wings and engine of the MQM-74C were retained, the expendable mission permitting the WR24-7 to be uprated to 0.87 kN (195 lb st) and the parachute recovery package to be replaced by an auxiliary fuel tank. Electrical power was increased, the lower rear fuselage fairing enlarged, and wingtip payload pods added.

Other differences from the standard MQM-74C included:

DIMENSIONS:
Wing span over pods	2.20 m (7 ft 2.75 in)
Length overall	4.36 m (14 ft 3.75 in)
Height overall	0.79 m (2 ft 7 in)

WEIGHTS:
Max launching weight:	
without boosters	233.5 kg (515 lb)
with boosters	265 kg (585 lb)

PERFORMANCE:
Max level speed at cruise altitude	
	500 knots (927 km/h; 576 mph)
Range at max speed	400 nm (740 km; 460 miles)

NORTHROP NV-135

The NV-135 was a candidate in the US Air Force's mid-1970s programme for a mini-RPV designed to harass enemy radar defences. Known at first as **VLCEHV** (very low cost expendable harassment vehicle), the programme was later retitled more simply as **HWS** (harassment weapon system).

Of sweptback flying wing configuration, with endplate fins, the NV-135 was of plastics construction, produced by a Northrop adaptation of the rotational moulding process. It was powered by an 8.2 kW (11 hp) two-cylinder two-stroke piston engine, driving a two-blade pusher propeller, and controlled by a programmed and command guidance system. Three prototypes were built and flight tested in 1976, but the expected request for production version proposals in 1979 did not materialise.

The 'flying wing' NV-135, built for a mid-1970s harassment drone programme

DIMENSIONS:
Wing span	2.44 m (8 ft)
Wing area	0.98 m² (10.5 sq ft)
Length overall	1.29 m (4 ft 2.9 in)
Body diameter (max)	0.28 m (11 in)
Propeller diameter	0.56 m (1 ft 10 in)

WEIGHT:
Max launching weight	68 kg (150 lb)

PERFORMANCE:
Max level speed	160 knots (296 km/h; 184 mph)
Ceiling	1,830 m (6,000 ft)
Design endurance	3–5 h

NORTHROP CHUKAR III

US Navy designation: BQM-74C

The BQM-74C is a US Navy target version of the MQM-74C Chukar II (which see) with added air launch capability and pre-programmed flight profiles. It can be used as a cruise missile simulator, in training pilots for air-to-air combat, and as a target for anti-aircraft gunnery and surface-to-air missiles. Design began in November 1977, and construction of 16 pre-production examples started in September 1978. Airframe is essentially similar to that of the MQM-74C, but with some components made of glassfibre-reinforced plastics.

Since 1980 Northrop has produced over 1,000 BQM-74Cs for the US Navy, including 350 in 1985. A further 132 (including some BQM-74C/Recces) were delivered in 1986; 70 were scheduled for delivery in 1987, and continuing contracts are planned well into the 1990s. In its first deployment overseas, the Chukar III in 1984 successfully simulated, in France, a sea skimming anti-ship cruise missile during test firings of the Thomson-CSF Crotale. Export deliveries have been made to France and Spain.

The BQM-74C target system includes pylon adaptors for air launching from several types of aircraft, and payload kits for mobile sea range (MSR) operations. MSR enables fleet commanders to conduct realistic 'war games' on open sea. The BQM-74C's role in these exercises is to simulate cruise missiles fired from multiple directions and latitudes. The BQM-74C's missions can be pre-programmed, and the target is capable of air or surface launch from beyond the horizon of target ships. It has been flown at an altitude of 3 m (10 ft) while simulating cruise missile flight profiles.

The **BQM-74C/Recce** version, developed at US Navy request, has a nose bay reconfigured to accommodate a non-gimballed daylight TV camera and zoom lens of the type installed in the Northrop RF-5E TigerEye, a video data link transmitter, a video cassette recorder with in-flight replay capability, and a control and interface unit. Air, ground or ship-launchable, and parachute-recoverable, this version has a growth potential extending to panoramic photography and real-time infra-red coverage. The reconnaissance kit allows ready conversion to and from target configuration, enabling either training or tactical missions to be flown using the same basic vehicle. Ten of the Recce version have been delivered to the US Navy. A successful flight demonstration programme has been conducted, and USN evaluation was continuing in 1987.

The following description applies to the current standard BQM-74C target version:

TYPE: Radio-controlled or programmable automatically recoverable multirole target.

BQM-74C Chukar III uploaded for air launch

TV camera nose identifies this Chukar as a BQM-74C/Recce

AIRFRAME: Shoulder-wing monoplane of aluminium alloy and GRP construction. Northrop G-9224-080 wing section of 8% thickness/chord ratio. No dihedral. Non-swept wings, each with electrically actuated aileron. Semi-monocoque aluminium body houses all equipment, power plant and fuel tank. Nose and tail skins removable for access to equipment and power plants. Underslung engine air intake. Inverted Y aluminium tail unit, comprising fixed vertical fin, fixed tailplane halves (anhedral 30°) and two electrically actuated elevators.

POWER PLANT: One Williams International WR24-7A (J400-WR-402) turbojet initially, rated at 0.80 kN (180 lb st). Standard engine from 1986 is 1.07 kN (240 lb st) J400-WR-404. Pressurised fuel tank in centre of fuselage, capacity as for Chukar II.

LAUNCH AND RECOVERY: Can be launched from ground or shipborne launcher in same manner as MQM-74C. Can also be air-launched from Grumman A-6E Intruder or McDonnell Douglas TA-4J Skyhawk (one under each wing); is also compatible with underwing launchers of Lockheed DP-2 Neptune or DC-130A Hercules. Parachute recovery, on land or from water, as for MQM-74C.

GUIDANCE AND CONTROL: Out-of-sight UHF radio control by automatic stabilisation and command; radar tracking in-sight control, with visual acquisition aids. Alternatively, can be pre-programmed. Proportional feedback stabilisation and control system for pitch and bank. Engine throttle positions, altitude hold initiation and recovery initiation are controlled by audio tone signals. Components include a Northrop digital avionics processor, vertical and yaw rate gyros, Motorola AN/DKW-3 integrated target control system, aileron and elevator servos, and altitude hold pressure transducer.

MISSION EQUIPMENT: Electrical power from engine driven alternator through a rectifier-regulator. 28V nickel-cadmium battery secondary power source. Onboard acquisition and tracking aids include fore and aft Luneberg lenses, for passive radar augmentation, and a smoke system. Main payload compartment is in forward fuselage section. Equipment includes locator beacon, radar altimeter, seeker simulator (to duplicate cruise missile emissions), radar transponder for IFF, and scoring. Provisions include flight profile programmer with UHF command override; active J-band, B-band, L-band and X-band radar augmentation; and Tacan receiver. System also includes payload kits with flotation gear for mobile sea range (MSR) operations (see introductory paragraph).

DIMENSIONS:

Wing span	1.76 m (5 ft 9.4 in)
Wing area	0.74 m² (8 sq ft)
Length overall	3.95 m (12 ft 11.5 in)
Body diameter (max)	0.36 m (1 ft 2 in)
Height overall	0.72 m (2 ft 4.2 in)

WEIGHTS (A: surface, B: air launch):

Basic operating weight empty:	
A	127 kg (280 lb)
B	133 kg (294 lb)
Max mission load	78.5 kg (173 lb)
Fuel	50.3 kg (111 lb)
Max launching weight:	
A	233 kg (514 lb)
B	199 kg (438 lb)

PERFORMANCE (at max launching weight. A: with J400-WR-402 engine, B: with -404):

Max level speed at 6,100 m (20,000 ft):	
A	500 knots (927 km/h; 576 mph)
B	530 knots (982 km/h; 610 mph)
Service ceiling:	
A	9,150 m (30,000 ft)
B	12,200 m (40,000 ft)
Max range: A, B	450 nm (833 km; 518 miles)
g limits:	
A	+2.3
B	+4

NORTHROP NV-144

Northrop's company funded NV-144 is a high-performance subsonic RPV that can be used as a target or for tactical RPV applications such as reconnaissance, weather data collection, electronic signal monitoring, electronic jamming and ordnance delivery. In 1987 it was one of the unmanned vehicles being considered as a new mid-range RPV for the US Navy, Marine Corps and Air Force. The USN is expected to award an FSD contract in 1988, with a fly-off between two contenders at the end of that year and a 1989 production contract to the winning vehicle.

TYPE: Subsonic recoverable drone.

AIRFRAME: Cantilever high-wing monoplane. Northrop NROC-2 wing section, with 8% thickness/chord ratio. No anhedral or dihedral. Incidence 1° 12 at root. Sweepback 22° 30' at quarter-chord. Wings are of vinylester sheet moulding compound; ailerons have a foam core with aluminium wraparound skin, and are operated by Superior electro-mechanical proportional actuators. Forward fuselage and pressurised fuel tank are of aluminium. Cowlings and fairings are of vinylester, as is the tailplane; twin endplate fins are of aluminium. Elevator actuation similar to that of ailerons. Construction makes use of some components and equipment from Chukar III.

POWER PLANT: One 3.70 kN (831 lb st) Microturbo TRI 60-2 turbojet, semi-recessed under rear of fuselage, for initial flight trials. Also test flown with 4.31 kN (970 lb st) Teledyne CAE 373-8. Single fuel tank in centre-fuselage, capacity 250 litres (55 Imp gallons; 66 US gallons), with refuelling point on top of fuselage.

LAUNCH AND RECOVERY: Air, land or ship launchable. Recovery by onboard parachute system.

GUIDANCE AND CONTROL: Can be radio controlled or pre-programmed by onboard computer, using Northrop digital avionics processor as developed for BQM-74C. Vehicle can operate with a variety of remotely controlled target control sytems such as ITCS, Vega, UHF and CTAS. Command override system to ensure target ship safety during simulated attacks.

SYSTEMS AND EQUIPMENT: Ram air pressurisation of fuel tank; 5.2 kVA alternator mounted in engine nose bullet; battery; power regulator; radar altimeter; and Northrop digital avionics processor.

Air launch of a Northrop NV-144 from an A-6E Intruder

DIMENSIONS:	
Wing span	3.26 m (10 ft 8.5 in)
Wing area	2.23 m² (24 sq ft)
Length overall	5.93 m (19 ft 5.5 in)
Body diameter (max)	0.51 m (1 ft 8 in)
Height overall	1.04 m (3 ft 5 in)
Tailplane span (over fins)	1.46 m (4 ft 9.5 in)
Payload volume	more than 0.31 m³ (11 cu ft)

WEIGHTS:	
Weight empty	431 kg (950 lb)
Max fuel	181 kg (400 lb)
Max payload	136 kg (300 lb)
Max launching weight	680 kg (1,500 lb)

PERFORMANCE:	
Never-exceed speed	Mach 0.975
Max level speed at S/L	580 knots (1,075 km/h; 668 mph)
Econ cruising speed at 11,430 m (37,500 ft)	300 knots (555 km/h; 345 mph)
Stalling speed	130 knots (240 km/h; 150 mph)
Operating height:	
min	6 m (20 ft)
max	16,000 m (52,500 ft)
Range at Mach 0.8 at 4,575 m (15,000 ft)	380 nm (703 km; 437 miles)
Max range at 15,240 m (50,000 ft)	more than 960 nm (1,779 km; 1,105 miles)
Endurance	2 h 45 min
g limit	+7

PACIFIC AEROSYSTEM INC

8695 Aero Drive, San Diego, California 92123

Pacific Aerosystem was incorporated in 1977 in order to support unmanned vehicle programmes in which the governments of Italy and other NATO countries have an interest. In particular, PAI works closely with Meteor of Italy (which see), whose President was a co-founder of PAI. The US company collaborated with Meteor in developing and producing the latter's Alamak ground control, tracking and telemetry system, has developed a remotely controlled and/or pre-programmed ocean fast boat for the Italian Navy, and carried out many other R & D programmes for the Italian government. For the US and international market, PAI has produced aircraft interface units for US Navy QF-86 target drones, and command receivers for the Australian Jindivik target drone.

PAI HERON 26

A primary feature of the Heron 26 is PAI's Mizar avionics system, developed to enable an unmanned aircraft to determine its own geographical position independently of any ground control station and to perform many of its manoeuvres automatically, thereby ultimately being capable of full pre-programmed 'launch and forget' operation. Mizar currently uses a differential/Omega/VLF system for navigation, backed up by dead reckoning, which will be replaced by GPS navigation when that system can offer worldwide coverage in about 1988. In 1984 the present Mizar system was adopted by the Italian government as part of its Sorao battlefield surveillance programme. The air vehicle used for this

Standard span short-range version of the Pacific Aerosystem Heron 26

demonstration was the Meteor Mirach 20 (which see); PAI is a subcontractor in this programme to Meteor, which produces the Mirach 20 for the Italian Army and Navy.

To cater for US and international markets requiring an aircraft with greater altitude, endurance and payload, PAI developed the Heron 26, starting the design in June 1983 and flying the first of three prototypes in July 1984. Ten production examples, ordered through Meteor by the Italian government, had been completed by February 1986. Demonstrations to potential US and foreign customers were continuing at that time, and the Heron 26 was a candidate in 1987 for the US Army's intelligence and electronic warfare RPV competition.

TYPE: Recoverable multi-role drone/RPV.

AIRFRAME: Shoulder-wing monoplane with central fuselage nacelle, twin tailbooms and twin fins and rudders. Conventional construction, mostly of carbonfibre and epoxy, with some Kevlar in tail unit. Wings have tapered trailing edge, with ailerons, and can be folded for transportation and storage. No anhedral or dihedral. Mainly rectangular-section fuselage, with crushable keel to absorb landing impact. 'Add-on' wing extension panels optional, to increase altitude capability. Very low radar, infra-red, acoustic and other signatures.

POWER PLANT: One 19.4 kW (26 hp) Herbrandson D-290 two-cylinder two-stroke engine, driving a two-blade fixed-pitch pusher propeller. Fuel tank in fuselage, capacity 30 litres (6.7 Imp gallons; 8 US gallons).

LAUNCH AND RECOVERY: Capability for fully automatic zero-length, high angle booster-assisted launch (9.8 kN; 2,205 lb thrust solid propellant rocket, burn time 0.7 s), which allows aircraft to be airborne in less than 1 s after clearing any reasonable obstacle in the surrounding area. For missions where mobility is less important and launch area is quite large, a pneumatic launcher installed on a 10 ton truck can be used. Aircraft can fly to a pre-programmed point for precise and automatic un-attended recovery by parachute, or acquired and controlled by a portable control station mounted on the launch/checking/recovery vehicle, the PCS operator guiding the Heron down to land on its keel.

GUIDANCE AND CONTROL: Multi-loop four-axis autopilot (pitch, yaw, roll and throttle). In 'launch and forget' mode the Mizar avionics navigator is pre-programmed to allow autonomous flight control in four axes, and to manage payloads. Where real-time data is not required, Heron 26 can fly beyond radio horizon and a ground control station is not needed. GCS can, however, receive any kind of real-time information when aircraft is in radio line of sight, and in this condition can also steer the aircraft. Five levels of redundancy allow mission continuation and/or return home in the event of navigation system and associated mission payload failures; substantial redundancy is also implicit in ability of ground operator to 'fly' vehicle following disruption of onboard navigation.

MISSION EQUIPMENT: The following alternative payloads can be carried: steerable, stabilised platform with daylight or LLL TV camera or FLIR, with or without laser designator; low or medium altitude panoramic film camera; high altitude vertical camera; infra-red linescan; or packages for communications relay, navigation relay or electronic warfare. Two underwing locations are available for external stores, including auxiliary fuel tanks, within the overall payload limitations.

DIMENSIONS:

Wing span:	
standard	4 m (13 ft 1.5 in)
extended	6 m (19 ft 8.25 in)
Wing area:	
standard	4.72 m² (50.8 sq ft)
extended	6.30 m² (67.8 sq ft)
Width, wings folded	2 m (6 ft 6.75 in)
Length overall	3.93 m (12 ft 10.9 in)

Fuselage: Length	2.72 m (8 ft 11 in)
Max width	0.36 m (1 ft 2.2 in)
Max depth	0.49 m (1 ft 7.3 in)
Height overall	1.16 m (3 ft 9.8 in)
Tailplane span (c/l of tailbooms)	1.37 m (4 ft 6.3 in)
Propeller diameter	0.74 m (2 ft 5 in)
Payload compartment volume	0.063 m³ (2.24 cu ft)

WEIGHTS (A: standard wings, B: extended span):

Weight empty:	
A	93.2 kg (205.5 lb)
B	99.2 kg (218.5 lb)
Max payload: A, B	35 kg (77 lb)
Max fuel: A, B	21.8 kg (48 lb)
Max launching weight: A, B	150 kg (330 lb)

PERFORMANCE (at max launching weight, A and B as above):

Max level speed at S/L:	
A	108 knots (200 km/h; 124 mph)
B	105 knots (195 km/h; 121 mph)
Econ cruising speed at S/L:	
A, B	85 knots (158 km/h; 98 mph)
Stalling speed:	
A	51 knots (95 km/h; 59 mph)
B	48 knots (89 km/h; 56 mph)
Max rate of climb at S/L:	
A	240 m (785 ft)/min
B	300 m (985 ft)/min
Service ceiling:	
A	3,500 m (11,480 ft)
B	6,000 m (19,675 ft)
Landing run: A, B	70 m (230 ft)
Range with max fuel, 20 min reserves:	
B	170 nm (315 km; 196 miles)
Endurance (A and B):	
with 34 kg (75 lb) payload	5 h
with 22.7 kg (50 lb) payload	7 h 12 min
with 11.3 kg (25 lb) payload	10 h

PARTNERSHIPS LIMITED INC

PO Box 6503, Lawrenceville, New Jersey 08648

Partnerships formerly produced the Model A Sport single-engined microlight aircraft, but turned its attention in 1983 to research RPVs. Its only design to date is the C-1, a high-altitude test vehicle developed under NASA contract.

PARTNERSHIPS C-1

Development of this aircraft began with a 1983 NASA contract aimed at providing technology for flight test at altitudes above 18,300 m (60,000 ft). There were three major project tasks: the airframe, a power system to carry it to very high altitudes, and a data and control system which could fly the aircraft when it was out of sight of the ground, perform a precise flight test pattern, and record the data for analysis on the ground.

The programme succeeded in its objectives of demonstrating a method of chemically supercharging a two-stroke engine with oxygen, which potentially can be used to reach extreme altitudes. Autonomous flight under computer control was demonstrated, and preliminary flight test data obtained. The system for storing the data in CMOS RAM on board, with automatic downloading to a portable computer on the ground

Partnerships C-1 high-altitude research UMA

and automatic data reduction and plotting, was also demonstrated.

After its first flight in December 1984 the airframe was modified from the original design to have a shorter wing span with 4° of dihedral and struts. It proved reliable in service and had accumulated a total of 56 flights by February 1986.

The current programme objective then was to improve the flight data instrumentation so that better data could be obtained to provide a competitive flight test capability. In addition, Partnerships planned to extend the DACS software to permit long-range autonomous flight. This was to involve increased navigation capability, as well as development of artificial intelligence concepts to deal with in-flight problems such as weather, ice and traffic. By mid-1987, however, the C-1 programme was inactive.

TYPE: High-altitude research RPV.

AIRFRAME: Strut-braced high-wing monoplane, of typical 'model aircraft' configuration. Constant chord wings, with Eppler 193 section, 2° incidence, 4° dihedral and single bracing strut each side. No ailerons. Box-section forward fuselage, of plywood and spruce with Dacron covering. Rear fuselage, wings and horizontal tail surfaces also of wood construction; fin and rudder made from composites. Elevators partially mass balanced and controlled by electric servo. Non-retractable tricycle landing gear, with 6 in diameter wheels and tyres on all units.

POWER PLANT: One 3.73 kW (5 hp) Quadra Q-50 modified two-stroke chain-saw engine, driving a two-blade fixed-pitch wooden propeller. Fuel tank in centre of fuselage, capacity (petrol/oil mixture) 15.1 litres (3.3 Imp gallons; 4 US gallons). Oxygen boost system permitted aircraft to attain a ceiling of 18,300 m (60,000 ft).

LAUNCH AND RECOVERY: Conventional T-O and landing.

GUIDANCE AND CONTROL: Kraft KPR8FD radio control receiver, mounted in rear fuselage. Autonomous navigation. Two onboard microcomputers, installed in forward fuselage to form part of data acquisition and control system.

MISSION EQUIPMENT: See introductory paragraphs.

DIMENSIONS:

Wing span	4.14 m (13 ft 7 in)
Wing area	1.89 m² (20.34 sq ft)
Fuselage:	
Length	3.66 m (12 ft)
Max width	0.359 m (1 ft 2.25 in)

Height overall	0.761 m (2 ft 6 in)
Tailplane span	1.82 m (5 ft 11.75 in)
Wheel track	0.675 m (2 ft 2.5 in)
Wheelbase	1.06 m (3 ft 5.75 in)
Propeller diameter	0.56 m (1 ft 10 in)
Payload compartment volume	0.0265 m³ (0.936 cu ft)

WEIGHTS:

Weight empty	19 kg (42 lb)
Max payload	3 kg (6.6 lb)

Fuel:

normal	3 kg (6.6 lb)
max	15 kg (33 lb)

T-O weight:

normal	25 kg (55 lb)
max	37 kg (81.5 lb)

PERFORMANCE:

Max level speed	70 knots (130 km/h; 81 mph)
Max cruising speed	35 knots (65 km/h; 40 mph)
Stalling speed	23 knots (43 km/h; 27 mph)
Max rate of climb at S/L	300 m (984 ft)/min
*Ceiling	18,300 m (60,000 ft)
Range with max fuel	
	1,084 nm (2,009 km; 1,248 miles)
g limits	+4/−2

*with chemical supercharging

PHALANX ORGANIZATION

2600 E Wardlow Road, Long Beach, California 90807

PHALANX MP-9 DRAGONFLEA

The MP-9 Dragonflea, for drone/RPV/cruise missile applications, is one of several announced versions of the Phalanx Dragon family, and was intended to be among the earliest versions to be completed and flown. Published details include:

POWER PLANT: One 13.3 kN (3,000 lb st) turbojet.

DIMENSIONS:

Wing span	2.74 m (9 ft)
Wing area	4.76 m² (51.25 sq ft)

WEIGHTS (estimated):

Weight empty	625 kg (1,378 lb)
Payload	270 kg (595 lb)
Fuel	270 kg (595 lb)
Max T-O weight	1,165 kg (2,568 lb)

PERFORMANCE (estimated):

Max level speed	Mach 0.96

ROCKWELL INTERNATIONAL CORPORATION (Missile Systems Division)

4300 East Fifth Avenue, Columbus, Ohio 43216

ROCKWELL ARPV

Together with Boeing Aerospace and Northrop, Rockwell International was one of three companies awarded a three-year study contract in April 1975 to design an ARPV (advanced remotely piloted vehicle) as a possible successor to the Teledyne Ryan BGM-34C (which see). The designs were required to incorporate a drone control and data retrieval system (CDRS) and data relay by Compass Cope type RPVs. Rockwell's proposal was for a sweptwing, V-tailed airframe with a dorsally-podded jet engine, capable of carrying an internally mounted camera, wingtip pods for EW missions, or underwing weapons for use in a harassment role. A retractable tricycle landing gear was proposed, the aircraft being intended for conventional runway take-off, with recovery by arrester wire and net barrier.

DIMENSIONS:

Wing span (excl wingtip pods)	5.89 m (19 ft 4 in)
Length of fuselage	7.62 m (25 ft)
Body diameter (max)	0.84 m (2 ft 9 in)
Height overall	2.06 m (6 ft 9 in)

WEIGHTS AND PERFORMANCE:
    No details known

Display model of Rockwell's proposed ARPV

ROCKWELL INTERNATIONAL CORPORATION
(North American Aircraft Division)
PO Box 92098, Los Angeles, California 90009

ROCKWELL HiMAT

Initiated jointly by NASA's Dryden Flight Research Center and the USAF Flight Dynamics Laboratory, the HiMAT programme (Highly Maneuverable Aircraft Technology) was aimed chiefly at speeding up the progress of advanced design technology into the flight test phase; assisting designers to take larger technological steps forward between generations of aircraft; and, more specifically, at providing a low-risk means of testing the advanced manoeuvring capability of future aircraft. NASA began developing control techniques for the HiMAT programme in 1975, first with three-eighths-scale unpowered glassfibre models of the F-15 fighter and later with two modified BQM-34F Firebee IIs.

Air vehicle designs were submitted by Grumman Aerospace, McDonnell Aircraft Co and Rockwell International, Rockwell winning an October 1975 contract for two prototype HiMAT RPRVs. Teledyne Ryan was major subcontractor for the airborne flight control system. The aircraft's design consisted of a basic core vehicle which included the engine and all essential subsystems. To this core were added, as modular units, the wings, canard and tail surfaces, engine intake, and afterburner/exhaust structure. This enabled the modular components to be replaced during the programme, at minimum cost, with others of alternative design, such as a two-dimension vectored-thrust exhaust nozzle, advanced supercritical wings, variable camber wings, deformable/self-trimming outer wings, CCV techniques, a digital fly-by-wire system, and an integrated propulsion control system.

The first HiMAT prototype was delivered to NASA on 7 March 1978, and made its initial free flight on 27 July 1979. The second HiMAT flew for the first time on 24 July 1981. By the time that flight testing was completed in early 1983, the two RPRVs had made 26 flights providing a total research time of 11 h 34 min and a total time aloft, including B-52 captive flight time, of 41 h 6 min. The flight envelope expansion and performance demonstration goals were all accomplished successfully, and the flight programme was supported by hundreds more hours of ground test and simulation time, yielding a comprehensive amount of data on advanced aerodynamics, structures, flight control systems, configuration development and RPV operations.

TYPE: Remotely piloted research vehicle.
AIRFRAME: Mid-wing monoplane, of roughly tandem delta configuration, with sharply sweptback main wings and foreplanes having graphite composite skins. Glassfibre outer leading edges; remainder of wings of aluminium, titanium and other materials. No dihedral or anhedral. Ailerons, elevons and elevators on trailing edges of main wings; sweptback NASA winglet at each wingtip. Dihedralled canard surfaces, fitted with elevators. Semi-monocoque area ruled fuselage, with graphite composite skin. Twin, sweptback, outward-canted pivoted fins on short booms extending from trailing edges of main wings at approx mid-span. Graphite composite fin skins. Retractable tricycle landing gear, of skid type for landing on dry lake bed at Edwards AFB. All units retract rearward, main units to form continuous fairing with wing/tail booms, nose unit into underside of engine air intake trunk.
POWER PLANT: One General Electric J85-GE-21 turbojet (15.6 kN; 3,500 lb st dry and 22.25 kN; 5,000 lb st with afterburning), mounted centrally in fuselage.
LAUNCH AND RECOVERY: Air-launched from B-52 carrier aircraft at about 13,720 m (45,000 ft). Recovered by conventional skid landing.
GUIDANCE AND CONTROL: Primary control from ground console, by TV, telemetry and radar link with onboard systems. Flown by operator in ground-based control centre in which all of aircraft's flight parameters were displayed via telemetry

Rockwell International's HiMAT advanced aerodynamic research RPV

from RPRV. Ground-based 'cockpit' equipped with conventional aircraft controls. Operator aided in landing manoeuvre by televised view of landing area taken with TV camera mounted in air vehicle. Provision for relaying backup inputs from RPRV to TF-104G chase-plane in event of loss of ground control. For occasions when TF-104G out of control range, RPRV fitted with onboard self-righting system to bring it into constant altitude, orbiting, subsonic flight until chase-plane able to resume control.

MISSION EQUIPMENT: Included flight and control parameter sensors, 164 research instrumentation sensors, signal processors, data links to ground control and chase-plane, backup flight control system computer, and TV camera.

DIMENSIONS:

Wing span	4.755 m (15 ft 7.25 in)
Length overall, incl nose probe	6.86 m (22 ft 6 in)
Height overall	1.31 m (4 ft 3.6 in)

WEIGHTS:

Weight empty	1,200 kg (2,645 lb)
Fuel	295 kg (650 lb)
Max weight for air launch	1,528 kg (3,370 lb)

PERFORMANCE:

Max level speed	Mach 1.6
Touchdown speed	180 knots (333 km/h; 207 mph)
Average research flight duration	30 min
g limit	+12

ROTEC ENGINEERING INC

PO Box 220, Duncanville, Texas 75138

Rotec developed an actuator package for its **Panther 2 Plus** microlight aircraft enabling it to be remotely controlled while carrying a 272 kg (600 lb) civil, military or personnel payload. Flight testing of the radio controlled version took place in the spring of 1986. The electrical actuators are powered by an 8Ah 12V battery, through a 15 × 10 × 4 cm (6 × 4 × 1.5 in) control box in the cockpit, provision for manual override being retained for emergency use.

RS SYSTEMS

5301 Holland Drive, Beltsville, Maryland 20705-2383

After supplying more than 90,000 aerial targets to the US Army, Navy, Marine Corps and foreign forces since 1979, RS Systems reorganised its remote controlled miniature aerial target (RCMAT) product line in 1987 into three main categories. Between those dates the product line expanded from a delta-winged gunnery target, the FQM-117A, to state-of-the-art three-dimensional one-ninth and one-fifth scale aerial targets carrying infra-red sources, two-axis stabilisers, sonic hit indicators, payload release devices, and an Airmiles airborne hit recording and signalling system.

RS SYSTEMS FQM-117A RCMAT

Between June 1979 and December 1983 the US Army received more than 30,000 examples of this expendable remote controlled miniature aerial target (RCMAT), as a training vehicle for air defence gunners and infra-red systems tracking; and for payload missions. Production also included quantities for four Middle East nations.

Graphic evidence of the survivability of RS Systems' little FQM-117A hand-launched target

At a distance of 200 m (650 ft) and a speed of 80 knots (148 km/h; 92 mph), the RCMAT simulates a full size aircraft 1,200 m (3,935 ft) away, travelling at 480 knots (890 km/h; 553 mph). The US Army converted a substantial number of existing FQM-117As to ARCMAT (Augmented RCMAT) standard.

TYPE: Radio-controlled miniature aerial target.

AIRFRAME: Simple fibreboard covered Styrofoam structure, of cropped delta monoplane planform with V tail surfaces. Aluminium components for radar enhancement. No landing gear.

POWER PLANT: One 0.93 kW (1.25 hp) K & B 0.6 cu in two-stroke model aircraft engine, mounted in nose. Standard fuel capacity 0.47 litre (0.8 Imp pint; 1 US pint). Auxiliary fuel tanks optional.

LAUNCH AND RECOVERY: Hand launched; normally non-recoverable (expendable), but with recovery provisions.

GUIDANCE AND CONTROL: Radio command guidance system.

MISSION EQUIPMENT: Visual hit indicator, passive radar augmentation, electronic or pyrotechnic infra-red attachment, and MILES adaptation.

DIMENSIONS:

Wing span	1.60 m (5 ft 3 in)
Length overall	0.91 m (3 ft)
Height overall	0.19 m (7.6 in)

WEIGHTS:

Weight empty	2.05 kg (4.5 lb)
Fuel	0.45 kg (1 lb)
Max payload	1.4 kg (3 lb)
Max launching weight	3.9 kg (8.5 lb)

PERFORMANCE:

Cruising speed	80 knots (148 km/h; 92 mph)
Launch speed	25 knots (47 km/h; 29 mph)
Landing speed	20 knots (37 km/h; 23 mph)
Ceiling	3,050 m (10,000 ft)
Endurance (standard fuel)	12 min

RS SYSTEMS FQM-117A AUGMENTED RCMAT

Early RCMAT models, because of their configuration and size, were unable to provide realistic visual profiles and flight patterns of genuine threat aircraft. They were also unstable in flight, and, initially, lacked an infra-red tracking source for heat-seeking air defence weapons. The Augmented RCMAT was therefore developed in 1980 and introduced in the following year. This utilised the same transmitters, receivers and flight packages as the FQM-117A delta, but airframe components were added to provide a more realistic visual representation of a threat aircraft. These involved replacing the nose crutch of the RCMAT delta with a three-dimensional nose section, and adding a two-dimensional fuselage and tail section. The result was an effective one-ninth scale representation of (initially) the MiG-27 'Flogger-D', although versions representing the MiG-21, Vought A-7 and General Dynamics F-16 were also produced for visual recognition training and target use.

More than 4,500 Augmented RCMATs were produced for the US Army, US Marine Corps and one overseas customer. In addition, the US Army upgraded a substantial number of its earlier FQM-117A deltas to ARCMAT standard by means of kits enabling the conversion to be made in the field in about 20 minutes.

POWER PLANT: One 1.5 kW (2 hp) 0.6 cu in engine, mounted in nose.
MISSION EQUIPMENT: As listed for FQM-117A RCMAT, plus single or dual axis gyro autopilot.
DIMENSIONS:

Wing span	1.70 m (5 ft 7 in)
Length overall	1.85 m (6 ft 1 in)

WEIGHTS:

Weight empty, incl fuel	2.7 kg (6 lb)
Max payload	2.3 kg (5 lb)
Max launching weight	5.4 kg (12 lb)

PERFORMANCE: As for FQM-117A RCMAT except:

Cruising speed	65 knots (120 km/h; 75 mph)

RS SYSTEMS HEAT

HEAT (highly expendable aerial target) was essentially a larger scale (one-seventh) development of Augmented RCMAT, tested and validated in August 1981 to execute scale manoeuvres of typical attack aircraft. It utilised an improved command link and electrostatic stabilisation, and could be launched mechanically or by hand. An IR source was tested in March 1982, enabling HEAT to be used as a target for such weapons as Redeye, Stinger and Chaparral, and more than 200 HEATs were delivered to the US Army in MiG-27 and F-16 configuration. An extended range version was essentially similar except for a hardened airframe structure able to carry alternative payloads. This had an empty weight (incl fuel) of 9.1 kg (20 lb), max launching weight of 15.9 kg (35 lb) and a 30-minute endurance; other data were as for the standard HEAT, which were as follows:

POWER PLANT: One 2.1 kW (2.8 hp) 2.2 cu in nose-mounted engine.
LAUNCH AND RECOVERY: Conventional T-O and landing, or bungee or rail launch with fail-safe recovery system.
DIMENSIONS:

Wing span	1.98 m (6 ft 6 in)
Length overall	2.39 m (7 ft 10 in)

WEIGHTS:

Weight empty, incl fuel	7.7 kg (17 lb)
Max payload	6.8 kg (15 lb)
Max launching weight	14.5 kg (32 lb)

PERFORMANCE:

Cruising speed	65 knots (120 km/h; 75 mph)
T-O speed	35 knots (65 km/h; 40 mph)
Landing speed	25 knots (46 km/h; 29 mph)
Ceiling	3,050 m (10,000 ft)
Endurance (standard fuel)	15 min

RS SYSTEMS HEAT 3D

First flown in December 1983, the HEAT 3D was developed under US Army contract and differed from the standard HEAT chiefly in being reconfigured to have a pusher engine installation to provide a scale IR signature. It was also faster, and had a greater payload capacity. Production was in MiG-27 and F-16 versions.

POWER PLANT: One 3 kW (4 hp) engine, mounted at rear and driving a two-blade pusher propeller.
LAUNCH AND RECOVERY: Launched from 4.88 m (16 ft) rail or T-O dolly.
DIMENSIONS:

Wing span:	
F-16	2.08 m (6 ft 10 in)
MiG-27	2.34 m (7 ft 8 in)
Length overall:	
F-16	2.82 m (9 ft 3 in)
MiG-27	2.62 m (8 ft 7 in)

WEIGHTS:

Weight empty, incl fuel:	
F-16	13.6 kg (30 lb)
MiG-27	14.5 kg (32 lb)
Max payload (both)	9.1 kg (20 lb)
Max launching weight:	
F-16	22.7 kg (50 lb)
MiG-27	23.6 kg (52 lb)

PERFORMANCE (both):

Cruising speed	80 knots (148 km/h; 92 mph)
T-O speed	38 knots (70 km/h; 44 mph)
Landing speed	32 knots (59 km/h; 37 mph)
Ceiling	3,050 m (10,000 ft)
Endurance (standard fuel)	30 min

RS SYSTEMS ONE-NINTH SCALE TARGETS

At this scale, RS Systems currently produces '3-D' representations of the MiG-27 'Flogger-D' and Su-25 'Frogfoot' as aerial targets, and the General Dynamics F-16 and McDonnell Douglas/BAe AV-8B for recognition training. The MiG-27, a replacement for the FQM-117A, is produced for the US Army (designation **FQM-117B**) and, in a 'commercial' version, for other customers. Both targets are used to fly realistic attack profiles, and can be tracked and engaged by air defence units using small arms, 20–40 mm gun systems or infra-red based weapons.

POWER PLANT: One 1.5 kW (2 hp) 0.6 cu in engine.
MISSION EQUIPMENT: Four principal training payloads can be used: a tactical hit indicator (THI), manual hit indicator (MHI), Airmiles, or an IR (infra-red) source. The THI automatically initiates up to ten flash-smoke 'target disabled' indications per flight, its sonic detection system providing users with an adjustable target size from 2–24 m (6.56–78.74 ft) and adjustable 'hits to disable' (1–15 rounds through the hit zone). Each time a pre-set 'disabled' criterion is met, the gunner receives an instant flash-bang-smoke

One-ninth scale MiG-27 target produced by RS Systems

This 'Hind-D' scale target by RS Systems flies like an autogyro

Wing span over rocket pods	1.22 m (4 ft)
Fuselage: Length	2.16 m (7 ft 1 in)
Max width	0.23 m (9 in)
WEIGHTS:	
Max payload	more than 0.9 kg (2 lb)
Max launching weight	4.5 kg (10 lb)
PERFORMANCE:	
Max level speed	43 knots (80 km/h; 50 mph)
Visual control range	500 m (1,640 ft)
Endurance	20 min

feedback. The MHI can provide up to ten similar indications per flight, via push-button actuation at the target controller's transmitter. Airmiles, which is compatible with US Army MILES (multiple integrated laser engagement system), will signal 'target disabled' automatically with the same indication as the THI and MHI, the 'disabled' criteria in its microprocessor varying according to lethality of the weapon fired. Airmiles has an optional eye-safe 'fire back' feature for use in 'cover and concealment' training by air defence units, through its laser gun which is mounted on the target and controlled by the target's pilot. In-flight remotely actuated flares can be carried by the target for infra-red based weapon tracking.

DIMENSIONS (MiG-27 and Su-25):
Wing span	1.68 m (5 ft 6 in)
Length overall	1.83 m (6 ft 0 in)
WEIGHTS (MiG-27 and Su-25):	
Max payload	2.3 kg (5 lb)
Max launching weight	3.6 kg (8 lb)
PERFORMANCE (MiG-27 and Su-25):	
Cruising speed	65 knots (120 km/h; 75 mph)
Service ceiling	3,050 m (10,000 ft)
Endurance (standard fuel)	12 min

RS SYSTEMS ONE-SEVENTH SCALE TARGET

This new (1987) target is a visual representation of the 'Hind-D' helicopter, claimed to be able to perform all flight patterns of the real Mi-24, and to simulate standoff weapons delivery tactics as well as close-in support profiles. Hand launched, it flies as an autogyro, the nose mounted engine being offset to starboard driving a small tractor propeller, with lift provided by the fixed wings and an autorotating main rotor; there is no tail rotor.

POWER PLANT: One 1.08 cu in methanol fuelled standard glow plug engine.
DIMENSIONS:
Rotor diameter	1.60 (5 ft 3 in)

RS SYSTEMS ONE-FIFTH SCALE TARGETS

MiG-27 and Su-25 versions at one-fifth scale are also available, the former being the replacement for RS Systems' earlier one-seventh scale HEAT series. The increased size, speed, range and endurance afford air defence trainees a low-cost realistic target that can be hand or mechanically launched from an unprepared training site.

POWER PLANT: One 6.0 cu in engine in nose.
MISSION EQUIPMENT: As for one-ninth scale targets. In addition, IR flares can be used for live-fire engagements.
DIMENSIONS:
Wing span (both)	2.84 m (9 ft 4 in)
Length overall: MiG-27	3.05 m (10 ft)
Su-25	2.78 m (9 ft 1.5 in)
WEIGHTS (both):	
Max payload	11.3 kg (25 lb)
Max launching weight	14.5 kg (32 lb)
PERFORMANCE (both):	
Max level speed	95 knots (177 km/h; 110 mph)
Visual control range	2.7 nm (5 km; 3.1 miles)
Endurance	30 min

SIMULATORS LIMITED INC (SLI)
PO Box 1644, Terre Haute, Indiana 47808

SLI MiG-27 'FLOGGER-D' TARGET

The Flogger-D was designed as a one-seventh scale representation of the Soviet MiG-27, with the objective of offering not only a visually realistic target, but one which could also perform the kind of aerial manoeuvres that might be expected of the Soviet type. At the same time, it can be produced at low cost, and can be operated by only two persons: a launchman/range observer and a flight controller.

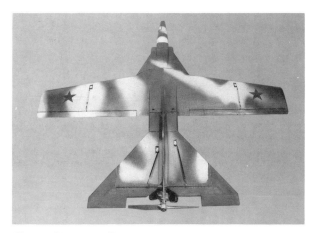
'Flogger-D' target by SLI is powered by a 'pusher' engine

TYPE: Radio-controlled aerial target.
AIRFRAME: Cantilever shoulder-wing monoplane (fixed wings), of modular construction to permit easy replacement of damaged components. Wings have a moulded core of polystyrene expanded foam plastics, reinforced with wooden stiffeners covered with a protective coating of vinyl and coated with a metallic based paint or metallic tape to enhance radar signature. Tail surfaces are of similar construction, and include a foldable underfin similar to that on the real MiG-27. The rectangular section fuselage has a central spine of plywood, strengthened on each side by foam plastics and covered in selected areas with an aliphatic resin and glassfibre cloth. Wings attach to fuselage by four bolts. Fuselage has a $5 \times 10 \times 25$ cm ($2 \times \times 10$ in) hollowed out ventral compartment for mission equipment. Interchangeable nose sections permit representation of either the MiG-23 or MiG-27 versions of 'Flogger'.
POWER PLANT: One 2.2 kW (2.9 hp) Tartan 2.68 cu in two-stroke engine, installed at rear of fuselage and driving a two-blade pusher propeller aft of elevator trailing-edge. Single fuselage fuel tank of 0.6 kg (1.25 lb) capacity standard; a second tank, of same capacity, is optional.
LAUNCH AND RECOVERY: Spring-launched from dolly on a 4.88 m (16 ft) long catapult. At conclusion of flight sequence, target can be flown into a previously deployed retrieval net, skid-landed on grass, or landed on open water. Entire system can be carried, launched, flown and recovered within a relatively self-contained area, including deployment on board ship or from a long-bed pickup truck.
GUIDANCE AND CONTROL: Four-channel proportional radio command guidance, using a proprietary model aircraft fidelity transmitter. Aerodynamic control by ailerons and elevator. Nose-mounted nickel-cadmium battery for operation of radio control equipment and aileron/elevator servos.
MISSION EQUIPMENT: Up to 2.3 kg (5 lb) of miss distance or other equipment in ventral compartment, to customer's requirements.

DIMENSIONS:

Wing span	2.07 m (6 ft 9.5 in)
Wing area	approx 1.11 m² (12 sq ft)
Length overall	2.30 m (7 ft 6.4 in)
Fuselage: Max width	0.24 m (9.5 in)
Max depth	0.20 m (8 in)
Height overall	0.51 m (1 ft 8 in)

WEIGHTS:

Operational weight empty, incl fuel	8.2 kg (18 lb)
Mission equipment	2.3 kg (5 lb)
Max launching weight	10.5 kg (23 lb)

PERFORMANCE:

Max level speed	45 knots (83 km/h; 52 mph)
Min flying speed	25 knots (47 km/h; 29 mph)
Ceiling	3,050 m (10,000 ft)
Min radio control range	1.6 nm (3 km; 1.9 miles)
Endurance	more than 10 min
g limit	+3

SLI ONE-NINTH SCALE MiG-27 and F-16 TARGETS

SLI also produces one-ninth scale targets of the MiG-27 and General Dynamics F-16. Construction, launch, recovery and guidance are generally as described in the preceding entry, but the targets carry a slightly smaller payload and are powered by a Fox 78RC or similar engine.

DIMENSIONS:

Wing span:	
F-16	1.09 m (3 ft 7 in)
MiG-27	1.67 m (5 ft 5.9 in)
Length overall:	
F-16	1.68 m (5 ft 6 in)
MiG-27	1.73 m (5 ft 8 in)
Tailplane span: both	0.61 m (2 ft)

WEIGHT:

Max payload: both	1.4 kg (3 lb)

PERFORMANCE (both):

Max level speed at S/L	over 40 knots (74 km/h; 46 mph)
Stalling speed	16–20 knots (30–37 km/h; 19-23 mph)
Ceiling	3,050 m (10,000 ft)
Endurance	more than 10 min

SLI FALCON

The Falcon mini-RPV was designed at the USAF Flight Dynamics Laboratory and was manufactured initially by Eglen Hovercraft Inc (which see). Production was subsequently transferred to SLI, the current version being built from thermovacuum formed plastics as a modularised aircraft with interchangeable wing, fuselage and nose components. It retains the size, configuration and capabilities of the original Falcon, and is large enough to perform electronic warfare, ECM, reconnaissance and other tactical missions. Other applications include electronic equipment testbed, target for testing the effectiveness of countermeasures, and training of RPV operators. Falcons have been supplied to NATO and other military and civil authorities. The complete system comprises a 'mini-squadron' of ten air vehicles plus launch, net recovery and control subsystems.

TYPE: Recoverable mini-RPV and target drone.
AIRFRAME: High-wing monoplane, with 2° 7′ dihedral, built mainly of moulded glassfibre, foam plastics and plywood, with epoxy paint finish. Skid landing gear. Nose (payload) modules interchangeable. Aircraft dismantles into four modules for transportation.
POWER PLANT: One 1.9 kW (2.5 hp) Homelite two-cylinder two-stroke engine, driving a two-blade pusher propeller.

SLI (formerly Eglen) Falcon mini

SLI Matador delta winged drone

Single fuel tank in fuselage, capacity 1.9 litres (0.4 Imp gallon; 0.5 US gallon).

LAUNCH AND RECOVERY: Pneumatic or spring-loaded catapult launch from ground, truck or ship's deck. Recovery by skid landing on ground or in net on board ship.

GUIDANCE AND CONTROL: Six-channel Collins Pro Line radio control system standard (four channels for flight control and two for payload operation). Eight-channel system available optionally. Aerodynamic control by ailerons, elevators and rudder.

MISSION EQUIPMENT: Standard airborne TV package includes Conic 8W CTM UHF 408V S-band TV transmitter with antenna; Sony AVC 1400 TV camera and lens (modified for airborne use); and battery pack. Optional equipment includes miss distance indicator, strobe light detection system, autopilot, underwing pods, retro-reflectors, 3.05 m (10 ft) span wings, and metallic reflection (chaff) for radar operations.

DIMENSIONS:

Wing span:	
standard	2.44 m (8 ft)
optional	3.05 m (10 ft)
Wing area:	
standard	1.11 m² (12 sq ft)
optional	1.39 m² (15 sq ft)
Length overall	1.87 m (6 ft 1.75 in)
Fuselage:	
Max width	0.165 m (6.5 in)
Max depth	0.235 m (9.25 in)
Height over fin	0.64 m (2 ft 1 in)

WEIGHTS:

Weight empty	11.3 kg (25 lb)
Max equipment load	11.3 kg (25 lb)
Balanced T-O weight	15.4 kg (34 lb)
Max T-O weight	22.7 kg (50 lb)

PERFORMANCE:

Max level speed	87 knots (161 km/h; 100 mph)
Ceiling	approx 3,050 m (10,000 ft)
Normal radio range	approx 1.75 nm (3.2 km; 2 miles)
Max endurance	2 h

SLI MATADOR

First flown in February 1978, the Matador was designed particularly for target use with Vulcan and Chaparral weapons, but can be used with any similar weapon system. It was produced originally, by Eglen Hovercraft Inc, for RCMAT (remotely controlled miniature aerial target) programmes; marketing is being continued by SLI.

TYPE: Recoverable target.

AIRFRAME: Delta wing monoplane, of foam plastics and wood construction. Full span flaps and ailerons on trailing edge. Sweptback fin at each wingtip. Landing skids under fuselage and each fin. Fins and propeller blades coated with aluminium paint to ensure radar engagement/lock-on within distances of up to 800 m (2,625 ft).

POWER PLANT: One 0.75–3 kW (1–4 hp) K & B piston engine, driving a two-blade propeller. Centre-fuselage fuel tank, capacity 0.5 litre (0.8 Imp pint; 1 US pint).

LAUNCH AND RECOVERY: Hand launch; skid landing.

GUIDANCE AND CONTROL: Four-channel proportional radio command system.

MISSION EQUIPMENT: Infra-red source or small internal or external payload.

DIMENSIONS:

Wing span	1.52 m (5 ft)
Length overall	1.37 m (4 ft 6 in)
Height overall	0.36 m (1 ft 2 in)

WEIGHTS:

Weight empty	2.9 kg (6.5 lb)
Max payload	0.9 kg (2 lb)
Max launching weight:	
standard	4.3 kg (9.5 lb)
with IR source	4.5 kg (10 lb)

PERFORMANCE:

Max level speed at S/L	80 knots (148 km/h; 92 mph)
Max cruising speed	69 knots (129 km/h; 80 mph)
Min flying speed	10 knots (19 km/h; 12 mph)
Ceiling	3,050 m (10,000 ft)
Radio control range	1.1 nm (2 km; 1.2 miles)
Endurance	more than 10 min

SPERRY DEFENSE SYSTEMS DIVISION OF HONEYWELL INC

PO Box 9200, Albuquerque, New Mexico 87119–9200

A pioneer of aircraft control systems, including some 40 years' association with remote control of full size aircraft, Sperry is one of the world's most experienced producers of full scale aerial targets (FSATs), and its work in this area has combined the activities of the former Sperry Corporation Flight Systems, Univac and Defense Systems Divisions. Programmes since the late 1940s have included remotely controlled versions of such widely differing aircraft as the Boeing B-17 and B-47, Lockheed F-80, T-33 and F-104, and Northrop T-38. More recent programmes have included an RPV surveillance version of the Beechcraft 36 Bonanza, and FSAT droning of the Convair F-102, North American F-86 and F-100. The latest contracts are for prototype target conversion of the Convair (General Dynamics) F-106, two prototype QF-104Js for Mitsubishi (which see), and the remote control system for an Orlando Helicopter Airways conversion of the Sikorsky S-55.

SPERRY (BEECHCRAFT) QU-22 BONANZA

Military examples of the Beechcraft Bonanza Model A36 utility aircraft were completed for use as drone aircraft in the US Air Force's **Pave Eagle** surveillance programme in Southeast Asia. These were of two types, designated **YQU-22A** (Pave Eagle 1, six converted for evaluation) and **QU-22B** (Pave Eagle 2, 27 converted for operational use). Under the programme management of Sperry's Univac Division, the Pave Eagle aircraft were modified at Marana, Arizona, for operation as pilotless relay vehicles for infiltration data, although in all missions actually flown a pilot was present in the cockpit, primarily as a monitor except during the take-off and landing phases.

Data-receiving equipment in the aircraft was manufactured by Radiation Inc, and the onboard stabilisation and control system by Sperry's Flight Systems Division. Remote operation of the QU-22s was carried out using a Univac UPQ-3 microwave command guidance system. A second data link system, independent of the UPQ-3, was used to relay to ground bases the mission data collected automatically during each flight.

The Pave Eagle 2 aircraft differed from the standard commercial Bonanza models chiefly in having as their power plant a 280 kW (375 hp) Continental GTSIO-520 engine, driving a three-blade large-diameter Hartzell W10178H-11 slow turning propeller through a reduction gear. A larger output engine-driven alternator, reportedly of 28V DC, was fitted on the starboard side of the engine; a second, belt-driven AC alternator of 8kW was installed above the propeller

reduction gearing, in a prominent bulged fairing above the engine, to provide power for the relay avionics. Compared with the YQU-22A, the QU-22B had a 0.91 m (3 ft) extension of each wing; wingtip auxiliary fuel tanks; and deletion of the aft pair of cabin windows on each side. Numerous small antennae were visible beneath the wings, and above and below the fuselage, and the cabin space aft of the pilot's seat was occupied by avionics equipment. The full-depth double doors to the cabin, aft of the wing trailing-edge on the starboard side, were retained to give access to the avionics compartment. Max T-O weight of the QU-22B has been estimated at approx 2,358 kg (5,200 lb).

The Pave Eagle aircraft were based at Nakhon Phanom, Thailand, and were employed instead of Lockheed EC-121R Super Constellations to relay infiltration data gathered by Igloo White acoustic sensors located south of the demilitarised zone in South Viet-Nam. Their operating ceiling was restricted to 5,790 m (19,000 ft), and the aircraft had an on-station endurance of about 18 hours. Operational deployment began in 1971 and included use as an FAC platform, but was terminated in late 1972, reportedly because of a high rate of loss attributed to a series of engine failures. All surviving Pave Eagle aircraft were placed in store during the winter of 1972–73, prior to the cease-fire in Viet-Nam.

SPERRY (CONVAIR/GENERAL DYNAMICS) PQM-102 DELTA DAGGER

Conversion of US Air Force F-102A fighters for remotely piloted operation, under the **Pave Deuce** programme, resulted in three versions, as follows:

QF-102. Prototypes, with provision for manned operation. Five converted by Fairchild Aircraft Service Division. Used for captive missile evaluation, crew training and systems checkout.

PQM-102A. Initial unmanned version, of which 63 produced under subcontract to Sperry by Fairchild Aircraft Service Division. Used for development testing, including pre-programmed repeatable manoeuvres.

PQM-102B. Principal unmanned version, of which 145 were converted by Sperry Flight Systems; deliveries completed in January 1982. Retained same operational characteristics as

Sperry (Beechcraft) YQU-22A Bonanza, converted for covert surveillance during the Viet-Nam war

'Nolo' (no local operator) Sperry PQM-102 conversion could be flown *only* in an unmanned state

PQM-102A except for one low-altitude mode, which could be implemented for special missions by installing radar altimeter. Improvements made to scoring system; smoke, brake and explosive destruct systems; and lift compensation in altitude hold mode. Modification of basic aircraft; avionics and operational complexity; and throttle quadrant, all simplified. Additional batteries reduced to one; second transformer deleted, a slightly modified form of the basic AC system in the F-102A being used; aircraft wiring simplified; and engine start done in cockpit, eliminating need for external control unit. Flight control avionics located in nose bay. Manoeuvres could be initiated and programmed from a fixed ground control site, using a PQM-102B auxiliary panel.

The PQM-102s were the first fighter aircraft converted for drone duties with no provision whatever for manned operation, and could not be flown except under remote control. Operational service began in October 1974, and missiles fired against them included AIM-9J/L Sidewinders, AIM-7E/F Sparrows, Stingers and Patriots. The last PQM-102 was expended in 1985, and the type was then replaced by the QF-100.

The following description applies to the PQM-102B:

TYPE: Full scale aerial target.
AIRFRAME: As original F-102A.
POWER PLANT: One Pratt & Whitney J57-P-23A turbojet, rated at approx 45.4 kN (10,200 lb st) dry and 71.2 kN (16,000 lb st) with afterburning.
LAUNCH AND RECOVERY: Dual Vega command guidance and telemetry systems. Fully redundant digital tracking and control system for command/telemetry link, in conjunction with AN/FPS-16 ground based range radar. Two targets could be controlled simultaneously.
GUIDANCE AND CONTROL: Flight control stabilisation system (FCSS), comprising flight reference computer, interface coupler and air data computer, providing eight longitudinal/vertical and four lateral/directional modes, plus interface between aircraft systems and command/telemetry system. Automatic control modes for take-off, loss of command carrier, take-off abort, and other safety modes. For cases of primary FCSS failure, a backup system provided independent control in pitch, roll and yaw, and of thrust and other vital functions. Backup operated by independent

electrical and hydraulic power systems. Redundant AC and DC power systems, and redundant dual autopilots. Manoeuvre programmer could be pre-programmed for three or four manoeuvres, to run in any required sequence, and provided backup for FCSS. Command/telemetry system provided for four proportional (pitch, roll and two spare) and 48 discrete commands, 22 proportional and 40 discrete telemetry channels; 11 additional commands (nine discrete and two proportional) available for standard payload control.

MISSION EQUIPMENT: Upper and lower fuselage avionics bays, missile bay, cockpit, and two pylon-mounted underwing pods, available for mission equipment. Digidops miss distance scoring system standard (antennae aft of cockpit, under fuselage, and in fairings each side of tailpipe). Two types of scoring camera used, covering forward and aft areas to provide missile approach angle, velocity and miss distance; these were mounted in front and at rear of cockpit. Manoeuvre destruct and explosive destruct systems incorporated. Visual augmentation (smoke) system, operable at any altitude or power setting. Radar and infra-red augmentation not required, due to size of aircraft.

DIMENSIONS:
Wing span	11.62 m (38 ft 1.5 in)
Wing area	64.57 m² (695 sq ft)
Length overall	20.84 m (68 ft 4.66 in)
Height overall	6.46 m (21 ft 2.5 in)
Payload volume (max, excl wing pods)	
	5.66 m³ (200 cu ft)

WEIGHTS:
Basic mission weight	9,076 kg (20,010 lb)
Payload (max)	1,905 kg (4,200 lb)
Mission operational T-O weight	14,186 kg (31,276 lb)

PERFORMANCE:
Max speed at altitude	
	Mach 1.2 (688 knots; 1,274 km/h; 792 mph)
Operating height range	
	61 m (200 ft) to 17,070 m (56,000 ft)
Range (dictated by effective control range of guidance radar)	more than 174 nm (322 km; 200 miles)
Normal endurance of mission	40–55 min
g limit	+8

QF-86 Sabre droned by Sperry for the US Navy

SPERRY (NORTH AMERICAN) QF-86F SABRE

During 1980–81, Sperry Flight Systems converted ten North American F-86F Sabre jet fighters into QF-86F target drones for the US Naval Weapons Center at China Lake, California. The programme was generally similar to those then current to convert F-100 and F-102A fighters for the US Air Force.

POWER PLANT: One 26.56 kN (5,970 lb st) General Electric J47-GE-27 turbojet.
DIMENSIONS:

Wing span	11.91 m (39 ft 1 in)
Wing area	29.12 m² (313.4 sq ft)
Length overall	11.43 m (37 ft 6 in)
Height overall	4.49 m (14 ft 8.75 in)

WEIGHTS (F-86F):

Weight empty	5,046 kg (11,125 lb)
T-O weight 'clean'	6,893 kg (15,198 lb)

PERFORMANCE (F-86F):

Max level speed at S/L
       588 knots (1,091 km/h; 678 mph)
Max rate of climb at S/L, AUW of 6,446 kg (14,212 lb)
       2,987 m (9,800 ft)/min
Service ceiling, AUW as above   15,120 m (49,600 ft)

SPERRY (NORTH AMERICAN) QF-100 SUPER SABRE

To fill the gap between the PQM-102 and a recommended target version of the F-4 Phantom, Sperry received an FSED contract in 1979 to convert USAF and ANG F-100 fighter-bombers into remotely piloted QF-100 full scale aerial targets. Nine FSED prototypes were converted by Sperry, the first of these making its initial unmanned flight on 19 November 1981. These were followed by a batch of 91 'production' conversions by Sperry, completed in June 1985, after which continuation of the QF-100 programme was assigned to Flight Systems Inc, under whose entry a detailed description of the target version is included.

SPERRY (SCHWEIZER) SURVEILLANCE/RELAY AIRCRAFT

Sperry carried out a design study in 1984 for an optional manned or unmanned surveillance and relay system aircraft, based on the airframe of the Schweizer SGM 2-37 Sprite motor glider. It was intended to be capable of carrying up to 544 kg (1,200 lb) of payload, and equally suitable for low-altitude quiet operation or for long-endurance missions at 15,240 m (50,000 ft). It was planned to test-fly such an aircraft during 1985, but the project was not funded beyond the concept stage. Schweizer has subsequently flown an SA 2–37A piloted version of the Sprite with a more powerful (175 kW; 235 hp) Avco Lycoming engine, a three-blade propeller and large exhaust mufflers flanking the engine cowling. Two of these have been acquired by the US government or armed forces for surveillance purposes, but Sperry is not believed to be associated with this programme.

SPERRY (CONVAIR/GENERAL DYNAMICS) QF-106 DELTA DART

As noted under Flight Systems Inc's entry, Sperry Defense Systems Division is prime contractor for the supply of QF-106 FSATs to the US Air Force, and has subcontracted FSI to produce the first six prototype conversions.

TELEDYNE RYAN AERONAUTICAL

2701 Harbor Drive, PO Box 80311, San Diego, California 92138–9012

The former Ryan Aeronautical Company was renamed Teledyne Ryan Aeronautical in December 1969.

Current activities include the design, production and field operation of high performance aerial jet targets and RPV systems. Major production items for many years have been the Firebee jet-powered targets and special purpose vehicles (pre-programmed and remotely piloted) for various types of reconnaissance mission.

TELEDYNE RYAN MODEL 124 FIREBEE I
(TARGET VERSIONS)

US Air Force designation: BQM-34A
US Army designation: MQM-34D
US Navy designations: BQM-34A and BQM-34S

The Firebee I was developed as a joint US Air Force/Army/ Navy project, in collaboration with the USAF Air Research and Development Command.

Glide flight tests of the original version began in March 1951, and the first powered flights were made that summer. A total of 1,280 of these early Q-2A and KDA versions were built eventually for all three US services and for the Royal Canadian Air Force.

Development of the current **BQM-34A** (originally Q-2C) improved Firebee began on 25 February 1958, and it flew for the first time on 19 December 1958. The first production model flew on 25 January 1960.

By April 1987 a total of 6,498 Firebee Is had been produced, including the early Q-2A and KDA versions, and had provided more than 32,000 flights in support of weapons systems and target research, development, test, evaluation, quality assurance, training and annual service practices conducted by the US Army, Navy and Air Force, and foreign governments. Target presentations have been made to virtually every surface-to-air and air-to-air weapon system in the US arsenal.

The US Army's **MQM-34D**, which is ground-launched, has extended span wings and a longer-burning rocket booster, enabling it to take off at a loaded weight some 454 kg (1,000 lb) greater than the BQM-34A. Prototypes were also built of an **MQM-34D/Mod II** (Ryan Model 251), but this was not proceeded with.

The total includes Firebees supplied to NATO for use in a missile test programme, and those sold to the Japan Defence Agency to support the training of surface-to-air and air-to-air missile and gunnery crews. The latter Firebees are built under licence by Fuji Heavy Industries. Current 1987 production by Ryan comprised 160 Firebee Is for the US Navy, deliveries beginning in September of that year, with a further 80 BQM-34S to follow in 1988. Firebees Is in the current operational inventory are powered by J69-T-29, J69-T-41A or J85-GE-7 turbojet engines.

Current Firebee targets for the US Navy incorporate a Motorola integrated target control system (ITCS) and have the designation **BQM-34S**; US Air Force BQM-34A targets have a Vega drone tracking and control system (DTCS).

One of the world's most familiar targets: a Teledyne Ryan BQM-34A Firebee I

US Army MQM-34D Mod II Firebee I, with nose intake *(US Army)*

RPVs using Model 147 airframes derived from that of the Firebee I are described separately. The following details refer to the current standard BQM-34A and S targets:

TYPE: Remotely piloted jet target vehicle.

AIRFRAME: Mid-wing monoplane, of aluminium alloy semi-monocoque construction. Three-spar wings, with leading edge droop. No dihedral or incidence. Sweepback at quarter-chord 45°. Single-spar ailerons, with Lear servo-actuators. Wingtips detachable. Provision for wingtip extensions. Tapered, circular section body, with chemical-etched components. Glassfibre tailcone and nose section. Keel under central portion, to absorb landing impact. All tail surfaces swept 45° at quarter-chord. Multi-spar fin, with glassfibre tip housing guidance and control antenna. Rudder operated electrically by servo-actuator. Single-spar tailplane, with glassfibre tips housing radar echo enhancing antennae. Ventral fin under tailcone, aft of main tail unit. Magnesium elevators powered by Lear servos.

POWER PLANT: One 7.56 kN (1,700 lb st) Teledyne CAE J69-T-29, one 8.54 kN (1,920 lb st) Teledyne CAE J69-T-41A, or one 10.9 kN (2,450 lb st) General Electric J85-GE-7 turbojet. Integral fuel tank in forward fuselage, capacity 378 litres (83.3 Imp gallons; 100 US gallons). Provision for one 68 litre (15 Imp gallon; 18 US gallon) auxiliary fuselage tank or underwing drop tanks.

LAUNCH AND RECOVERY: Either air launching, from suitably modified aircraft, or surface launching, using 50.3 kN (11,300 lb st) (nominal) solid propellant JATO bottle. US Navy has launched BQM-34As from ships under way at up to 15 knots (27.5 km/h; 17 mph). Two-stage parachute recovery system operates automatically in event of loss of radio wave carrier from remote control station, engine failure, or upon command by remote control operator. To prevent damage by dragging, recovery system incorporates disconnect which releases parachute from Firebee on contact with ground or water.

GUIDANCE AND CONTROL: Remote control methods include choice of radar, UHF radio, active seeker and automatic navigator, developed and designed by Teledyne Ryan. Normal method is through Motorola ITCS (integrated target control system) in BQM-34S; BQM-34A fitted with

Vega DTCS (drone tracking and control system). Target can be controlled either from manned aircraft or from surface station. Remote command includes activation of special scoring and augmentation equipment in target. Basic commands consist primarily of on/off functions, received by onboard receiver and relayed to appropriate subsystem. Other types of remote command and tracking system can include microwave command and guidance to control Firebee beyond line of sight from ground station through airborne relay station. BQM-34A equipped with three-axis flight control system for tactical air combat simulation which gives target capability to perform 4, 5 or 6g manoeuvres. Other systems include active and passive radar augmentation, and afterburning plume devices. Radar altimeter low altitude control system (RALACS), when added to Firebee I control system, permits precision low altitude flights at 6 m (20 ft) over water and 30 m (100 ft) over land.

SYSTEMS: Electrical power only. Primary power furnished by 28V 200A DC engine-driven generator. Power for control systems furnished by 400 Hz 115V 250W AC inverter; 28V 12.5Ah lead-acid battery provides power for electric devices of recovery system and for control during pre-landing glide phase.

MISSION EQUIPMENT: ITCS DKW-2 guidance transponder, or DTCS Model 685-2 guidance system. A/A37G-8A or A/A37G-14 flight control system. Wide range of 'building block' operational equipment includes visual or radar-reflecting banner targets; radar or infra-red Towbee towed targets or wingtip mounted infra-red pods; two underwing drop tanks, 500 lb bombs or bomblet dispensers; AN/ALE-33 or other ECM containers; wingtip tow launchers, camera pods, scoring equipment, flares or other forms of infra-red augmentation, or reflector pods for radar augmentation. BQM-34A can be equipped with adjustable travelling wave tube amplifiers for use as radar echo enhancers in L, S, X and C frequency bands.

DIMENSIONS:

Wing span	3.93 m (12 ft 10.8 in)
Wing area	3.34 m² (36 sq ft)
Length overall	6.98 m (22 ft 10.8 in)
Body diameter (max)	0.94 m (3 ft 1.2 in)
Height overall	2.04 m (6 ft 8.4 in)

*WEIGHTS:

Weight empty	680 kg (1,500 lb)
Basic gross weight	934 kg (2,060 lb)
Max launching weight	1,134 kg (2,500 lb)

*PERFORMANCE:

Never-exceed speed	Mach 0.96 (635 knots; 1,176 km/h; 731 mph at 15,240 m; 50,000 ft)
Max level speed at 1,980 m (6,500 ft)	600 knots (1,112 km/h; 690 mph)
Max cruising speed at 15,240 m (50,000 ft) at 816 kg (1,800 lb) AUW	547 knots (1,015 km/h; 630 mph)
Stalling speed, power on, at 816 kg (1,800 lb) AUW	101 knots (187 km/h; 116 mph)
Max rate of climb at S/L at 1,000 kg (2,200 lb) AUW	5,486 m (18,000 ft)/min
Operating height range	6 m–18,300 m (20 ft to more than 60,000 ft)
Endurance at 15,240 m (50,000 ft), incl 2 min 40 s glide after fuel expended	1 hr 15 min 30 s
Max range	692 nm (1,282 km; 796 miles)
Flotation time with 25% fuel	24 h

*Same for aircraft with J85-GE-7 engine

TELEDYNE RYAN MODEL 147 (RPV VERSIONS)

USAF designations: AQM-34 and XAQM-103

The Model number 147, and the basic USAF designation AQM-34, encompass a large family of surveillance, reconnaissance and ECM RPVs derived from the subsonic Firebee I target. Most were air-launched from DC-130 Hercules mother-planes which combined the functions of command, tracking, data relay and recovery aircraft.

From August 1964, various types of Model 147 were despatched on flights over China, North Viet-Nam and other areas. Early versions were deployed initially from the SAC air base at Kadena, Okinawa, as part of the USAF's **Blue Springs** programme for overflying the Chinese mainland. The Chinese claimed to have destroyed eight RPVs by May 1965, and exhibited the remains of several of them at the Chinese People's Revolutionary Museum in Beijing. In the late 1960s, detachments of the 100th Strategic Reconnaissance Wing from Davis-Monthan AFB, Arizona, operated 147-type RPVs from Bien Hoa in South Viet-Nam, bringing them back to Da Nang air base for mid-air recovery by helicopter. In all, the 100th SRW flew 3,435 operational sorties with Model 147s in Southeast Asia between August 1964 and June 1975.

Versions of the Model 147 were also used extensively to test the effectiveness of new combat equipment in an operational environment without risk to personnel.

By 1973, nearly a thousand Model 147s had been delivered for operational use. Details of these follow, together with the appropriate USAF designation where applicable. All surviving examples were placed in store in the late 1970s, when they were stated to be 'available for reactivation if required'.

Model 147A. Original version, basically a BQM-34A Firebee I with new guidance system and increased fuel. Developed in 1962 (first flight 11 April) as part of USAF **Big Safari** intelligence-gathering programme. Four prototypes built.

Model 147B. First reconnaissance drone version (37 built). Longer fuselage, wing span more than doubled, for high altitude photo-reconnaissance. First operational launch 20 August 1964.

Model 147C. Externally similar to 147A (interim short-wing test and training version pending development of 147B); seven built.

Model 147D. Externally similar to 147A. Three modified from 147C with CIA elint payload.

Model 147E. Combined airframe of 147B (but with blunter, more bulbous nosecone and longer dorsal spine) and elint package of 147D. Three built.

Model 147F. Modified 147B (one only) as ALQ-51 ECM payload testbed for US Navy.

Model 147G. Upgraded 147B (longer fuselage, uprated engine); narrow probe-like fairing on nose and small antenna fairing on top of fin. Nose-mounted TV camera, with zoom lens; L-band TV transmitter; modified three-axis proportional control system. Total of 56 built; 12 later modified to 147J. One modified as **XAQM-103** with structure strengthened to withstand 10g.

Model 147H (AQM-34N). High-altitude reconnaissance version. Extra-long-span wings, otherwise externally similar to 147G except for flatter ventral bulge. Longer range, and detachable camera noses. Flew 138 operational sorties in SEA 1967–71.

Model 124I. Hybrid Model 124/147, about a dozen of which said to have been supplied to Israel in 1971 and later used for

Model 147NX decoy (foreground), flanked by a 147J (left), 147G (right) and the big-wing 147H (rear)

high-altitude photographic reconnaissance overflights of Arab territory. Endplate auxiliary fins and elongated nose, similar to USAF's AQM-34L/M. Used in October 1973 war for day/night reconnaissance and to decoy Arab surface-to-air missiles.

Model 147J. Low-altitude photo-recce version of 147G; 39 built, including 12 modified from 147G.

Model 147N. Expendable decoy prototypes: ten built. Shorter fuselage, with recovery parachute deleted.

Model 147NA (AQM-34G). Medium-altitude ECM version. Extended-span wings, strengthened to carry active (jamming) or ALE-2 passive (chaff) ECM pod under each wing. Small antenna fairing on top of fin. Similar equipment to 147NC, but no onboard programmer; 24 built under USAF **Compass Bin** and **Combat Angel** programmes. Used by TAC.

Model 147NC (AQM-34G and H). Medium-altitude drone for ECM/chaff (43 as AQM-34G) and propaganda leaflet

Ryan 147NA/NC with underwing chaff pods

dropping (as AQM-34H). Former similar to 147NA but with flight programmer added.

Model 147NC (M1) (AQM-34J). Interim low altitude day photo and training version of 147NC, without underwing pylons, pending definitive 147SC. Total of 52 built. Some updated to AQM-34V.

Model 147NP. Interim day photo version (first flight 1 June 1967); eight built. Externally similar to 147NC (M1) except for absence of auxiliary fins.

Model 147NQ. Low-altitude version of 147NX; ten built.

Model 147NRE. 'Night reconnaissance electronic' modification of 147NP. Four completed; first flight 25 May 1967.

Model 147NX. Similar to 147N but with parachute retained. Ten built for decoy and medium-altitude daytime reconnaissance.

Models 147S and SA. Improved daytime photographic versions (long fuselage, short-span wings). Forty produced 1967–68 for low-altitude tasks.

Model 147SB. Improved 147SA (40 built 1968–69).

Model 147SC (AQM-34L and YAQM-34U). Definitive low-altitude photographic reconnaissance version. Externally similar to 147SA/SB. Several hundred built under USAF **Compass Bin** and **Buffalo Hunter** programmes. Only reconnaissance RPV permitted to overfly North Vietnam after cessation of bombing on 15 January 1973. Flew 1,651 missions with 100th SRW from January 1969 to June 1973, with 87 per cent return rate. Some equipped with real-time TV. Six modified to YAQM-34U by Lear Siegler in 1972 Update programme, to improve low-level navigational accuracy and reliability of RPV avionics system. Five YAQM-34U later converted as BGM-34C prototypes (which see).

Model 147SD (AQM-34M). Low-altitude photo-reconaissance version, externally similiar to AQM-34L but with real-time data link. Total of 87 built for USAF **Compass Bin** and **Buffalo Hunter** programmes. Some converted to **147SD Loran-AQM-34M(L)** and one as **Compass Robin** elint testbed, to eject micro-elecronic radio receivers near a radar target to facilitate attack by strike aircraft. Highest mission survival rate (97.3 per cent) of any operational 147 model.

The Teledyne Ryan drone 'family', with (where appropriate) their related USAF programmes

Model 147SK. Ten evaluated by US Navy for zero-length ship/shore launch in 1969–70. Later operational (low-altitude day photo-recce) from USS *Ranger*.

Model 147SRE (AQM-34K). Low-altitude night reconnaissance version of 147SB: 20 built 1968–69.

Model 147T (AQM-34P). High-altitude surveillance version, based on 147G airframe with uprated J100 engine.

Model 147TE (AQM-34Q). High-altitude comint (communications intelligence) version of 147T, with J100 turbojet. Four prototypes and 15 production examples. Flew 268 operational sorties 1970–73, and with 147TF was one of two models used in USAF's **Combat Dawn** programme. Slender tubular wingtip pods, large bulbous data link antenna fairing on top of fin, and other aerials projecting from fuselage.

Model 147TF (AQM-34R). Second **Combat Dawn** version for comint and elint: 20 built. Airframe as for 147TE, but probe-type fairing on nose omitted and small blade antenna on top of the nosecone. Range increased by underwing drop tanks.

Model 255 (AQM-34V). Upgraded AQM-34H and -34J with increased active/passive ECM capability (E-Systems/Melpar active jamming equipment and ALE-2 or ALE-38 chaff dispenser pods underwing). Forty-seven converted from AQM-34H/J, plus 16 new-built vehicles.

POWER PLANT: All Model 147s powered by a single Teledyne CAE turbojet, as follows: 7.56 kN (1,700 lb st) J69-T-29 in A, B, C, D, E, F, and all N series; 8.54 kN (1,920 lb st) J69-T-41A in G, H, J, all S series, and 124I; and 12.45 kN (2,800 lb st) J100-CA-100 in T, TE and TF.

DIMENSIONS (approx):

Wing span:

A, N, NQ, NX, S, SA, SB, SC, SD, SRE	3.96 m (13 ft)
B, E, F, G, J	8.23 m (27 ft)
C, D, NA, NC, NP, NRE, SK, 124I	4.57 m (15 ft)
H, T, TE, TF	9.75 m (32 ft)

Wing area:

A, N, NQ, NX, S, SA, SB, SC, SD, SRE	3.34 m² (36 sq ft)
B, E, F, G, J	7.43 m² (80 sq ft)
C, D, NA, NC, NP, NRE, SK, 124I	3.72 ² (40 sq ft)
H, T, TE, TF	10.59 m² (114 sq ft)

Length overall:

A, B, C, D, E, F	8.23 m (27 ft)
G, J, S, SA, SB, SC, SD, SK, SRE	8.84 m (29 ft)
H, T, TE, TF	9.14 m (30 ft)
N, NQ, NX	7.01 m (23 ft)

Model 147SD, for low-altitude real-time surveillance

MARS helicopter retrieval of a long-span Ryan Model 147TF

BGM-34A with underwing Maverick missile

NA, NC	7.92 m (26 ft)
NP, NRE	8.53 m (28 ft)
124I	9.45 m (31 ft)

WEIGHTS:
Max launching weight:

NA	1,671 kg (3,684 lb)
NC (AQM-34H)	1,700 kg (3,749 lb)
NC (AQM-34V)	2,041 kg (4,500 lb)
NC (M-1)	1,299 kg (2,865 lb)
SC	1,390 kg (3,065 lb)
SC (TV-1)	1,429 kg (3,150 lb)
SD, SD Loran	1,412 kg (3,113 lb)
SRE	1,527 kg (3,367 lb)
T	1,720 kg (3,792 lb)
TE	1,755 kg (3,870 lb)
TF:	
without underwing stores	1,859 kg (4,100 lb)
with underwing stores	2,812 kg (6,200 lb)
124I	1,474 kg (3,250 lb)

PERFORMANCE:
Not officially released, but broadly similar to that of correspondingly powered BQM-34 models, subject to allowance for higher operating weights

TELEDYNE RYAN MODELS 234 and 259

USAF designation: BGM-34

Although retaining a Firebee I parentage, the designation change from AQM to BGM indicated that these RPVs were developed specifically for tactical strike and other defence suppression roles, reflecting plans in the mid-1970s to provide combat drones for various missions otherwise requiring manned aircraft.

Three versions were produced:

BGM-34A (Ryan Model 234). Four built to evaluate feasibility of using RPVs to deliver defence suppression weapons by day, under real-time control. Trials involved release of Shrike, Maverick and HOBOS weapons, with good results, against simulated SA-2 'Fansong' ground radars and other targets. Powered by 7.56 kN (1,700 lb st) Teledyne CAE J69-T-29 turbojet. Air launched and directed from DC-130 Hercules; equipped with Sperry radio command control system and nose mounted TV camera for real-time navigation guidance.

BGM-34B (Ryan Model 234A). Generally similar to BGM-34A, but with 8.54 kN (1,920 lb st) J69-T-41A turbojet, modified tail unit, enlarged control surfaces, and added operational capability. Eight built. One or two fitted with extended, modified nose containing LLL TV camera and Ford stabilised laser designator/receiver, enabling RPV to act as pathfinder, locating and locking on to a target and signalling its position to other, weapon carrying, RPVs. One other BGM-34B fitted with Hughes high resolution FLIR sensor in nose instead of TV installation.

BGM-34C (Ryan Model 239). Multi-mission validation version, with modular noses for reconnaissance, EW and air-to-ground strike missions. Combined, in interchangeable nose modules, capabilities of AQM-34V electronic warfare, AQM-34M reconnaissance and BGM-34B TV guided Maverick strike RPVs. Five converted from YAQM-34Us, with structure strengthened for ground launch. Flight testing (completed March 1978) utilised three 'reconnaissance' noses, two 'strike' noses and one 'electronic warfare' nose. Controlled during mission by DC-130H with multiple (up to eight) drone control capability.

DIMENSIONS:

Wing span	4.42 m (14 ft 6 in)
Length overall:	
A	7.19 m (23 ft 7.2 in)
B	7.92 m (26 ft)
C	8.69 m (28 ft 6.2 in)
Body diameter (max)	0.94 m (3 ft 1.2 in)

WEIGHTS:
Max launching weight:

A	1,270 kg (2,800 lb)
B	1,465 kg (3,230 lb)
C	2,268 kg (5,000 lb)

PERFORMANCE (BGM-34C):
Cruising speed at 9,140 m (30,000 ft)
410 knots (760 km/h; 472 mph)

Operating height:	
min	15 m (50 ft)
max	more than 15,240 m (50,000 ft)
Max range	760 nm (1,408 km; 875 miles)

TELEDYNE RYAN MODEL 154

USAF designation: AQM-91A

First confirmation of the flight status of this advanced RPV (known unofficially as the Firefly) came in the summer of 1969, when a Model 154 on a test flight from Holloman AFB made an emergency parachute descent on to a roadway at Los Alamos Scientific Laboratory, New Mexico, and was photographed for a news agency before it could be removed.

Developed under a 1966 contract, this large high-altitude reconnaissance and electronic surveillance RPV was launched, controlled and recovered by a Lockheed DC-130 Hercules director aircraft. It was developed basically for operation over China, under the USAF's **Compass Arrow** programme. The flattened undersurface of the airframe, with smooth curves elsewhere, and the over-fuselage mounting of the 23.44 kN (5,270 lb st) General Electric J97-GE-100 turbojet, underline the care taken to minimise radar reflectivity and susceptibility to lock-on by infra-red missiles, following the loss of a number of earlier types of drone to Chinese ground defences.

The tail fins were toed inward towards the tips, also to reduce radar reflectivity, and the high aspect ratio sweptback wings were made largely of plastics. No landing gear was fitted, as the Model 154 utilised a MARS parachute recovery system.

Navigation to and from the target area was by self-contained system utilising a Teledyne Doppler sensor, inertial stabilised platform and digital computer. Final recovery was by Sperry Univac UPQ-3 microwave command guidance system, with a range of about 175 nm (320 km; 200 miles), operated from either a recovery aircraft or a ground station via transponders on the drone.

The basic reconnaissance sensor was an Itek KA-80A optical bar panoramic camera, able to take some 1,500 exposures on

The Compass Arrow Ryan 154/AQM-91 'Firefly'

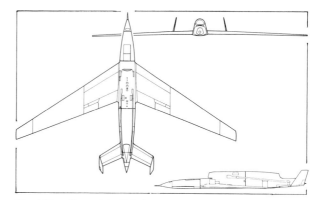

'Stealth' outlines of the Teledyne Ryan Model 154

each mission. Raytheon elint and HRB Singer infra-red sensors were also carried.

All existing Model 154s were placed in storage in July 1973.

DIMENSIONS:

Wing span	14.63 m (48 ft)
Length overall	10.36 m (34 ft)
Body diameter	0.975 m (3 ft 2.4 in)

WEIGHT:

Max launching weight	2,379 kg (5,245 lb)

PERFORMANCE:
No details known

TELEDYNE RYAN MODEL 166 FIREBEE II

US Navy designations: BQM-34E and BQM-34T
USAF designation: BQM-34F

The Firebee II is an advanced development of the Firebee I to provide target presentations above 18,300 m (60,000 ft) at a supersonic dash speed of Mach 1.5 for up to 14 minutes.

Fourteen XBQM-34E development Firebee IIs were built under US Navy contract, and evaluated in 1968-69.

Three versions were built, as follows:

BQM-34E. For US Navy: 116 delivered. First operational flight 29 March 1972. In service from 1973.

BQM-34F. For US Air Force: 99 delivered. Slightly heavier than BQM-34E, with corresponding adjustment of performance, due to different augmentation and scoring systems and addition of recovery parachute for mid-air retrieval. Recently retrofitted with Vega drone tracking and control system (DTCS).

BQM-34T. Follow-on version for US Navy (54 delivered), incorporating Motorola integrated tracking and control system (ITCS).

Although out of production since 1980, the Firebee II remains in service, with 58 still in inventory in March 1987.

TYPE: Remotely piloted supersonic jet target.

AIRFRAME: Shoulder-wing monoplane. Sweepback 53° at leading edge. Basic wing structure of aluminium honeycomb core, steel skins and leading edge, machined aluminium trailing edge and detachable aluminium wingtips. No ailerons. Conventional aluminium semi-monocoque fuselage of frames, bulkheads and formers. Glassfibre nose radome. Sweptback (45°) all-moving horizontal tail surfaces and sweptback (53°) tapered fin and rudder. Aluminium honeycomb cores, with steel skins. Aluminium leading and trailing edges. Fin tip is a glassfibre housing for UHF antennae. Tail control surfaces actuated electro-hydraulically.

A BQM-34F Firebee II supersonic target drone

POWER PLANT: One 8.54 kN (1,920 lb st) Teledyne CAE J69-T-406 turbojet. Wing centre section and main fuselage total fuel tank capacity 119 kg (263 lb) in BQM-34E and T; 151 kg (333 lb) in BQM-34F. External fuel pod capacity 181 kg (400 lb); weight of fuel plus tank, 210 kg (463 lb). With all tanks, the target will perform subsonic flight missions with similar performance capability, endurance and range to those of subsonic BQM-34A. For supersonic flights, external pod is jettisoned. Provision for 50.3 kN (11,300 lb st) (nominal) solid propellant JATO bottle.

LAUNCH AND RECOVERY: Launched from ground or shipborne launcher, or from modified DP-2E Neptune or DC-130A or E Hercules aircraft. DP-2E can carry two Firebees underwing, DC-130 four; launched at altitudes up to 5,485 m (18,000 ft) at approx 200 knots (370 km/h; 230 mph). Recovery by two-stage parachute system similar to that of Firebee I. Can also be recovered from water or (BQM-34F only) by helicopter mid-air retrieval system. In a MARS recovery, helicopter snares 5.72 m (18 ft 9 in) diameter engagement parachute which extends above 24.08 m (79 ft) main parachute. Once engaged, main parachute is released automatically. Provision for emergency recovery. In all versions, recovery parachutes are housed in fuselage tailcone. Recovery sequence preceded, at altitudes above 4,575 m (15,000 ft), by power-off glide, and can be initiated by remote command at any time during glide. When necessary to gain altitude and reduce speed for safe parachute deployment and recovery, a power-off climb is initiated automatically below 4,575 m (15,000 ft), either by normal recovery command or if there is loss of engine power or generator failure.

GUIDANCE AND CONTROL: Frequency-modulated UHF radio guidance system, with 20 separate command channels, utilising AN/DRW-29 onboard radio receiver with compatible transmitter at remote control station. Motorola ITCS (integrated tracking and control system) in BQM-34T performs functions of tracking beacon, radio control receiver and telemetry system. Six-element automatic flight control system (AFCS) comprises three-axis rate gyro, vertical gyro, air data computer, flight control box, low-altitude control box, and three-axis electro-hydraulic actuator assembly. Positioning data provided by onboard radar tracking beacon, antennae for which are located on top of nose compartment and in lower rear portion of fuselage. Ten-channel telemetry system comprises data collection, conversion and FM/FM transmitting equipment in drone and receiving and data display units in remote control station. Flight control system continues to operate when engine or generator power is shut down at high altitude.

SYSTEMS: Electrical power only. Primary power furnished by a 28V 200A DC engine-driven starter/generator. Power conversion by means of a 250VA 400 Hz 115V AC static inverter. Power for recovery system and for drone control during glide phase furnished by a 28V 10Ah nickel-cadmium battery.

MISSION EQUIPMENT (BQM-34E and T): AN/DLQ-3 ECM equipment, AN/DRQ-4 missile scoring system, AN/APX-71 L-band beacon, X- or C-band tracking beacons, special low-altitude radar altimeter kit for 15 m (50 ft) altitude, AN/DRW-29 radio control receiver, Dorsett AN/AKT-21 telemetry system. Motorola ITCS in BQM-34T. Radar augmentation includes travelling wave tube (TWT) in S-, C- and X-band nose mounted Luneberg lens passive radar reflector. Infra-red augmentation by wingtip-mounted Mk 37 Mod 0 flares. In general, Firebee II can be equipped with active and passive radar augmenters, electronic and photographic scoring systems, ECM, low-altitude radar sensing systems and IR flares or pods. Other augmentation equipment can include target identification, GCI tracking, variable radar-image size, augmented IR radiation and smoke system. Positive electronic identification provided by L-band IFF beacon.

DIMENSIONS:

Wing span:	
E and T	2.71 m (8 ft 10.8 in)
F	2.95 m (9 ft 7.9 in)
Length overall	8.89 m (29 ft 1.9 in)
Body diameter (max)	0.61 m (2 ft)
Height overall	1.71 m (5 ft 7.2 in)
Tailplane span	1.46 m (4 ft 9.6 in)

WEIGHTS:

Weight empty:	
E	658 kg (1,452 lb)
F	780.8 kg (1,721.4 lb)
Equipment payload:	
E	67 kg (147.6 lb)
T	50.5 kg (111.4 lb)
Max launching weight:	
E, air launch	855.7 kg (1,886.5 lb)
F, air launch	951 kg (2,097 lb)
E, ground launch	1,036 kg (2,285 lb)
F, ground launch	1,110 kg (2,447 lb)
T, ground launch	1,030 kg (2,270 lb)

PERFORMANCE:

Max level speed:	
at S/L	Mach 1.1
at 13,715 m (45,000 ft):	
E	Mach 1.8
F	Mach 1.78
Operating height range	15 m (50 ft) to 18,300 m (60,000 ft)
Service ceiling:	
E	18,300 m (60,000 ft)
F	16,765 m (55,000 ft)

Control range   200 nm (370 km; 230 miles)
Typical range, external tank on:
 low altitude, subsonic cruise/transonic dash
          221 nm (409 km; 254 miles)
 high altitude, subsonic cruise/supersonic dash
        606 nm (1,123 km; 698 miles)
 high altitude, subsonic cruise throughout
        617 nm (1,142 km; 710 miles)
Max range   774 nm (1,434 km; 891 miles)
Endurance (total time)   1 h 14 min
Flotation time   24 h

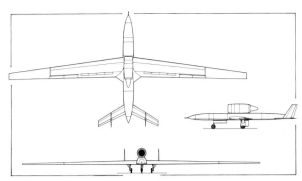

General arrangement of the Model 235/YQM-98 R-Tern

TELEDYNE RYAN MODEL 235 R-TERN

USAF designation: YQM-98A

This aircraft was ordered in 1972 for evaluation against the Boeing B-Gull (which see) in the USAF's **Compass Cope** programme for a high-altitude sensor platform RPV.

Representing a third-generation vehicle to follow the Model 147TF/AQM-34R and Model 154/AQM-91A, the Model 235 had extremely high aspect ratio wings and an overfuselage pod mounting for its power plant. The engine installation was designed to give low infra-red signature, low radar reflectivity, very low smoke and noise emissions, and a capability for very high altitude operation.

Two YQM-98A prototypes (72-01871 and '872) were ordered in 1972, and the first flight took place on 17 August 1974. During the demonstration programme, which was completed at Edwards AFB on 27 November 1974, the YQM-98A made five flights totalling more than 36 h. On its fifth flight, on 3/4 November, it set an unofficial endurance record for RPVs by remaining airborne for well over 24 h and reached an altitude in excess of 16,765 m (55,000 ft).

Flight testing resumed on 8 May 1975, from Cape Canaveral AFB, as part of a joint USAF/Ryan programme to determine any design changes necessary for an operational Compass Cope RPV. Seventeen flights were made during this phase, one prototype being damaged in a night landing in the autumn of 1975.

Teledyne Ryan's R-Tern contender in the Compass Cope programme

As indicated in the Boeing entry, the Compass Cope programme was terminated in 1977.

TYPE: Prototype high-altitude long-endurance RPV.

AIRFRAME: Low-wing monoplane, of very high aspect ratio. Approx 1° anhedral from roots. Sweepback approx 7° at quarter-chord. Two-section ailerons on each wing trailing edge, inboard of outer panels. Four-section spoilers on each upper surface. Triangular fillet on each trailing edge at root. Conventional stressed skin wing structure, with selected use of composite materials. Detachable 4.27 m (14 ft) outer panels with aluminium core and graphite composite skin; trailing edges and fairings making extensive use of glassfibre. Semi-monocoque fuselage, of approximately rectangular cross-section with rounded upper edges, tapering towards front and rear. Undersurface flared and flattened to reduce radar reflectivity. Nosecone, forward fuselage and tailcone detachable for transportation. Low-set swept tailplane, with twin sweptback fins and overhanging rudders at approx half span. Full-span elevators. Nose, tailcone, tailplane and parts of fuselage taken from AQM-91A. Retractable tricycle landing gear. Single-wheel main units, modified from those of a Cessna A-37, retracting inward into wings; nosewheel unit, from a Canadair CF-5, retracting rearward.

POWER PLANT: One Garrett ATF 3 (YF104-GA-100) turbofan, rated at 18.0 kN (4,050 lb st), pod-mounted on shallow pylon on top of fuselage, in line with wings. Fully automatic electronic fuel control system. Fuel tank in each inboard wing panel, each with refuelling point on wing upper surface, and in fuselage.

LAUNCH AND RECOVERY: Conventional runway T-O and landing.

GUIDANCE AND CONTROL: Teledyne Ryan radio command guidance system.

MISSION EQUIPMENT: Main payload compartment in lower forward fuselage, with provision for additional payload in rear of fuselage. Singer Kearfott Talar IV tactical airborne landing approach radar. Details of other systems and equipment not released.

DIMENSIONS:
Wing span	24.75 m (81 ft 2.5 in)
Wing area	32.24 m² (347 sq ft)
Length overall	approx 11.68 m (38 ft 4 in)
Fuselage: Length	11.38 m (37 ft 4 in)
Max depth	0.79 m (2 ft 7 in)
Height overall	2.44 m (8 ft)
Tailplane span	6.53 m (21 ft 5 in)
Wheel track	approx 2.29 m (7 ft 6 in)
Wheelbase	3.07 m (10 ft 1 in)

WEIGHTS (approx):

Weight empty	2,540 kg (5,600 lb)
Payload for 24 h mission	317.5 kg (700 lb)
Max T-O weight	6,490 kg (14,310 lb)

PERFORMANCE (estimated):

Cruising speed at altitudes from 15,240 to 21,340 m (50,000 to 70,000 ft)	Mach 0.5 to 0.6
T-O field length	1,067 m (3,500 ft)
Max endurance	30 h

TELEDYNE RYAN MODEL 262

This 'stealth'-shaped glassfibre mini-RPV was developed as a feasibility demonstrator for locating, identifying and targeting surface vessels, under the US Navy's **STAR** (ship tactical airborne RPV) programme of the mid-1970s. Its delta wing was specially designed to emit very low radar, visual and infra-red signatures, and its ducted propulsion unit for very low noise emission. Three Model 262s were built under USN contract, successfully demonstrating automatic 'hands-off' net recovery during a series of land based tests in 1976–77. The contract programme was completed in mid-1977.

TYPE: Experimental tactical mini-RPV.

AIRFRAME: Delta-form 'flying wing', carefully shaped for low observable signatures. Twin inward canted fins and rudders, just outboard of propeller duct. Construction mainly of glassfibre or other composite materials. Provision for landing gear.

POWER PLANT: One 18.6 kW (25 hp) McCulloch MC-101 flat-twin engine, driving a four- or five-blade ducted propeller at rear. Engine and fuel tank fully buried within delta wing.

LAUNCH AND RECOVERY: Designed for ship or shore launch from compressed air rail-type launcher; net recovery. Could also be fitted with landing gear for conventional runway T-O and landing.

GUIDANCE AND CONTROL: Radio command guidance system, with hybrid autopilot employing analog technique for inner control loop and digital for outer loop.

MISSION EQUIPMENT: Believed to include Honeywell electro-optical sensors, Raytheon radar, and Naval Research Laboratory EW equipment.

Teledyne Ryan Model 262 glassfibre mini-RPV

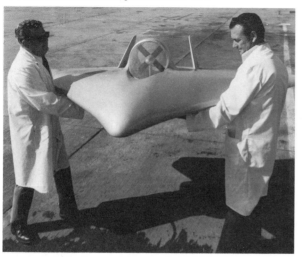

DIMENSION:

Wing span	2.29 m (7 ft 6 in)

WEIGHT:

Max launching weight	approx 75 kg (165 lb)

PERFORMANCE:

Design endurance	up to 8 h

TELEDYNE RYAN FIREBRAND

US Navy designation: ZBQM-111A

Initial US Navy funding was announced in May 1977 for this supersonic target, designed to imitate Soviet anti-shipping missiles in tests of USN shipboard defence weapons under simulated combat conditions. The contract called for completion of nine test vehicles, with flight testing to begin in 1983, but the programme was cancelled in January 1982 for budgetary and other reasons.

TYPE: Recoverable supersonic target drone.

AIRFRAME: All-metal shoulder-wing monoplane, with small delta wings set well back on tapered, circular section body. Differentially operating elevons and rudder.

POWER PLANT: Two Marquardt ramjets, mounted one each side of rear fuselage. Fuel tank in centre of fuselage. Thiokol booster rockets.

LAUNCH AND RECOVERY: Air or surface launch; parachute recovery.

GUIDANCE AND CONTROL: Pre-programmed radio command system, with provision for manual override.

MISSION EQUIPMENT (intended): ECM, active and passive radar augmentation, IR augmentation, expendable H/I/J-band emitter, and scoring system.

DIMENSIONS:

Wing span	2.74 m (9 ft)
Wing area	3.72 m² (40 sq ft)
Length overall	10.36 m (34 ft)
Body diameter (max)	0.71 m (2 ft 4 in)

WEIGHTS (surface launch):

Fuel	998 kg (2,200 lb)
Mission payload	113 kg (250 lb)
Max launching weight, incl boosters	2,812 kg (6,200 lb)

TELEDYNE RYAN MODEL 305 FIREBOLT

US Air Force and Navy designation: AQM-81A

Firebolt is a continuation and refinement of the high altitude supersonic target (HAST) development programme conducted by Beech Aircraft Corporation. Teledyne Ryan won the FSED contract for this target, of which nine test vehicles were ordered in December 1979 (later increased to 21, including six each to specific Air Force and Navy configurations). The programme included 28 test flights, the first of which took place at Eglin AFB on 13 June 1983. Five subsequent flights that year encompassed altitudes of 12,200 to 30,500 m (40,000 to 100,000 ft) and speeds from Mach 1.2 to Mach 4.0.

US Navy Firebolt prototypes are similar to the USAF version except for changes made for Navy integrated target control systems (ITCS) capability, FPS-16 range radar tracking augmentation, flight profile requirements, and compatibility with Navy water recovery procedures. The FSED phase was completed in 1985; as at spring 1987, no follow-on production programme was planned by USAF or USN.

TYPE: Supersonic air launched recoverable target drone.

The cancelled Ryan ZBQM-111A Firebrand

AIRFRAME: Mid-wing monoplane, constructed mainly of stainless steel. Clipped-tip slim delta wings are of constant thickness except for tapered leading edge, which has 75° sweepback. No anhedral, dihedral or incidence. Full-span stainless steel ailerons. Arrow planform stainless steel foreplanes for pitch control. Stainless steel fixed endplate fin at tip of each main wing for lateral stability. Cylindrical body divided into four portions: forward equipment compartment and oxidiser tank (both pressurised), centre section (for parachute and ducted power unit), and controlled thrust assembly. Electric servos for control surface actuation.

POWER PLANT: CSD hybrid rocket motor. Propellant comprises 68 kg (150 lb) of polybutadiene and polymethylmethacrylate, with 227 kg (500 lb) of IRFNA oxidiser. System is inherently safe, since propellants will not burn unless external ignition is applied. Engine is throttleable, with thrust variable from 0.53 to 5.34 kN (120–1,200 lb). The 0.33 m (13 in) thrust chamber forms integral part of fuselage assembly. Oxidiser pressurisation and electrical power provided by Marquardt ducted power unit, powered by ram air turbine with air intake and exit on lower side of fuselage mid-section. Manoeuvring requirements dictate positive expulsion system for oxidiser.

LAUNCH AND RECOVERY: Air launched from F-4 carrier aircraft at speeds between Mach 1.2 and 1.5. Recovery by 13.72 m (45 ft) diameter ring-sail parachute from land, water or mid-air. Flotation bag for water retrieval.

GUIDANCE AND CONTROL: Command and control link. Digital microprocessor for command updates; hybrid digital/analog flight control system; built-in test equipment. Manoeuvres can be either pre-programmed or initiated via ground command radio link. Manoeuvres of between 5g at 10,670 m (35,000 ft) and 1.15g at 27,400 m (90,000 ft) were part of flight test programme; vehicle also capable of 'S' and 180° turns in horizontal plane and altitude changes in vertical plane.

MISSION EQUIPMENT: Range radar and FAA/GCI augmentation; radar augmentation for weapons users. The flight test vehicles include provisions for a Scaler miss distance scoring system and a point source radar augmentation system.

DIMENSIONS:
Wing span	1.02 m (3 ft 4 in)
Wing area	1.71 m² (18.43 sq ft)
Foreplane area	0.27 m² (2.88 sq ft)
Length	5.18 m (17 ft)
Height (stabiliser)	0.66 m (2 ft 2 in)
Body diameter (max)	0.33 m (1 ft 1 in)
Mission equipment volume	0.033 m³ (1.14 cu ft)

WEIGHTS:
Max payload	24 kg (53 lb)
Solid propellant	68 kg (150 lb)

AQM-81A Firebolt high altitude supersonic target

Oxidiser 227 kg (500 lb)
Max launching weight 558 kg (1,231 lb)

PERFORMANCE:
Max level speed at 30,500 m (100,000 ft)   Mach 4.0
Service ceiling 30,500 m (100,000 ft)
Endurance at Mach 3   5 min

TELEDYNE RYAN MODEL 324

Brief details of this new tactical reconnaissance RPV can be found in the Addenda.

TELEDYNE RYAN MODEL 328

This mini-RPV entered flight test in February 1985, and systems evaluation was still under way in July of that year, when details of the Model 328 were first made public. At that time it had been evaluated primarily in an airfield damage assessment role at Wendover AFB, Utah, equipped with an infra-red linescanning system. In early 1986 it was stated that further development had been postponed indefinitely.

TYPE: Multi-purpose recoverable mini-RPV.
AIRFRAME: High-wing pod and boom monoplane, built mainly of epoxy composites with some metal reinforcement; configuration based on USAF Flight Dynamics Laboratory XBQM-106. Wings are of glassfibre with a foam core.
POWER PLANT: One 18.6 kW (25 hp) KFM 107E two-cylinder two-stroke engine, driving a two-blade pusher propeller. Fuel capacity 38 litres (8.2 Imp gallons; 10 US gallons).
LAUNCH AND RECOVERY: In suitable terrain, can take off and land conventionally using a non-retractable tricycle undercarriage. When this is not fitted, launch is either by portable pneumatic rail launcher or zero-length 2.75 in rocket booster, and recovery by explosively deployed 7.32 m (24 ft) diameter parachute to a landing on twin skids.
MISSION EQUIPMENT: Gimballed stabilised TV or still camera, or IRLS, in retractable underfuselage 'bubble' mounting.

DIMENSIONS:
Wing span 3.61 m (11 ft 10 in)
Length overall 3.12 m (10 ft 3 in)

WEIGHTS:
Weight empty 117 kg (258 lb)
Max T-O/launching weight 142 kg (314 lb)

PERFORMANCE:
Max level speed 104 knots (193 km/h; 120 mph)
Cruising speed 69 knots (129 km/h; 80 mph)
Typical operating altitudes
915–3,050 m (3,000–10,000 ft)
Service ceiling 5,030 m (16,500 ft)
Endurance (depending on equipment and mission)
up to 7 h

Teledyne Ryan Model 328 testbed mini

TELEDYNE RYAN 'HIND-D' MINI-RPH

Originally conceived as a low-cost Army target for AA artillery weapons, this aircraft took the form of a quarter-scale representation of the Mil M-24 'Hind-D', and was in the development flight test stage in mid-1985. Main rotor blades are of glassfibre, with a metal leading edge strip and foam core. The prototype was powered by a 37.3 kW (50 hp) microlight aircraft engine. Development was shelved in early 1986.

DIMENSIONS:
Main rotor diameter 4.27 m (14 ft)
Length of fuselage 3.96 m (13 ft)
Height overall 1.07 m (3 ft 6 in)

WEIGHTS:
Payload 22.7–45.5 kg (50–100 lb)
Max T-O weight 129 kg (285 lb)

PERFORMANCE: (estimated: proposed tactical version except where indicated):
Max level speed 90 knots (167 km/h; 103 mph)
Service ceiling 3,050 m (10,000 ft)
Max range 200 nm (370 km; 230 miles)
Endurance: target 2 h
tactical version 3–5 h

TELEDYNE RYAN SPIRIT

This high-altitude long-endurance (HALE) RPV was for a variety of tactical missions, with a prototype first flight originally intended for early 1987. Primary missions were meant to include communications relay, elint, sonobuoy monitoring for ASW ships and aircraft, and long-range weather monitoring. Future applications were envisaged for OTH targeting, and cruise missile early warning and tracking, but further development was suspended in early 1986. No prototype was completed.

The nose compartment, which was to incorporate a cockpit in the prototype for manned initial test flying, was designed to accept interchangeable payload modules according to the mission being undertaken. The engine was to be fitted with a two-stage supercharger enabling the rated power of 119 kW (160 hp) to be maintained up to an altitude of 19,810 m (65,000 ft).

TYPE: High-altitude, long-endurance recoverable RPV.
AIRFRAME: Low/mid-wing monoplane, of very high aspect ratio, with central nacelle, and twin tailbooms supporting an arched tailplane fitted with elevators. Small rudder beneath rear of each tailboom for pitch and yaw control. Construction almost entirely of composite materials, including graphite/epoxy load-bearing members, Kevlar wing leading edges and glassfibre secondary structures. Tricycle landing gear, mainwheels of which retract into tailbooms.
POWER PLANT: One 119 kW (160 hp) Teledyne Continental liquid-cooled and turbocharged six-cylinder piston engine, driving a large diameter pusher propeller having Kevlar blades with a foam core.

DIMENSIONS (approx):
Wing span 25.91 m (85 ft)
Length overall (depending on payload nose module)
12.19 m (40 ft)
Height over tail 4.27 m (14 ft)
Propeller diameter 6.10 m (20 ft)

WEIGHTS (approx):
Weight empty 1,134 kg (2,500 lb)

'Hind-D' mini-RPH built by Teledyne Ryan in 1986

Payload	136–544 kg (300–1,200 lb)
Max T-O weight	2,041 kg (4,500 lb)
PERFORMANCE (estimated):	
Design cruising speed	130 knots (241 km/h; 150 mph)
Normal operating altitude	15,850 m (52,000 ft)
Absolute ceiling	nearly 22,860 m (75,000 ft)
Endurance	80 h, equivalent to range of
	14,000 nm (25,945 km; 16,120 miles)

TELEDYNE RYAN MODEL 410

Details of this surveillance RPV are given in the Addenda.

Artist's impression of the 1986 Ryan Spirit proposal for a HALE RPV

TRACTEL CORPORATION

2761 Laguna Canyon Road, Laguna Beach, California 92651

TRACTEL AMT-RPV1

The general appearance of the AMT-RPV1 is shown in an accompanying drawing.

TYPE: Recoverable surveillance mini-RPV.

AIRFRAME: Canard configuration, comprising mid-mounted non-swept foreplane with elevators, and shoulder-mounted sweptback main wing, with ailerons, at rear. Main wingtips upswept to form winglets. Box-section fuselage. Non-retractable tricycle landing gear. Kevlar fuselage and epoxy/foam wings, of modular construction to facilitate in-the-field replacement of individual components.

POWER PLANT: Single piston engine (type not known), mounted at rear to drive a two-blade pusher propeller. Fuel capacity 7.6 litres (1.7 Imp gallons; 2 US gallons).

LAUNCH AND RECOVERY: Launched from rail launcher; recovered by conventional wheeled landing or, optionally, by net system.

GUIDANCE AND CONTROL: Ground control station includes two video monitors with controls for video imaging and for proximal guidance of RPV utilising forward-looking dedicated camera for flight control. Two 9.14 m (30 ft) mast antennae, linked with telemetry and remote from base station, provide telemetry link for location and control functions. Computer with logic function, to determine plot and assist control, is linked to plotting board mounted for accepting standard military maps as graphics. Options include distal navigation system, with memory for pre-programmed flight data, and laser disc storage facility for map data and sequencing data link.

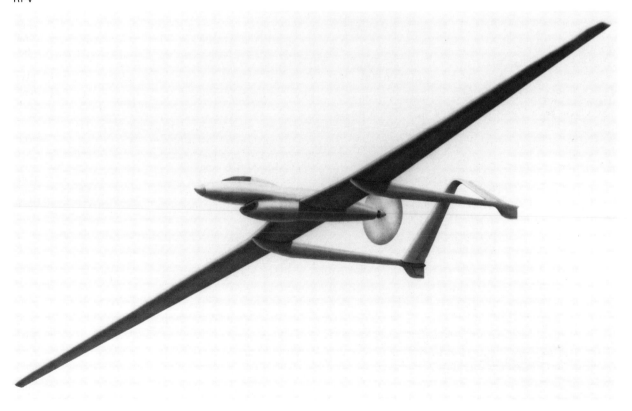

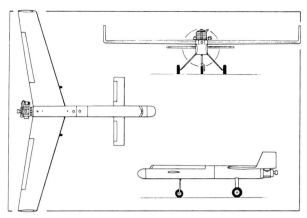

Tractel AMT-RPV1 surveillance mini-RPV *(Michael A. Badrocke)*

MISSION EQUIPMENT: Standard payload of two infra-red video cameras, one forward-looking and one-downward looking, with any available 8 mm lens system including telephoto, wide angle or fisheye. All video cameras are solid state and CCD (charged coupled device) technology, available in three configurations: 288 or 560 horizontal line resolution black and white, or 330 line colour. Transmitter in range 400 MHz to 1.2 GHz. Camera options include 256 greyscale daytime recognition processor (which can be set to night-time sensitivity for anything greater than ambient light, such as muzzle flash or vehicle headlights); passive second generation fixed focal point lens for night observation; or 35 mm motor-driven single-lens reflex camera with telephoto lens for still photography. Signal options include digitally encrypted transmitter (requiring special receiver), and frequency hopping facility to prevent jamming of signal.

DIMENSIONS:
Wing span	3.05 m (10 ft)
Length overall	2.18 m (7 ft 2 in)

WEIGHTS:
Weight empty	12.7 kg (28 lb)
Max launching weight	20.4 kg (45 lb)

PERFORMANCE:
Endurance	4 h

US AIR FORCE/ARMY/NAVY
See under 'Department of the Air Force' etc.

WINDECKER INDUSTRIES

WINDECKER/LMSC SAVOIR

SAVOIR (Small Aerial Vehicle for Observation, Intelligence and Reconnaissance) was a mid-1970s joint programme by Windecker and LMSC. It combined the fuselage and rear-mounted propulsion unit of LMSC's Aequare (which see) with high-mounted fixed wings and a non-retractable gear for normal runway take-off and landing. Lockheed integrated the airborne equipment.

The SAVOIR programme resulted in improvements in RPV autopilot design, payload integration, and ground launch and recovery techniques.

WING MANUFACTURING
Crystal Lake, Illinois

WING CRUISE 3

This RPV was designed and built by Wing Manufacturing for testbed use by the US Naval Air Development Center at Warminster, Pennsylvania. It has high-mounted wings with prominent leading-edge root extensions, sweptback tail surfaces, and a fuselage with a long, slender nose. A single piston engine is installed in the rear of the fuselage, driving a pusher propeller, and the Cruise 3 is catapult-launched and parachute-recovered.

DIMENSIONS:
Not known

WEIGHTS:
Weight empty	11 kg (24 lb)
Max payload	9 kg (20 lb)

PERFORMANCE:
Cruising speed	60 knots (111 km/h; 69 mph)
Ceiling	3,050 m (10,000 ft)
Range	43–78 nm (80–145 km; 50–90 miles)

Wing Cruise 3 for the US Naval Air Development Center *(Jane's/Mike Keep)*

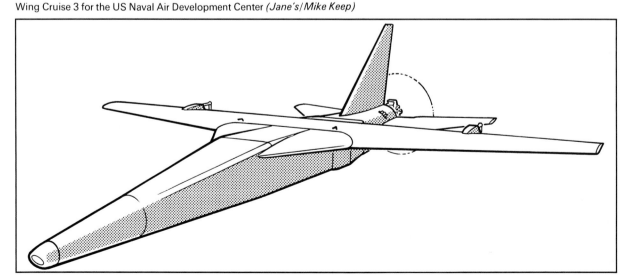

APPENDIX 1

Abbreviations

AFB	Air Force Base
AFCS	automatic flight control system
AUVS	Association for Unmanned Vehicle Systems (USA)
CCV	control configured vehicle
CEP	circular error probability
ECM	electronic countermeasures
EPU	emergency power unit
ESM	electronic support measures
EW	electronic warfare
FDL	Flight Dynamics Laboratory (USAF)
FLIR	forward looking infra-red
FSED	full scale engineering development
GCS	ground control station (or system)
GFE	government furnished equipment
GPS	Global Positioning Satellite
GRP	glassfibre reinforced plastics
GSE	ground support equipment
IGE	in ground effect
IOC	initial operational capability
IR	infra-red
IRCM	infra-red countermeasures

IRFNA	inhibited red fuming nitric acid
IRLS	infra-red linescan
LLL	low light level
MARS	mid-air retrieval system
MoD	Ministry of Defence (UK)
MoS	Ministry of Supply (UK)
NBC	nuclear, biological and chemical (warfare)
OGE	out of ground effect
OTH	over the horizon
PCM	pulse code modulated (radio)
PCS	portable control station (or system)
PCU	portable (or powered) control unit
RAE	Royal Aircraft Establishment (UK)
RAN	Royal Australian Navy
RPA	remotely piloted aircraft
RPH	remotely piloted helicopter
RPRV	remotely piloted research vehicle
RPV	remotely piloted vehicle
RSRE	Royal Signals and Radar Establishment (UK)
UMA	unmanned aircraft
WRE	Weapons Research Establishment (UK/Australia)

APPENDIX 2

Military designations of US drones, targets and RPVs

Since introduction of the tri-service designation system in 1962, a common series of design numbers has been used for missiles, RPVs, drones, targets, probes and rockets, the three principal prefix letters being allocated on the following basis:

Launch environment
- A   Air
- B   Multiple
- C   Coffin (container)
- F   Individual
- G   Runway
- H   Silo stored
- L   Silo launched
- M   Mobile
- P   Soft pad
- R   Ship
- U   Underwater

Mission
- D   Decoy
- E   Special electronic installation
- G   Surface attack
- I   Aerial intercept
- Q   Drone
- T   Training
- U   Underwater attack
- W   Weather

Vehicle type
- M   Guided missile/drone
- N   Probe
- R   Rocket

Example   Y   M   Q   M – 105   A

- Status prefix (service test)
- Launch environment (mobile)
- Mission (drone)
- Vehicle type (missile/drone)
- Design number
- Series (first version of this design)

Designations in this series allocated to RPVs, drones and targets include:

BQM-6	Target version of Vought RGM-6 Regulus 1 missile	MQM-57	Northrop Falconer target (NATO AN/USD-1)
MQM-8 Vandal	Target version of Bendix RIM/RGM-8 Talos missile	MQM-58	Aerojet General Overseer target
CQM-10	Target version of Boeing MIM-10 Bomarc missile	AQM-60	Lockheed Kingfisher target
		MQM-61	Beechcraft Model 1025 Cardinal target
GQM/MQM-15	Target versions of Vought RGM-15 Regulus 2 missile	BQM/MQM-74	Northrop Chukar target
		AQM-81	Teledyne Ryan Firebolt target
ADM-20	McDonnell Quail decoy for North American Rockwell AGM-28 Hound Dog missile	BQM-90	US Navy target (cancelled)
		AQM-91	Teledyne Ryan 'Firefly' RPV
MQM-33	Northrop KD2R-5 basic training target	XQM-93	E-Systems L450F RPV
AQM/BQM/ BGM/MQM-34	Teledyne Ryan Firebee I and II targets and Models 147/234 RPVs	YQM-94	Boeing B-Gull RPV
		YQM-98	Teledyne Ryan R-Tern RPV
AQM-35	Northrop target version of Bendix RIM-35 missile	PQM-102	Sperry target (converted Convair F-102)
		XAQM-103	Teledyne Ryan Model 147G RPV
MQM-36	Northrop KD2R Shelduck target	YMQM-105	Lockheed (LMSC) Aquila RPV
AQM-37	Beechcraft Model 1019 (et al.) target	XBQM-106	USAF (FDL) Teleplane RPV
AQM-38	Northrop Models RP-76 and RP-78 targets	MQM-107	Beechcraft Model 1089 Streaker target
MQM-39	Beechcraft Model 1001 Cardinal target	XBQM-108	US Navy (NWC) VATOL research RPV
MQM-40	Globe US Navy target	ZBQM-111	Teledyne Ryan Firebrand target
AQM-41	Fairchild Petrel target	FQM-117	RS Systems RCMAT series targets
MQM-42	North American Rockwell Roadrunner target	XCGM-121	Boeing (BMAC) Pave Tiger drone
		BQM-126	Beechcraft Model 997 target
PQM-56	Nord (Bell modified) CT.41 target	YAQM-127	Martin Marietta SLAT target

Addenda

Australia

ATA (page 12)

ATA JINDIVIK

Current production of the Jindivik ended in 1986 with delivery of the last UK Mk 4A. In all, 502 Jindiviks, in 13 versions, were built for the WRE, UK, US Navy, Royal Australian Navy and Sweden.

In a major overhaul of the basic airframe design, ATA has proposed a considerably modified **Mk 5** version. Changes would include new-design wings with electrically operated flaps, landing spoilers, redesigned vertical and horizontal tail surfaces, a new engine, digital autopilot and GPS navigation system. The redesign is to meet a new Australian specification for a 6g target aircraft with a very low radar signature, able to operate at speeds of up to Mach 0.95 (550 knots; 1,019 km/h; 633 mph), at altitudes from 15 m (50 ft) to 18,300 m (60,000 ft), and for periods of up to 2 h. Roles other than target use are also being studied.

Brazil

CTA (page 20)

CTA ACAUÃ

First flight of the Acauã was made in March 1986, and early prototypes were all-metal. One built using composites was due to fly in 1987. Power plant is a 14.9 kW (20 hp) two-stroke engine. Other data include a wing span of 5.00 m (16 ft 4.75 in), length of 4.72 m (15 ft 5.75 in), T-O weight of 100 kg (220 lb) and max level speed of 65 knots (120 km/h; 74 mph).

Canada

CANADAIR (page 24)

CANADAIR CL-227 SENTINEL

Phase 3 vehicles have larger rotors (diameter 2.80 m; 9 ft 2.25 in) and a higher gross weight (190 kg; 419 lb), with useful load increased to 88 kg (194 lb). Joint US/Canadian DoD evaluation was taking place in 1987–88.

China (People's Republic)

CHANG HONG 1

A Chinese (presumably 'reverse engineered') version of the Teledyne Ryan Model 147 is in service as a high-altitude photo-reconnaissance RPV. It has the Chinese name Chang Hong 1 (or CH-1 for short), although the Westernised designation D-1 is also used in some Chinese publications. The CH-1 is air launched (carrier aircraft not known) and MARS recovered.

NRIST (page 33)

NRIST YK-7

Design of this mini-RPV began in February 1986. Prototype construction started four months later, and the first flight was made in October of that year. It is intended to simulate, at one-fifth scale, a typical low-level ground attack aircraft, providing a versatile target for tactical exercises and for training of air defence and short-range surface-to-air missile crews. In addition, the YK-7 has development potential as a surveillance, photographic or scientific research mini-RPV.

TYPE: Re-usable target/mini-RPV.

AIRFRAME: Shoulder-wing monoplane. Wings are of GRP with a foam plastics core, and have a NASA GA(W)-1 aerofoil section, 5° dihedral, 0° incidence, and 15° sweepback at quarter-chord. Conventional tail surfaces are of similar construction. Oval section streamline fuselage is a GRP composite structure, with a landing skid under the forward portion.

POWER PLANT: One 3.7 kW (5 hp) single-cylinder piston engine, fitted with contactorless magneto, fuel pump and barostat and driving a two-blade wooden propeller.

LAUNCH AND RECOVERY: Launched from bungee-powered rail launcher, on cradle which is jettisoned after take-off. Recovery by conventional skid landing or, optionally, by parachute; latter can be commanded either manually, or automatically by fail-safe function incorporated in remote control system. At conclusion of mission, launcher can be folded to become transport trailer for air vehicle.

GUIDANCE AND CONTROL: Remote control by high power digital proportional PCM radio system, plus optical system for out of sight operation. Conventional aerodynamic control surfaces.

MISSION EQUIPMENT: No details known

DIMENSIONS:

Wing span	2.115 m (6 ft 11.25 in)
Wing area	0.825 m² (8.88 sq ft)
Length overall	2.05 m (6 ft 8.75 in)
Propeller diameter	0.50 m (1 ft 7.75 in)

WEIGHTS:

Weight empty	12.5 kg (27.6 lb)
Max payload	1 kg (2.2 lb)
Max launching weight	14 kg (30.9 lb)

PERFORMANCE:

Max level speed	105 knots (194 km/h; 120 mph)
Max rate of climb at S/L	660 m (2,165 ft)/min
Operating height: min	50 m (165 ft)
max	1,000 m (3,280 ft)
Effective control range	1.6–2.7 nm (3–5 km; 1.9–3.1 miles)
Endurance	40 min

YK-7 target/mini-RPV developed by the NRIST in Nanjing

France

AÉROPAR

AÉROPAR SURVEILLANCE RPV

Aéropar has developed a surveillance RPV from a small target drone which it designed in 1984, and has teamed with SAT (responsible for the ground control station) to offer the vehicle to the French Army. Of delta wing configuration, the RPV has a narrow, unswept canard surface at the nose, sweptback fin and rudder, tricycle landing gear, a payload bay in the centre fuselage, and a rear-mounted piston engine driving a two-blade pusher propeller. Reports suggest that Aéropar may have had one Middle East customer for the RPV in 1986, and was negotiating with another in 1987. Payload includes two cameras (one in the nose for navigation, one ventrally mounted for surveillance) and a video downlink.

DIMENSIONS:
  Not known
WEIGHTS:
  Max payload   64 kg (141.1 lb)
  Max T-O weight   128 kg (282.2 lb)
PERFORMANCE:
  Max cruising speed   151 knots (280 km/h; 174 mph)
  Max speed for camera operation
                               59 knots (110 km/h; 68 mph)
  Endurance with 40 kg (88.2 lb) payload   7–8 h

Israel

TECHNION ISRAEL INSTITUTE OF TECHNOLOGY (TIIT)

Kiryat Hatechnion (PO Box 4910), 32000 Haifa

Test flying began on 27 April 1987 of a small RPV powered by two small turbojets fitted with two-dimensional thrust-vectoring nozzles. The nozzles can be vectored by the ground controller through $\pm 20°$ in pitch and $\pm 35°$ in yaw, or activated differentially to control roll, generating additional lift to augment the aircraft's natural manoeuvrability. Conventional elevators, rudder and ailerons are available as a backup. Twelve designs, ranging from the original 2.13 m (7 ft) $\times$ 1.22 m (4 ft) prototype to 5.49 $\times$ 5.49 m (18 $\times$ 18 ft), are being studied, and four more prototypes were due to be involved in the flight test programme during 1987. The project is being carried out by the TIIT's Jet Propulsion Laboratory under the leadership of Prof Benjamin Gal-Or.

United Kingdom

AEL (RPV) LTD (page 77)

AEL SNIPE

AEL now has two new-generation versions of the Snipe Mk II, known as **Mk 22 and Mk 23**. The former, with a 100 cc engine, is used chiefly for operator training, but can be used as a target in its own right, being able to tow banners or sleeves, and carry up to 16 smoke canisters as well as radar or acoustic miss distance indicators.

The faster Snipe Mk 23 uses the Mk 22 fuselage, but has an 18.6 kW (25 hp) NGL WAEL 342 flat-twin engine and a more 'advanced' wing, enabling it to out-perform the now-obsolete Snipe Mk III. The Mk 23 also can carry a full payload of smoke canisters and a radar MDI. Construction of both versions is similar to that of the Sparrowhawk RPV.

The Snipe **Mks IV and V**, both larger and faster than the original Mk II, are in customer service and are still current products.

DIMENSIONS:
Wing span: IV		3.21 m (10 ft 6.5 in)
V		3.06 m (10 ft 0.5 in)
22, 23		2.44 m (8 ft)
Length overall: IV, V		2.77 m (9 ft 1 in)
22, 23		2.50 m (8 ft 2.5 in)

WEIGHTS:
Weight empty: IV	46 kg (101.4 lb)
V	45 kg (99.2 lb)
22	25 kg (55.1 lb)
23	31 kg (68.3 lb)
Standard fuel: IV	10 kg (22.0 lb)
V, 23	7.25 kg (16.0 lb)
22	3.4 kg (7.5 lb)
Max payload (incl fuel): IV	31 kg (68.3 lb)
V	14 kg (30.9 lb)
22	9 kg (19.8 lb)
23	17 kg (37.5 lb)
Max launching weight: IV	77 kg (169.8 lb)
V	59 kg (130.1 lb)
22	34 kg (75.0 lb)
23	48 kg (105.8 lb)

PERFORMANCE:
Max level speed: IV	130 knots (241 km/h; 150 mph)
V	147 knots (273 km/h; 170 mph)
22	95 knots (177 km/h; 110 mph)
23	183 knots (340 km/h; 211 mph)
Max range (visual tracking):	
IV, V	4.9 nm (9 km; 5.6 miles)
22, 23	3.2 nm (6 km; 3.7 miles)
Max range (with tracking system):	
all versions	27 nm (50 km; 31.1 miles)
Endurance at max speed: IV	1 h 35 min
V, 22	1 h 10 min
23	1 h 15 min
Endurance at cruising speed: IV	2 h 23 min
V, 23	1 h 44 min
22	1 h 50 min

FLIGHT REFUELLING (page 89)

FLIGHT REFUELLING RAVEN 2

In recent British Army exercises, a Raven 2 was subjected to an estimated 4,000 rounds of small-arms and light anti-aircraft gunfire and was hit by only one round, which passed harmlessly through its structure. On 16 July 1987 a Raven 2 made what FRL believes to be the first nocturnal demonstration flight by a fixed-wing surveillance RPV.

The Raven 2 differs from the XRAE-2 prototypes as follows:

AIRFRAME: NACA 4415 section wings, with 5° incidence and no Kevlar; fuselage of glassfibre, plywood and Kevlar.
POWER PLANT: One 5.2 kW (7 hp) or 7.5 kW (10 hp) engine; fuel capacity 12 litres (2.6 Imp gallons; 3.2 US gallons).

DIMENSIONS:
Wing span (no change in area)	3.63 m (11 ft 11 in)
Length overall	2.85 m (9 ft 4.25 in)
Height overall	0.65 m (2 ft 1.5 in)

WEIGHTS:
Max payload	15 kg (33.1 lb)
Max launching weight	45 kg (99.2 lb)

PERFORMANCE:
Max level speed	90 knots (167 km/h; 104 mph)
Stalling speed	40 knots (75 km/h; 47 mph)
Ceiling	2,440 m (8,000 ft)

United States of America

BEECHCRAFT (page 123)

BEECHCRAFT MQM-107 STREAKER

Beech received a US Army contract for 146 MQM-107D Streaker targets in the autumn of 1987, bringing total MQM-107 series orders by the US government to 1,126, of which more than 800 had been delivered at that time. Deliveries of this latest batch will run from spring 1988 to December 1989.

CALIFORNIA MICROWAVE (page 135)

CALIFORNIA MICROWAVE CM-30 and CM-44

The CM-30 and CM-44 are part of an overall RPV programme designated **I-30**, three contracts for which were received in FY 1986. The CM-30 has been the development model, retaining provision for manned as well as unmanned operation, while the CM-44 is the prototype for a more advanced UMA. Airframes are of GRP composites, the outer

California Microwave CM-30, a modified Rutan Long-EZ

wings and canard surfaces being detachable for transportation and storage. The nosewheel unit retracts electrically, with mechanical backup; the main gear is non-retractable. The vehicle has autonomous navigation, and normally flies a pre-programmed course. A GCS is not required for vehicle tracking or course corrections, but one can optionally be used to modify the flight plan if data telemetered from the onboard sensors make this necessary. Mission payloads can include FLIR, video and/or photographic imagers, communications relay equipment, systems for monitoring communications or electronic emissions, synthetic aperture side-looking radar, moving target indication radar, jamming devices, and chaff or flare dispensers. The RPV can also be used to airdrop supply packages (up to 163.3 kg; 360 lb in the case of the CM-30).

POWER PLANT: One 119 kW (160 hp) Avco Lycoming IO-320-D1C flat-four engine in CM-30 (156.5 kW; 210 hp TIO-360-C1A6D in CM-44), driving a three-blade wooden pusher propeller. Fuel capacities 276 litres (61 Imp gallons; 73 US gallons) and 348 litres (76.5 Imp gallons; 92 US gallons) respectively.

DIMENSIONS (A: CM-30, B: CM-44):

Wing span: A	7.92 m (26 ft)
B	9.30 m (30 ft 6 in)
Length overall: A	4.88 m (16 ft)
B	5.49 m (18 ft)

Prototype California Microwave CM-44 unmanned air vehicle, developed from the CM-30. Note the toed-in winglet/fins and modified flush intakes, to reduce radar and IR signatures

WEIGHTS:

Max payload: A	181 kg (400 lb)
B	272 kg (600 lb)
Max T-O weight: A	839 kg (1,850 lb)
B	1,197 kg (2,600 lb)

PERFORMANCE:

Max cruising speed (75% power):	
A at 4,575 m (15,000 ft)	161 knots (298 km/h; 185 mph)
B	190 knots (352 km/h; 219 mph)
Loiter speed (40% power):	
A at 4,575 m (15,000 ft)	83 knots (153 km/h; 95 mph)
Service ceiling: A	3,660 m (12,000 ft)
B	7,620 m (25,000 ft)
Absolute ceiling: A	4,575 m (15,000 ft)
B	over 9,150 m (30,000 ft)
T-O and landing distance: A	457 m (1,500 ft)
B	274 m (900 ft)
Range with max fuel, 45 min reserves:	
A	1,200 nm (2,224 km; 1,382 miles)
B	1,700 nm (3,150 km; 1,957 miles)
Endurance with max fuel: A	12 h
B	18 h

DEPARTMENT OF THE ARMY (page 137)

IEW-UAV

The US Army suspended its IEW-UAV competition in June 1987 when the two remaining competing vehicles (Developmental Sciences SkyEye R4E-50 and California Microwave CM-30) had completed only approx 80 per cent of the fly-off tests. Claiming that neither candidate had met all of its requirements, the Army planned to issue a revised request for proposals later in the year.

DEPARTMENT OF THE NAVY (page 137)

MR-RPV

As the next stage in its MR-RPV procurement programme, the US Navy awarded Northrop and Martin Marietta each a seven-month design study contract in September 1987. From these, one design will be selected for a 14-month prototype demonstration phase, with a production contract expected to follow in the second quarter of FY 1989. The losing manufacturer may become second-source supplier of the design chosen for production.

DEVELOPMENTAL SCIENCES (page 139)

SKYEYE R4E-50

This new version of the SkyEye has an enlarged and redesigned airframe, powered by a 34.4 kW (46 hp) Teledyne Continental GR-18 rotary engine, and was first flown in November 1986. Launch, recovery, guidance and control are essentially as for the R4E-40, but the -50 incorporates a new Lear Siegler flight control system hardened against electromagnetic interference, and navigation capability is enhanced significantly by integration of a GPS (Global Positioning Satellite) receiver.

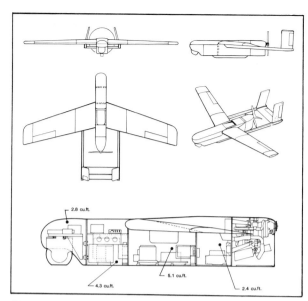

R4E-50 version of the Developmental Sciences SkyEye, with flush-type air inlet scoop to reduce radar cross-section

WEIGHTS:

Weight empty	195 kg (430 lb)
Max payload	90.7 kg (200 lb)
Max standard fuel	45.5 kg (100 lb)
Max launching weight	331 kg (730 lb)
Max weight for parachute recovery	295 kg (650 lb)

PERFORMANCE:

Max level speed ('clean')	125 knots (232 km/h; 144 mph)
Max rate of climb at S/L	198 m (650 ft)/min
Service ceiling:	
without turbocharger	4,575 m (15,000 ft)
with turbocharger	9,150 m (30,000 ft)
Max endurance	10 h

INTERNATIONAL AEROSPACE TECHNOLOGIES INC (IAT)

7738 Governors Drive West, Huntsville, Alabama 35806

IAT MK 103

This lightweight (hand launched?) mini-RPV is intended for civil applications such as aerial mapping and survey, industrial and environmental surveillance, and for use in remote or restricted areas inadequate for the employment of separate launch and recovery systems. Power plant is a 5 kW (6.7 hp) engine, driving a two-blade pusher propeller (see accompanying illustration); stabilised payloads can include a daylight or LLL photogrammetric camera, IR camera, or a video camera with real-time data transmission.

DIMENSIONS:

Wing span	3.20 m (10 ft 6 in)
Length overall	2.85 m (9 ft 4.25 in)

WEIGHTS:

Payload	6 kg (13.2 lb)
Max launching weight	15 kg (33.1 lb)

PERFORMANCE:

Speed range	13.5–75.5 knots (25–140 km/h; 15.5–87 mph)
Max endurance	1 h

Alternator power is increased to 1.2 kW, and increased payload volume permits carriage of multiple sensor packages (eg, a comint or elint sensor combined with a FLIR or daylight video imager for target identification). Various single and combined ('cuer-viewer') sensor packages have been demonstrated, with the main emphasis on EW applications. The R4E-50 is the version which was entered in the US Army's 1987 IEW-UAV competition, and was one of two finalists before the competition was suspended in mid-1987.

DIMENSIONS:

Wing span	6.10 m (20 ft)
Wing area	5.20 m² (56.0 sq ft)
Length overall	4.15 m (13 ft 7.25 in)
Height overall	1.10 m (3 ft 7.5 in)
Propeller diameter	0.99 m (3 ft 3 in)

International Aerospace Technologies MK 103 civil mini-RPV

LOCKHEED (AUSTIN DIVISION) (page 167)

LMSC AQUILA

Lockheed's Austin Division has proposed a naval real-time reconnaissance version of the Aquila, to which it has given the name **Stingray**.

SPERRY (page 188)

Honeywell's Sperry Defense Systems Division announced two new contracts in August 1987. One was from Mitsubishi of Japan, for whom Sperry will provide drone avionics and engineering for two prototype and 29 'production' conversions of ex-JASDF **F-104J Starfighters** into target drones. The other, from the US Army, is for a control system for an unmanned target version of the **Sikorsky S-55**. This is the first-ever major programme for a helicopter FSAT, and will involve two prototypes (first flight spring 1988) and 11 'production' conversions. Airframe modifications, to create a physical resemblance to the Soviet Mi-24 'Hind-E', will be undertaken by Orlando Helicopter Airways.

TELEDYNE RYAN (page 191)

TELEDYNE RYAN MODEL 324 SCARAB

The Model 324 is a 'midi' sized tactical reconnaissance UMA for use by, and co-production with, Egypt. Flight testing was nearing completion in late 1987, with deliveries of 29 Scarabs to the Egyptian Army scheduled for early 1988.

TYPE: Recoverable reconnaissance/surveillance drone/RPV.

AIRFRAME: Built mainly of Kevlar and other composites, with low-set sweptback wings and tailplane and flat-bottomed fuselage. Sweptback fins and rudders at mid tailplane span. Dorsal engine intake. No landing gear.

POWER PLANT: One 4.31 kN (970 lb st) Teledyne CAE 373-8C turbojet engine. Fuel capacity 568 litres (125 Imp gallons; 150 US gallons).

LAUNCH AND RECOVERY: Launch from truck-mounted zero-length launcher, boosted by Morton Thiokol jettisonable rocket motor (burn time 4 s) adapted from that of Harpoon missile. Parachute/airbag recovery, deployed automatically or on command.

GUIDANCE AND CONTROL: Vega C-band command/control system for line of sight control. Beyond line of sight, mission is basically pre-programmed, with provision for in-flight update/override. Speed, payload, Litton LN-81 INS guidance/navigation, propulsion, fuel, electrical and recovery systems governed by a Teledyne Ryan mission logic control unit, with Collins Navcore 1 onboard GPS receiver for INS update.

MISSION EQUIPMENT: Reportedly includes CAI/Recon Optical KS-153A reconnaissance camera.

DIMENSIONS:
Wing span	3.66 m (12 ft)
Length overall	6.10 m (20 ft)

WEIGHTS:
Payload	113.4 kg (250 lb)
Max launching weight	1,134 kg (2,500 lb)

PERFORMANCE:
Max level speed	Mach 0.8
Service ceiling	13,720 m (45,000 ft)
Max range	1,700 nm (3,150 km; 1,957 miles)

TELEDYNE RYAN MODEL 410

This new high-altitude, long-endurance RPV, which made its first flight in October 1987, can accommodate standard off-the-shelf modular payloads from a wide variety of sources. It has a pod-and-twin-tailboom configuration, with high-mounted wings, fixed mainwheels, retractable nosewheel, and a 119 kW (160 hp) Avco Lycoming TIO-320-C1B turbocharged flat-four engine in a 'pusher' installation. Capability is claimed for day or night, all-weather STOL operation, with autonomous navigation, high top speed, slow loiter and stalling speeds, and a long range/endurance. Missions can be pre-programmed, or re-programmed in flight, over a wide range of military or civil requirements. The GCS and airborne data link do not require a tracking antenna at the ground centre, and one GCS will be able to control up to eight air vehicles. A larger (11.28 m; 37 ft 0 in span, 1,088 kg; 2,400 lb gross weight) version, with greater endurance, is also envisaged.

The following data apply to the first prototype:

DIMENSIONS:
Wing span	9.45 m (31 ft)
Propeller diameter	1.60 m (5 ft 3 in)
Payload volume	0.68 m³ (24 cu ft)

WEIGHTS:
Max payload	136 kg (300 lb)
Max T-O weight	726 kg (1,600 lb)

PERFORMANCE:
Max level speed	190 knots (352 km/h; 219 mph)
Typical operating speed range	
	85–140 knots (157–259 km/h; 98–161 mph)
T-O run	229 m (750 ft)
Max endurance:	
with 45.4 kg (100 lb) payload	2 days
with max payload	1 day

INDEX

Aircraft (non-droned)